BOOK 1

FROM CELLS TO CONSCIOUSNESS

The Open University

This publication forms part of an Open University course SD226 *Biological psychology: exploring the brain.* The complete list of texts which make up this course can be found on the back cover. Details of this and other Open University courses can be obtained from the Student Registration and Enquiry Service, The Open University, PO Box 197, Milton Keynes MK7 6BJ, United Kingdom: tel. +44 (0)845 300 60 90, email general-enquiries@open.ac.uk

Alternatively, you may visit the Open University website at http://www.open.ac.uk where you can learn more about the wide range of courses and packs offered at all levels by The Open University.

To purchase a selection of Open University course materials visit http://www.ouw.co.uk, or contact Open University Worldwide, Walton Hall, Milton Keynes MK7 6AA, United Kingdom for a brochure. tel. +44 (0)1908 858793; fax +44 (0)1908 858787; email ouw-customer-services@open.ac.uk

The Open University
Walton Hall, Milton Keynes
MK7 6AA

First published 2004. Second edition 2006. Reprinted 2007

Edited, designed and typeset by The Open University.

Printed and bound in the United Kingdom by The University Press, Cambridge

ISBN 978 0 7492 1430 2

2.2

SD226 COURSE TEAM

Course Team Chair

Miranda Dyson

Course Managers

Alastair Ewing

Tracy Finnegan

Course Team Assistant

Yvonne Royals

Authors

Saroj Datta

Ian Lyon

Bundy Mackintosh

Heather McLannahan

Kerry Murphy

Peter Naish

Daniel Nettle

Ignacio Romero

Frederick Toates

Terry Whatson

Multimedia

Sue Dugher

Spencer Harben

Will Rawes

Brian Richardson

Other Contributors

Duncan Banks

Mike Stewart

Consultant

Jose Julio Rodriguez Arellano

Course Assessor

Philip Winn (University of St Andrews)

Editors

Gerry Bearman

Rebecca Graham

Gillian Riley

Pamela Wardell

Graphic Design

Steve Best

Sarah Hofton

Pam Owen

Picture Researchers

Lydia K. Eaton

Deana Plummer

Indexer

Jane Henley

Contents

CHAPTER 1

INTRODUCTION TO BRAINS, MIND AND CONSCIOUSNESS

1.1 Scene-setting

1.1.1 Introduction

This course, *Biological Psychology*, explores the relationship between the brain, mind, consciousness and behaviour. The role of Chapter 1 is twofold. First, it will review some of the biological psychology which you might have come across already from, for example, previous courses or the media. It will highlight some pitfalls that one needs to appreciate to gain a scientifically based understanding of such material. Second, it will introduce the range of material that is included in this course, and show some of the relationships between the different topics that are introduced.

The first section of this chapter considers a few well-known case reports taken from the area of brain and behaviour research. This is designed to give you a feel for the kind of issues that will arise throughout the course and the type of approaches that biological psychologists take towards explaining them. But bear in mind that case reports are by their nature based on the study of a single individual and that, in general, scientists are wary of generalizing from a single example.

1.1.2 Exceptional ability – an exceptional brain?

A fascinating and controversial question is whether an exceptional ability is associated with an 'exceptional' brain. In a rather trivial sense, of course, this just has to be the case, since the brain is the part of us that is responsible for our thoughts and behaviour. However, a more interesting and still open question is whether there are identifiable differences in the structure of the brains of people that in some way can be mapped onto differences in their performance.

The eminent physicist Albert Einstein described how his rich scientific imagination involved the manipulation of mental images that had a visual form. When he died in 1955 at the age of 76 years, his brain was removed before the cremation of the rest of his body and was preserved. It was found that most features of his brain, including its overall weight, were unexceptional. However, tantalizingly, certain very localized deviations from an average structure were noted and these were only in the regions of the brain associated with the manipulation of visual imagery.

It is possible that that was no more than a chance occurrence. However, it is interesting to raise the question of whether the peculiar features of Einstein's brain contributed to his predilection to pursue theoretical physics and his capacity to solve some of its major problems. Or, alternatively, to what extent is the brain structure the product of a lifetime's experience of particular challenges? Could it be that doing advanced mathematics and physics changes the structure of the brain? This might sound implausible but an important lesson is that scientists try to keep open minds and never take anything for granted. In violinists, certain structures of the right side of the brain that are concerned with the control of the left hand are particularly well developed. The left hand is used for the manipulation of the strings of the violin. Could it be that persons initially having such an asymmetrical brain structure are attracted to playing the violin and show talent at it, rather than, say, piano playing?

Perhaps more probable is the idea that extensive practice at the violin changes particular parts of the brain in certain respects. Another possibility is that there is some truth in both of these ideas.

Herein lies a challenge: exceptional cases might point to ways in which brains function. However, as you will see, biological psychology often appears to raise more questions than it can answer.

1.1.3 A rational scientific explanation – Huntington's disease

George Huntington, an American, recorded the following experience from his boyhood when he was out riding with his father in 1860:

> Driving with my father through a wooded road leading from East Hampton to Amagansett, we suddenly came upon two women, mother and daughter, both tall, thin, almost cadaverous, both twisting, bowing, grimacing. I stood in wonderment, almost in fear. What could it mean? My father paused to speak with them and we passed on.
>
> (cited by Vessie, 1932, p. 564)

The condition from which the two women were suffering is now termed Huntington's disease, named after this same George Huntington. In 1872, Huntington described various features of this disorder – namely that it runs in families, the onset of symptoms occurs in adulthood and the slow deterioration of those affected. By 1932, painstaking research had revealed that almost all the people with Huntington's disease living on the East coast of the USA were descendents of a family group who emigrated to America in 1630, from Bures, in Suffolk, England.

Study of this disease raises the issue of how the brain controls behaviour. We can now identify a specific region of the brain that is affected in Huntington's disease and which is said to 'form its biological basis'. One of the roles of the brain region affected is in the control of muscles. A growing scientific insight into this condition, involving both its genetic basis and the region of the brain that is implicated, stands in stark contrast to a pre-scientific understanding. In the 17th century, people behaving in this way were said to be possessed by demons. Indeed, they were lucky if they managed to escape death by hanging, the charge of witchcraft being made particularly against women sufferers. As more and more insight into the brain is gained, so a broader range of behavioural abnormality is understood scientifically. Throughout the course, you might like to reflect on the ethical implications of accounting for behaviour in terms of the brain.

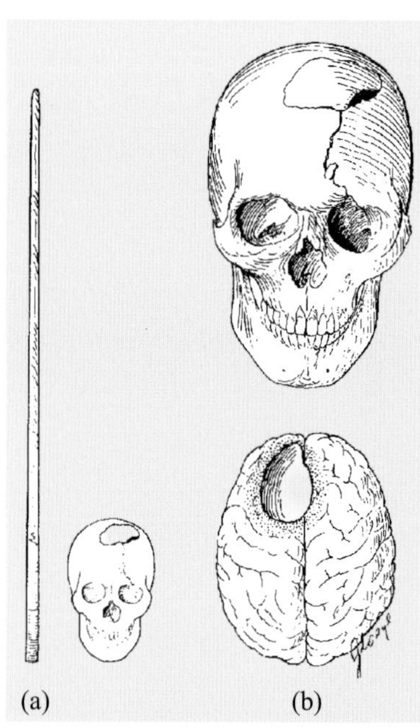

Figure 1.1 Phineas Gage. (a) The skull and the tamping iron drawn to scale. (b) The skull and brain (viewed from a different angle) showing the damage done by the tamping iron.

1.1.4 A tragic accident – Phineas Gage

One of the most famous names in the history of biological psychology is that of an American railroad construction worker, Phineas Gage. Probably little in Gage's background could have prepared him for his role in history! In 1848, in Vermont, during the course of his work, an accidental explosion sent a large tamping iron through the front part of his brain. (See Figure 1.1.) Miraculously, Gage survived the accident. However, his behaviour was altered. Previously he appeared to have been a well-respected 'upright' citizen and conscientious worker. After the accident, Gage started swearing and showing irritable and irresponsible behaviour.

Might we gain any understanding of the function of the front region of the brain from considering the changes in Gage's behaviour? Of course, this is a case of just one individual. Caution is always needed in interpreting the evidence of brain-damaged patients. The damage is extensive and unique; no one else will ever have exactly the same damage. Accidents rarely produce 'neat' damage to just one brain region. Also, we could never know the extent to which pain and trauma associated with the accident contributed to his change in behaviour. In such a one-off case of brain damage, there would be inordinate difficulty in assembling a group of similar individuals for comparison purposes, i.e. those experiencing trauma but without brain damage.

Such accidents cannot be considered in any sense to be scientific experiments. Normally in an experiment, something deliberate would be done to a group of individuals, the **experimental group** (e.g. they take specified amounts of a drug). The result would be compared with that from a group of similar individuals who did not receive the intervention (known as the **control group**). Clearly, this cannot be done in the case of accidental human brain damage.

However, it does indeed appear that the front region of the brain, which was damaged in the case of Gage, normally serves, amongst other things, to exert restraint on the expression of impulsive emotional behaviour. With damage to this region, a source of restraint is lifted. Later studies on this same brain region, using various techniques, suggest that it is involved in setting priorities and goals and in the inhibition of tendencies that act counter to the goal. Subsequent evidence from people who have had tissue removed from this region for the treatment of cancer is broadly in agreement with such an interpretation. Studies on non-human animals, point in the same direction. Herein lies an ethical issue: is it legitimate to inflict damage on the brains of animals in order to better understand the human condition?

One task of biological psychology is to try to identify the role that different brain regions play in the production of behaviour and the mental events described as 'mind'. The following two examples also illustrate this.

1.1.5 Classifying memory – H.M.

H.M. was born in Manchester, Connecticut, in 1926. When he was aged 9, H.M. fell off his bicycle, seriously injured his head and lost consciousness. At the age of 10 years, H.M. started to suffer from epilepsy, which was believed to be associated with the accident. The epilepsy became worse over the years and was resistant to all treatments. When H.M. was 27 years old and suffering constant severe fits which made living an independent life impossible, doctors decided upon the radical intervention of removing parts of H.M.'s brain on both sides.

Following the surgery, H.M.'s epilepsy improved but it was found that he had acquired some profound disturbances to his memory. He could recall very little of the events in the 12 years prior to the operation. For example, his favourite uncle had died 3 years prior to the operation but H.M. could recall nothing of this.

H.M. was also unable to remember people whom he met after the operation. A psychologist could spend the morning testing H.M. but in the afternoon H.M. would show no sign of recognizing the psychologist. Visitors to H.M.'s home were not recognized. H.M. would read, and then reread, the same magazine, showing no evidence of having seen it before.

Study of H.M. suggested that the brain regions that had been surgically removed would normally play a role in memory. However, although certain aspects of H.M.'s memory were severely disrupted after the operation, there were other aspects that were well preserved. For example, H.M. could engage in a fairly normal conversation. This is a skill that involves role-taking between speaker and listener and a memory of word meanings, grammar and 'who said what' in the immediate past. H.M. also showed an intact memory for motor skills such as how to mow a lawn. In the laboratory, he was tested on a novel task, that of reverse-mirror drawing, where new eye-hand coordination has to be acquired. In spite of H.M.'s success at this task, measured by an improvement in performance over days, at each stage he claimed to know nothing of having performed the task before.

As with Phineas Gage, brain damage gives clues as to the normal functioning of the brain. Patients such as H.M. give a valuable insight into memory and the issues surrounding how to classify it. They provide evidence that memory is not a unitary store of information. There are different types of memory, some of which can be lost with damage to a particular part of the brain, whereas others remain intact.

You might wonder about the ethics of performing such radical surgery with its associated drastic consequences. Of course, nowadays all other possibilities would be exhausted before surgery is carried out on the brain. We have learned a lot and these days surgery would be more finely tuned and targeted so as to avoid or minimize such risks.

1.1.6 Consciousness – the last great frontier?

Psychologists have amassed a considerable understanding of the kind of information processing that is carried out by conscious and **unconscious** processes. The term 'unconscious' refers to that part of the processing of the mind to which the individual under consideration is unaware. (See Box 1.1.) In other words, the individual has no conscious access to it.

Box 1.1 What term should we use?

Any writer in this area is bound to agonize over terminology. Here you might wonder – could we have employed either the term 'subconscious' or 'non-conscious' instead of that used here: unconscious? The term 'unconscious' is often associated with psychoanalysis and Sigmund Freud. However, its use here does not imply any attachment to such principles, which were developed largely in a different context from biological psychology. Another use of 'unconscious' is in a medical context to mean being in a state from which it is difficult or impossible to arouse the person concerned. Again, this is a rather different use from that to which the term is being applied here.

The result of a recent experiment on unconscious determinants of behaviour might surprise you. As far as the participants were concerned, the task was one of identifying the gender of a face but this was only a 'cover story' for the real intention of the study. As shown in Figure 1.2, psychologists presented images of happy, angry or neutral faces very rapidly on a screen just before presentation of another face of which the gender was to be guessed by the participant. The time of exposure of the first image was so rapid that no participant reported seeing anything of it at all. Such 'brief exposure images' are termed 'subliminal'. However, the subsequent behaviour of the participants showed that they were influenced by these subliminal images. Figure 1.3 shows the amount of a drink poured and drunk under the three conditions. On being asked to assess the drink, in terms of how much they would be prepared to pay for a can of it, participants exposed to the happy face gave a figure of twice as much as those exposed to the angry face.

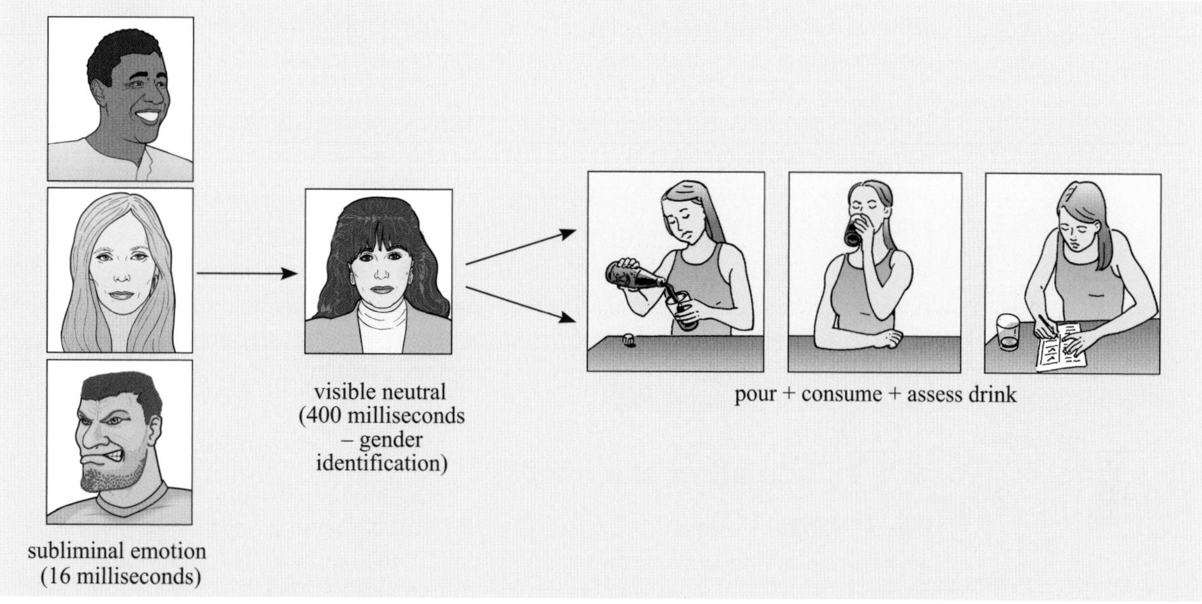

Figure 1.2 Experimental task. First, a subliminal image is presented for 16 milliseconds. The image is of either a happy, an angry or a neutral face. This is followed by the presentation of a visible neutral face. Then participants are asked to pour and consume a drink and then assess its value.

It is therefore relatively easy to demonstrate that the behaviour of all of us is subject to unconscious determinants, i.e. determinants about which we might know nothing. Biological psychologists would like to know how such information is processed and which parts of the brain are involved. Are different regions engaged with unconscious processing as compared to conscious processing? There are various techniques employed for investigating the responsibility of different brain regions but perhaps once again the most insight has come from looking at patients with brain damage.

A classic example of this is the patient known as D.B. and studied at the University of Oxford. D.B. was born in a market town in England in 1940. Up to the age of 14, nothing abnormal was noted in D.B.'s health. Then he started suffering from headaches associated with the right side of his head. Phantom flashing lights appeared before the onset of the headaches. In his twenties, D.B. noted that he had a blank region in his field of vision, i.e. a region of space in which he did not see anything.

An abnormality in the region at the back of D.B.'s brain, associated with processing visual information, was discovered and surgery on this part of the brain was performed to remove diseased tissue. The surgery was a success and the headaches and phantom flashes of light became something of the past.

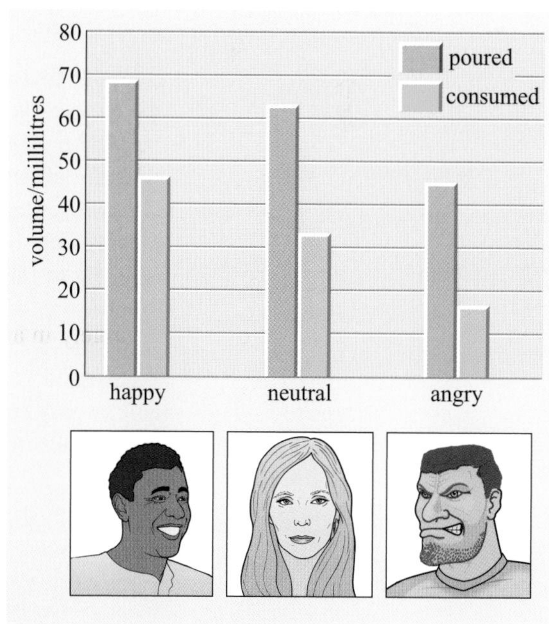

Figure 1.3 Result of the study showing the amount poured and drunk depending on which face was presented subliminally.

Following the operation and based on the results of controlled presentation of visual stimuli, D.B. did indeed appear to be blind in parts of his visual field: he reported that he could see nothing in particular regions of the visual world. These were the regions where he was expected to be blind, based on the location of the brain tissue removed. Closer scrutiny of D.B. found that the blindness was a relative thing: D.B. was blind in so far as having **conscious awareness** of events corresponding to the affected area of the visual field. That is, he did not give verbal reports of the events. However, D.B. showed evidence of *reacting to* such events. For example, he made eye movements toward visual stimuli that he claimed not to see. He reported being unable to see an outstretched hand but nonetheless reacted to it with a degree of accuracy by shaking it. D.B. could point to objects whilst denying that he could see them. The term **blindsight** is used to describe this feature of the vision of patients such as D.B.

We tend to feel that we have very good insight into the determinants of our own behaviour and that we can report these based on conscious insight. Patients such as D.B., as well as simple laboratory studies that are rather easily done on any of us, suggest a caution here. The nature of conscious and unconscious determinants of behaviour will feature in Chapter 4.

1.1.7 It's all in the mind?

People who have angina feel a pain in their chest which is caused by an inadequate supply of blood to the heart muscles. In the 1950s, one way of treating this condition was to perform an operation that involved binding up a number of vessels that ran near to the heart but which were not conveying blood to it. The expectation was that this would stimulate the sprouting of blood vessels supplying the heart and so relieve the pain. Large numbers of patients received the operation and for many it was judged to be a success. However, researchers were unable to find any evidence that such a sprouting of vessels was triggered.

Suppose that it was simply the procedure of the operation that had an effect, i.e. the expectation on the part of the patients that the operation would make them feel better. An effect involving an improvement based upon an expectation is termed a **placebo effect**. How could the possible role of a placebo effect be tested? In the USA in the late 1950s, a controlled study was performed. One group of patients received the operation just described. Another group was subjected simply to an opening of the skin but the blood vessels in the region of the heart were not touched (this is the control group). Both groups were treated the same in all other respects, and both were told that they were being given an operation upon some of their blood vessels. Neither the patients nor the doctors involved in the subsequent assessment knew the group to which any given patient had been allocated. Such a study is termed **double-blind**.

Patients in both groups reported a significant reduction in pain. The distance that they were able to walk without pain increased and their need for drugs declined.

Placebo effects are found in a wide range of different medical interventions. Perhaps the best known are those that involve the administration of drugs. Suppose that a particular drug has a known specific effect in targeting a specific pathological condition in the body. For example, morphine is widely recognized as a treatment for severe pain. Its chemical composition is known. Researchers can identify where it acts in the body and relate this to the experience of pain. Suppose someone expects to receive morphine but instead is simply injected with, say, a solution having exactly the same composition as the fluid of the blood. If they report some reduction in pain, this would be described as a placebo effect.

The implications of the existence of a placebo effect are vast and they greatly complicate the study of biological psychology. Patients come to a treatment with some expectation of its outcome, and so normally trust that what the doctor is doing will have some beneficial effect. This raises several serious ethical issues. For example, suppose that a doctor is deliberately using a placebo. Then, a patient asks the doctor to explain the nature of their treatment. Is the doctor to lie by describing some active chemical ingredient of the medicine? Similarly, human participants might well come to an experiment with some expectation of what the experimenter 'is after', e.g. that an injection will speed up subsequent reaction time.

Does the placebo effect mean that an apparent recovery can be due to events that are 'all in the mind'? The term 'all in the mind' raises important issues as to the nature of explanation and these will be discussed later in this chapter. However, even leaving such issues aside for the moment, there would be no justification to assume an action to be 'all in the mind' as a general truth. For example, morphine has effects that are more universal and stronger than any associated placebo. Such specificity is usually the case. However, the placebo effect certainly points to the important role that expectation and insight can also have when dealing with humans. It is important for biological psychologists to be aware of its ubiquitous presence. Some more of its implications will be explored later in this chapter.

1.1.8 Some issues in brain and behaviour

The examples just given are of course highly selective. However, they should have given you a feel for the kind of issues that occupy biological psychologists. A fundamental question underlying all of these studies is – how does the brain play a role in the production of mind and behaviour? In order to try to answer this, investigators consider both normal brains and brains that deviate from 'normal' in some respect. Among the questions posed are – what is the effect of brain damage? What is the link between brain processes and conscious awareness? What are the links between genes, brains and behaviour? The ways in which such questions are explored will be looked at in subsequent sections.

Alas, most of the examples chosen in the present section concern malfunction in one form or another. This is because insight can indeed be gained into the normal functioning of something by seeing what happens when things go wrong. However, from this you should not gain the impression that biological psychology only concerns things going wrong – there is the occasional happy moment in its study as well.

Summary of Section 1.1

Insights in biological psychology can be gained by looking at differences in brains and behaviour among individuals. A controversial issue is whether unusual abilities are associated with unusual features of brain structure. If such a relationship is found it raises further issues of how it is to be explained. The loss of a particular brain region or its malfunctioning can sometimes give rise to rather specific changes in behaviour and provide valuable insight into how brains normally function. An example of abnormality is Huntington's disease, an inherited condition that affects brain regions concerned with motor control.

One-off case reports include that of Phineas Gage who suffered damage to the front region of his brain and as a result his behaviour was changed. Another is that of H.M. which illustrates a distinction between types of memory. Damage to his brain disrupted one type of memory but left another intact. There are both conscious and unconscious brain processes involved in behaviour. D.B. exemplifies this in the case described as 'blindsight', where he was shown to react to events of which he was not consciously aware. The term 'placebo' raises profound issues on the nature of brain and mind and refers to an effect that relies upon a human's conscious insight into a procedure, whether therapeutic or experimental.

1.2 What is 'biological psychology'?

1.2.1 Introduction

Biological psychology attempts to build a picture that draws upon and integrates inputs from both biology and psychology. Its study has traditionally involved primarily the use of biology to explain phenomena of interest to psychology, e.g. the use of insight into the biology of the brain in understanding the altered behaviour of the patients H.M. and D.B.

Clearly, the brain plays a role in the production of behaviour and in our mental life. This course is concerned with such things as how different brain regions interact and how chemicals released in various parts of the body affect the working of the brain. We shall look at how genes play a role in determining the structure of the brain. However, the brain does not, of course, operate in isolation. Brains exist in bodies and brains require a supply of substances such as nutrients and oxygen in order to operate. In turn, bodies operate in a physical and social context. Therefore, the nature of the complex *interdependence* between brains, the bodies of which they form a part and their environment will necessarily engage our study.

1.2.2 Bodies and brains

Description and explanation

The body can be described in a number of different ways. One such description is in terms of the various **organs**, such as brain, heart, lungs and kidneys that make up the body. Organs are defined primarily in terms of their structure. Of the body's organs, the brain will form our principal focus.

Another description of the body is in terms of **systems** that perform particular functions, such as the cardiovascular system, made up of the heart, blood and blood vessels. This classification concerns what parts of the body do, e.g. to circulate blood around the body. In such terms, a principal focus of ours will be the **nervous system**, which is made up of the brain amongst other things. Defined in terms of function served, the nervous system is concerned with transmitting and processing information. This course will investigate the bases within the nervous system of such phenomena as perception, learning, emotion and motivation.

The body is composed of billions of small building blocks termed **cells** (which are described in detail in Chapter 2). Each organ is made up of millions of particular cells. Thus, muscle cells make up muscle and kidney cells make up the kidney. Some cells, such as red blood cells, move around the body.

Figure 1.4 is a representation of a number of cells of the body and their associated blood supply. Note the existence of a membrane surrounding each cell, the supply of nutrients (e.g. glucose) from the blood vessel to these cells and the removal of waste products from them. As far as cell types are concerned, our principal interest is a type that is found within the nervous system, termed **neurons**. (Neurons are described further in Section 1.3.2.)

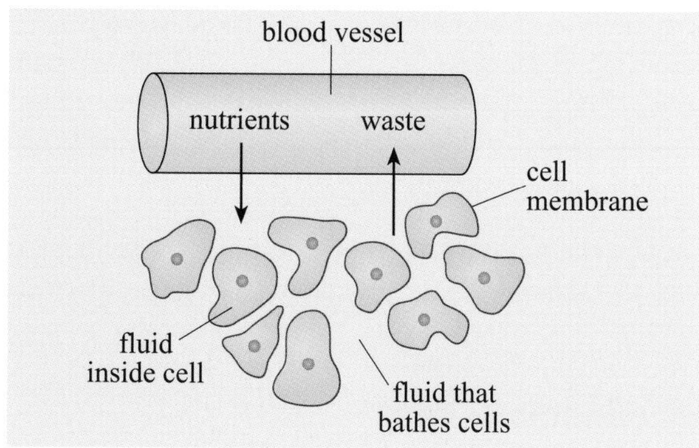

Figure 1.4 Schematic representation of some typical cells of the body shown in relation to their fluid surroundings and a blood vessel.

On a still smaller scale of analysis, we could look at the components such as the molecules and atoms that make up all the cells of the body, including those of the nervous system.

At various times, we shall need to consider each of these different levels of description and get to know how to relate them to one another. Without going far into the details, it is sufficient at this stage to note that, at each level, the body including the brain can be described in what is known as *material* terms. The meaning of this expression is much like the common-sense usage: to describe that which makes up the world 'out there', a world of so-called 'physical matter'. Cells, including neurons, are comprised of chemicals that can be weighed and analysed through various techniques and so, in chemical and biological terms, we form an account of what makes up the brain. Thus, at one level, the brain can be described in the terms of physics and chemistry, i.e. by the physical matter that comprises it. Similarly, a computer or television set can be described in physical terms, e.g. as something made of copper wires and silicon chips.

Of course, just knowing what makes up a brain, computer or television set does not give us an explanation of *how* it works, though such knowledge might provide some useful clues. For the moment, let us just consider that the task of understanding brain and behaviour is one of looking at how complex systems made up of physical components operate.

Explanation in terms of properties

Sometimes it is convenient and informative to explain events within the body and also behaviour in terms of certain important properties that the body exhibits. To exemplify this, the present section considers **homeostasis**. This term refers to the property of the body that, when one of its many key parameters shifts from its optimal level, action is taken to bring it back to the optimal level. Since the brain and behaviour are involved in homeostasis, this property of the body is of fundamental interest to biological psychologists. You will all be familiar with the concept of homeostasis from some of its better-known examples. Thus, when your body starts to overheat as in a sauna, sweat will soon appear on the body surface.

Sweating serves to lower body temperature. Conversely, in a cool environment, we start to shiver. This generates heat and increases body temperature. In other words, the body has an optimal temperature and deviations from this trigger action, which returns the body to its optimal state. With the exception of the somewhat strange behaviour of sitting in a sauna, we tend to take action to maintain body temperature, such as putting on extra clothes in winter and taking them off in summer.

Similarly, another illustration of the principle of homeostasis is the imperative for survival that body-fluid level does not depart far from its optimal level. Loss of water (dehydration) triggers thirst and the motivation (discussed in Book 6, Chapter 1) to seek water, whereas an excess of fluid triggers urination. At a time of dehydration, our minds can be preoccupied with thoughts of finding water.

So far, we have focused upon physical events within the body, though we have just noted an example of how these relate to mental events. The next section explores the nature of this relationship.

1.2.3 Brains, minds and consciousness

Introduction

An important theme that underlies biological psychology is the nature of the mind and its interdependence with brain and behaviour. One aspect of the mind, namely consciousness, came explicitly into focus in considering D.B.'s visual capacity. It was more implicit in the consideration of H.M.'s memory. The relationship between brain and mind is a perplexing topic that has taxed a number of eminent brains and minds for centuries. For the moment, the role of this section will be to state as clearly as we can the nature of the problem raised by asking how brains and minds are related.

If we first focus on the brain, we note that there are daunting problems involved in explaining how it works. Nonetheless, we have a good idea of how to pose the appropriate questions, as you will see in this chapter. Also, at least we know what a brain is, in terms of its constituent cells and some associated chemicals. We can also make an intelligent speculation on what kind of explanation is likely to emerge from any investigation, e.g. in terms of the patterns of activity in particular groups of neurons. When we come to try to explain the mind and consciousness, the difficulties are much greater, since even trying to define them is problematic. However, this is no reason for despair. Rather, we will start to define some basic terms in albeit an inadequate way and so gain some (provisional) understanding.

There are various ways of trying to gain insight into the nature of the relationship between brains, minds, consciousness and behaviour. We can experiment, e.g. presenting subliminal images and investigating their effect on behaviour (Section 1.1.6). Also, patients with brain damage can be investigated, as in the case of H.M. and D.B.. Moreover, each of us can engage in 'armchair philosophy' utilizing our own individual mental capacities. Based upon experimentation and personal insight, we can try to construct theories on the nature of the relationship between brain, mind, consciousness and behaviour.

Investigating conscious and unconscious processing – the link with the brain

By means of what is termed **introspection**, we can gain some insight into our own minds. Introspection is the process by which we inspect the contents of our conscious awareness and report on it. Reports on the content of our conscious awareness can then be compared across different individuals. We can note the way that these contents flow and shift over time. Sometimes our awareness is captured by immediate events in the world around us, such as a bird singing outside the window, and at other times it is engaged with thoughts of the past or plans for the future. For example, at the moment I am consciously aware of tapping the keys on my computer keyboard and producing the present text. A moment ago, I was consciously engaged with the thought of whether to leave for home or continue writing this chapter. Our conscious awareness or, as it is sometimes termed, our 'conscious mind' is perhaps the aspect of ourselves about which we have the most insight.

Employing the methods of traditional science, biologically orientated psychologists research how chemical manipulations alter mood, as, for instance, in antidepressant and anti-anxiety medication. Changes in behaviour following administration of a drug can be observed. However, perhaps the most reliable index of the efficacy of such medication is the subjective ('introspective') report of patients on their emotional state. This exemplifies the link between events in the physical body as targeted by drugs and events in the mind as subjectively experienced.

You will recall that the patient D.B. provided reports on the contents of his conscious awareness. These were of the kind, 'I saw nothing happen then'. That is, he was able to stop and reflect on the contents of his conscious awareness. Based upon our own introspection, we can speculate about the minds of others.

- For example, might the operation on H.M.'s brain to alleviate epilepsy have changed his conscious awareness?

- In the absence of an ability to update a memory of events, H.M.'s conscious awareness of the world (e.g. of people he recently met) would presumably be radically different from that of someone with this ability.

Note the different status of the knowledge gained about the mind by introspection, as compared to that gained about the brain. As an introspector, only *I* have knowledge of my own conscious awareness; no scientist, even with the most sophisticated technical equipment, has the privileged access that I have. The basis of this knowledge gained is very different from that concerning the brain. When it comes to brains, it is the objective scientist measuring such things as electrical activity and blood flows in the brain and analysing chemical composition that has privileged access. This might lead you to consider what was once seen only as a science fiction type of scenario, in which the scientists can get reliable knowledge on what you are thinking. Such considerations might still be premature but nonetheless they serve to remind us that biological psychology exists within a social context of concerns, responsibilities, ethics and principles.

- In what sense did the scientists studying D.B. have privileged access to his behaviour?

- They were able to monitor such things as his eye movements, which indicated to them that D.B. was reacting to events that he did not consciously perceive.

As we have just demonstrated, by introspection, we have access to that aspect of the mind that reaches conscious awareness. However, there is broad agreement in biological psychology that there also exists an unconscious aspect to the mind. A moment's reflection will show you that this is the case. For example, imagine the following scenario.

Mary What was the name of that American guy we met at the party last weekend?

John I have no idea – it's completely gone.

Mary Well try.

John I am trying.

Mary Try harder then.

John It's no good – but I think his name began with C. Let me stop trying for a moment.

Mary OK – let's water the garden.

John (5 minutes later) I have it – Charles – as always when I stop trying, it just pops from nowhere.

The considerable length of time between initiating a search for an answer and when the answer seems to 'pop from nowhere' is indicative of processing at an unconscious level. As introspectors, we have almost no idea at all of what sort of information processing is involved in such retrieval of stored information. The processing is not available to our conscious awareness. Only the result of the processing is what pops into consciousness. Such processing is sometimes described as occupying our unconscious mind.

Theories and models

What is the relationship between mind and the physical brain, and what kind of methods are employed in researching this question? One way of trying to describe minds and brains is to suggest that the mind is 'what the brain does'. This way of searching for explanations is within the bounds of traditional science, though it is compatible with insight also being gained by such methods as introspection. From this perspective, the term 'mind', in both its conscious and unconscious aspects, somehow captures the notion of the information processing carried out by the brain. A term that is commonly used in this context is **cognition**. This term refers to the information processing that is carried out by the brain, and lying between the incoming sensory information and the execution of behaviour.

For those of you who are fond of your computer, it can provide an **analogy** (or 'model') that might illuminate such issues for you. An analogy is a comparison between something that we already understand well and something that we wish to understand. Examination of what is familiar can illuminate the unfamiliar. The physical hardware of the computer, e.g. the memory system, keyboard, screen and printer can be compared to the physical brain.

◆ In terms of such an analogy, what would correspond to the mind?

◆ The software. That is the kind of operations run on the computer and the kind of information held in store, e.g. a calculation of tax owed or the text of your next TMA.

Thus, one can try to design computer programs that mimic some of the essential operations that engage mental processing such as adding numbers, finding a crossword clue or recognizing faces. This appears to describe something fundamentally different from the physical hardware of the computer.

However, the programs run on the computer and the memories stored in it depend upon the physical hardware. They cannot exist in its absence. Destroy the computer and you destroy the memory (including your next TMA, unless of course you remember to take a back-up copy – always a wise strategy!).

Could this provide a useful analogy of the distinction between brain (hardware) and mind (programming or software)? It certainly seems to help our thought processes and might thereby provide useful insight but this analogy, like any other, should not be taken too far. The brain and mind are, of course, not exactly like a computer. The analogy is a useful one in that it gives the logic as to why biological psychologists generally reject the notion of **dualism**. This term summarizes a belief in a duality, i.e. there is a fundamental independence between brain and mind, and the mind can have an existence even in the absence of a body.

This section and the previous one should have given you some initial feel for biological psychology. We now need to turn in the next section to some details of basic biology, with a focus on the brain.

Summary of Section 1.2

The body can be described in different ways, e.g. in terms of organs, systems and cells. Amongst systems, biological psychologists have the most interest in the nervous system and, amongst the types of cell, the principal interest is with neurons. Features of how the body functions (e.g. homeostasis) also provide a valuable source of insight into brain and behaviour.

Study of the mind creates profound problems of understanding since defining the issues is more difficult than in the study of the brain. The mind has both conscious and unconscious aspects. A means of investigating conscious awareness is introspection. One way of viewing the relationship between brain and mind is to suggest that the mind is what the brain does. A possibly useful analogy of brain and mind is in terms, respectively, of the hardware and software of a computer.

1.3 Some basics of biology

1.3.1 Systems

Earlier, in Section 1.2.2, we introduced the idea that we can employ the notion of systems to describe the body. Biological psychology involves consideration of several such systems but our principal focus is the nervous system. This section will first describe the basics of this system and then briefly introduce another, closely interacting, system: called the endocrine system. It should be noted at the outset that drawing boundaries around systems and defining them as 'nervous' or 'endocrine' is a matter of only temporary convenience. In reality, the interactions between systems are such as to make fuzzy any such boundaries.

1.3.2 The nervous system

Basic features

Figure 1.5 shows the human nervous system. A basic classification is into the **central nervous system (CNS)**, which consists of the brain and **spinal cord**, and the **peripheral nervous system**, which consists of all of the nervous system outside the CNS.

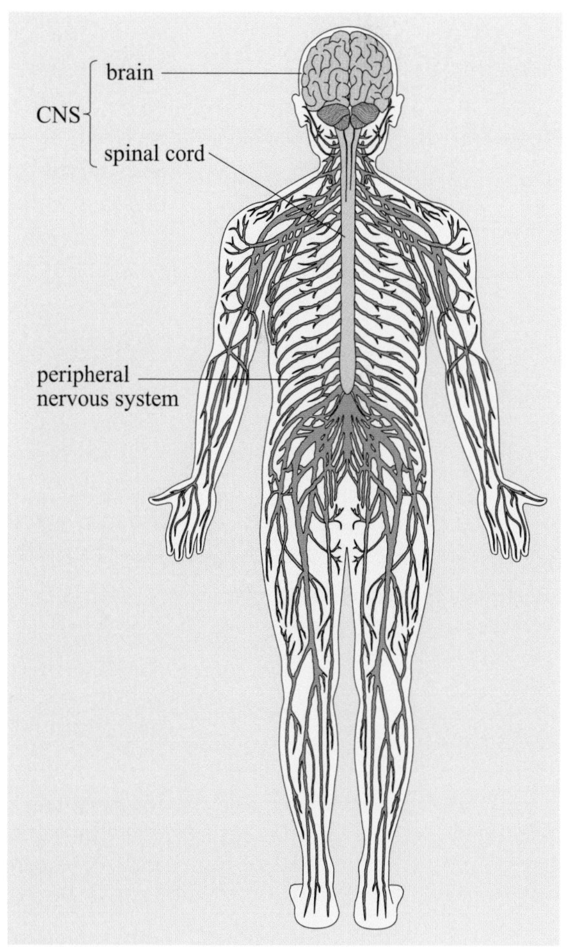

Figure 1.5 The human nervous system.

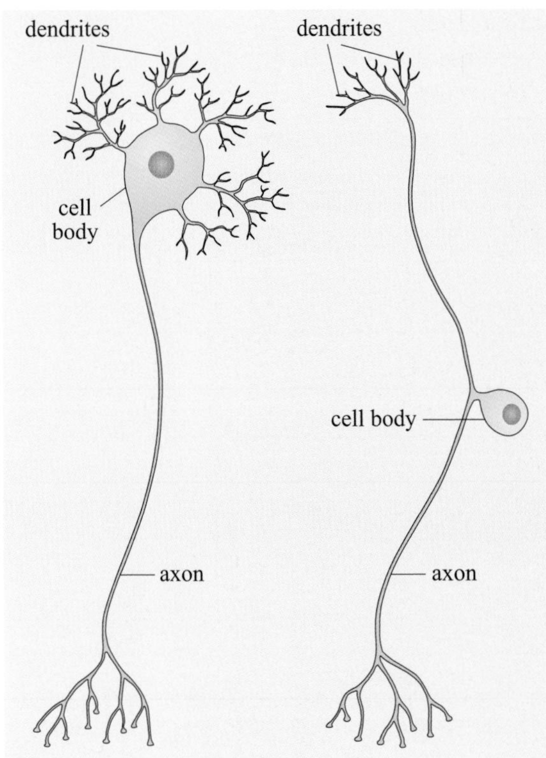

Figure 1.6 Two types of neuron.

As described earlier (Section 1.2.2), one type of cell that is found in the nervous system is the neuron. Neurons come in various shapes, two of which are shown in Figure 1.6.

Note that neurons are made up from component parts which are identifiable by their shape, e.g. the **axon**, **cell body** and dendrites. Like other cells of the body, a neuron is characterized by the small electrical voltage that exists between its inside and outside. Inserting a very fine electrode, called a **microelectrode**, into a neuron registers the presence of this voltage. In this regard, the neuron is like a miniature battery. Typically, the inside of a neuron, relative to the outside, shows a voltage of −70 millivolts (mV). The details are not important at this stage but just note that the minus sign signifies that the inside of the cell is described as 'negative' with respect to the outside. For us, the significance of this electrical voltage is that information is communicated by neurons in the form of changes in this electrical voltage.

Different neurons serve different roles. For example, a certain class of neuron (known as a sensory neuron) is sensitive to physical events in the environment. One important topic of this course will be how information about the world is encoded by neurons and this is discussed in detail in Book 4, Chapter 1. For example, the fact that you can detect whether water is hot or cold is due to the presence of neurons with their temperature-sensitive ends in your fingers. (This is illustrated by neuron 1 in Figure 1.7.) Note the axon and cell body of this neuron.

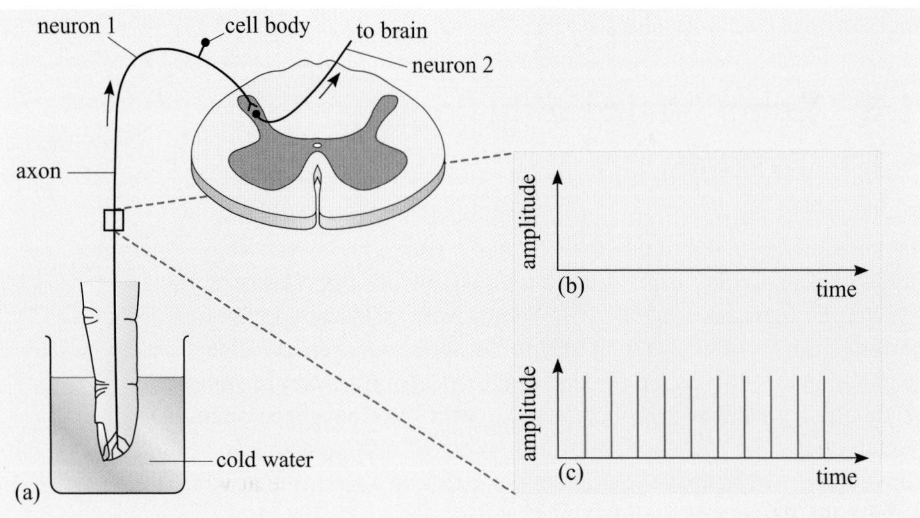

Figure 1.7 Detection of cold at a finger. (a) Two neurons and a slice of spinal cord. The graphs on the right show the response, measured as the amplitude of the signal sent by the neurons, when the finger is in (b) water at a neutral temperature and (c) very cold water.

Suppose you were able to record the electrical activity of a particular neuron with its tip at the skin. At first, the neuron exhibits a stable electrical voltage of −70 mV. Then you put your finger into some very cold water. As indicated in Figure 1.7, the neuron suddenly changes its electrical activity. That is to say, there is a sudden appearance of 'spikes' of electricity. These are termed **action potentials**. A neuron that is generating action potentials is sometimes described as 'firing'. Action potentials arise at the tip of the neuron under study, in response to the presence of cold. They are conveyed along the length of the axon of the neuron and, via another connecting neuron (neuron 2), thereby signal the information to the brain that there is cold present at the end of the finger. The axon of neuron 1 in this example is described as 'projecting' from the end of the finger to the spinal cord.

A collection of such axons all lying alongside each other in the peripheral nervous system is termed a **nerve**. (See Figure 1.8.) In the context of the peripheral nervous system, **afferent** means towards the CNS and **efferent** away from the CNS.

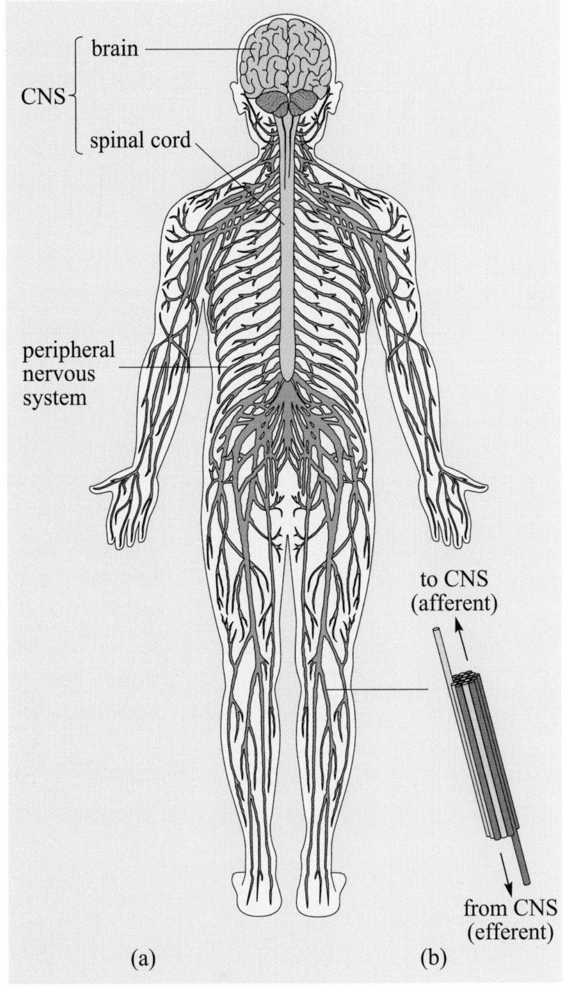

Figure 1.8 (a) The human nervous system, highlighting a nerve (b) consisting of a bundle of axons.

Another class of neuron (known as motor neurons) serves to alter the state of contraction of muscles. There are three types of muscle in the body – two are shown in Figure 1.9. The contraction of **skeletal muscle** alters the position of the limbs of the body. Amongst other roles, they effect what we all experience as willed action (often termed *voluntary* action), e.g. by changing the state of skeletal muscle, we can freely choose to get up to make tea. By contrast, we usually have rather little willed control over the contraction of **cardiac muscle**, which gives rise to the beats of the heart. The heart has its own intrinsic rhythm although its frequency of beating can be altered by changing circumstances. Changes in emotion (Book 6, Chapter 2) are a trigger to changes in the rate at which the heart beats and how intensely it beats. For example, when the central nervous system detects a threat and instigates the action of, say, fleeing or fighting, the activity of neurons immediately causes the heart to beat faster (route of neurons 3, 4 and 5 in Figure 1.9). Stress can also be associated with abnormally high activity of the heart.

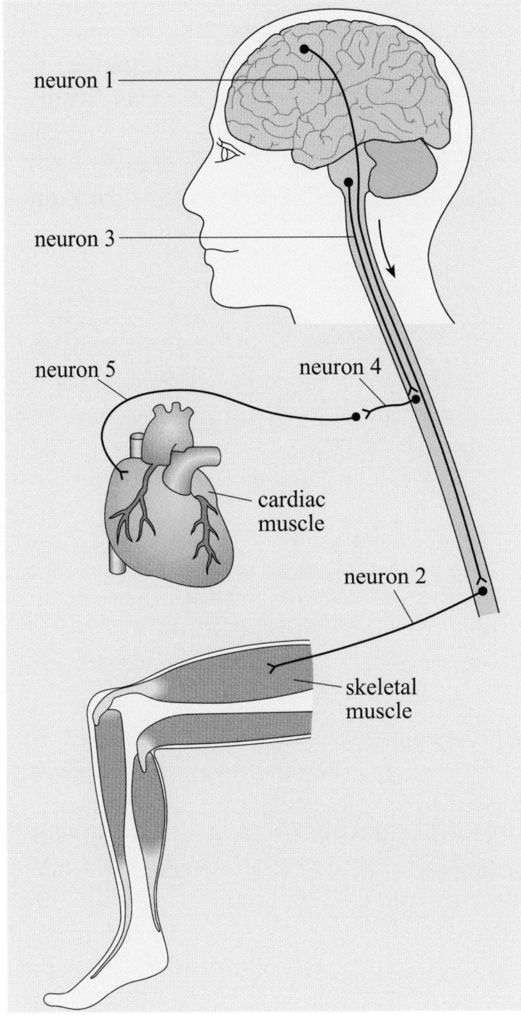

Figure 1.9 Two types of muscle and their controlling neurons.

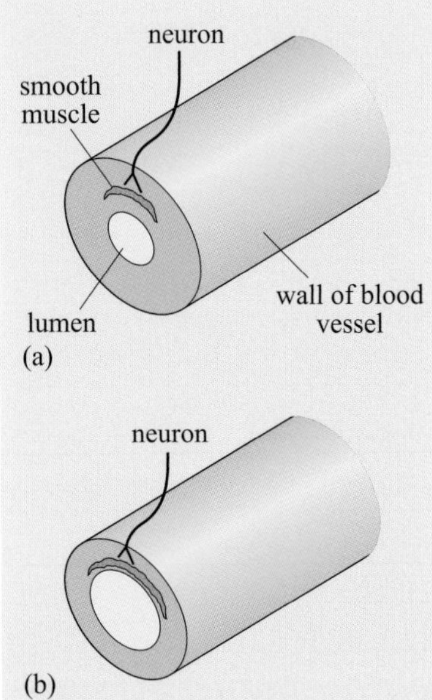

Figure 1.10 Smooth muscle embedded in the wall of a blood vessel. (a) Vessel and muscle relatively constricted, (b) vessel and muscle relatively relaxed.

Again with rather little willed involvement, **smooth muscle** controls amongst other things the diameter of the blood vessels of the body. As shown in Figure 1.10, the smooth muscle is contained within the vessel wall. When the skeletal muscles in, say, a leg are active in running, blood vessels supplying blood to the leg dilate, permitting a higher flow of blood. This brings more oxygen and glucose to the muscle, a necessary condition for its increased activity. The dilation occurs because of a change in the activity of the neurons associated with the muscle.

In Figure 1.7, note that the neuron that detects cold conveys information from the periphery to the spinal cord. A further neuron then conveys the information to the brain. In Figure 1.9, note that two neurons convey information from the brain to the skeletal muscle (neurons 1 and 2) whereas three convey information from the brain to the heart (neurons 3, 4 and 5).

As you can see there is a minute gap between two cells, whether neuron–neuron or neuron–muscle. This is the region at which one neuron influences another cell. Whether the latter is a neuron or a muscle cell, this region is described as a **synapse**. (See Figure 1.11.) At a synapse, information in the form of action potentials in one neuron is able to influence the activity in an adjacent cell. The action potential does this by triggering the release of a chemical from the neuron. This chemical, termed a **neurotransmitter**, very rapidly migrates across the minute gap between the cells. On attaching to **receptors** at the second cell the neurotransmitter influences the second cell's activity.

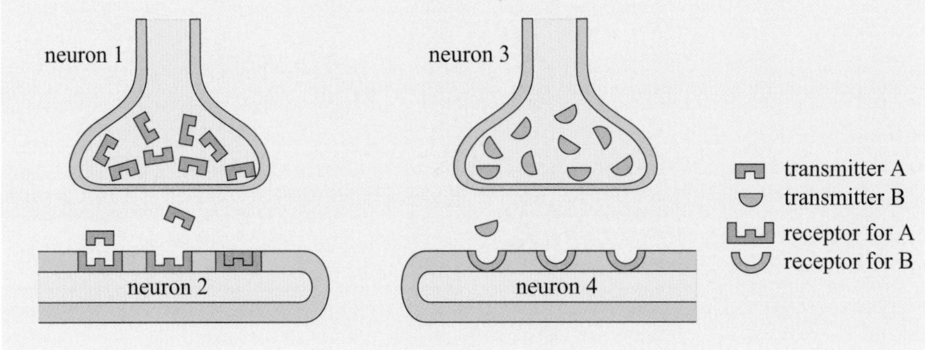

Figure 1.11 Two synapses. At one synapse, neuron 1 influences neuron 2, whereas at the other synapse, neuron 3 influences neuron 4. Note the two different types of neurotransmitter released by neurons 1 and 3 as indicated by different shapes and colours. Note also that the receptors are specific for the corresponding neurotransmitter.

Different neurons release different neurotransmitters and, as a first approximation, a neuron can be characterized by the type of neurotransmitter that it releases at synapses. For example, suppose that in Figure 1.11, neuron 1 releases a substance that is termed glutamate. It would be described as 'glutamatergic'. Suppose that neuron 3 releases acetylcholine. It would be described as 'cholinergic'. A neuron that releases dopamine is termed 'dopaminergic'.

Description of the nervous system

In order to explain the actions of the nervous system, we need first to know something of the conventions of its description. Figure 1.12 shows the meaning of the terms **dorsal**, **ventral**, **rostral** and **caudal** with regard to the human nervous system. When applied to the spinal cord, the term 'dorsal' means towards the back, but, in the head it means towards the top of the brain. The term 'ventral' means towards the front with regard to the human spinal cord and towards the bottom with regard to the brain. The term 'rostral' means towards the head when applied to the spinal cord, and towards the nose when applied to the brain. 'Caudal' means towards the tail with regard to the spinal cord and towards the back with regard to the brain.

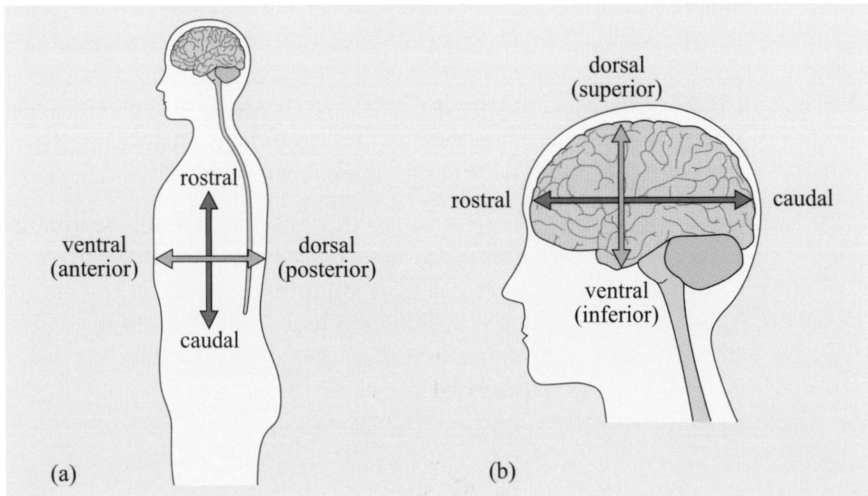

Figure 1.12 Anatomical notation to describe (a) the spinal cord and (b) the brain.

Figure 1.13 shows an outside view of the human brain, looked at from the front (an 'anterior' view). As shown, the terms **medial** and **lateral** refer, respectively, to a location near to the centre-line of the body and away from the centre-line of the body. Note that a large part of the brain can be divided into left and right hemispheres. Hidden from view but represented by black lines is a collection of neurons that project between one half of the brain and the other. One such projection constitutes a structure termed the **corpus callosum**. Figure 1.14 shows an outside view of the brain from the side, a so-called 'lateral view'. Note that large parts of the brain can be divided into four lobes: the **frontal**, **parietal**, **occipital** and **temporal lobes**.

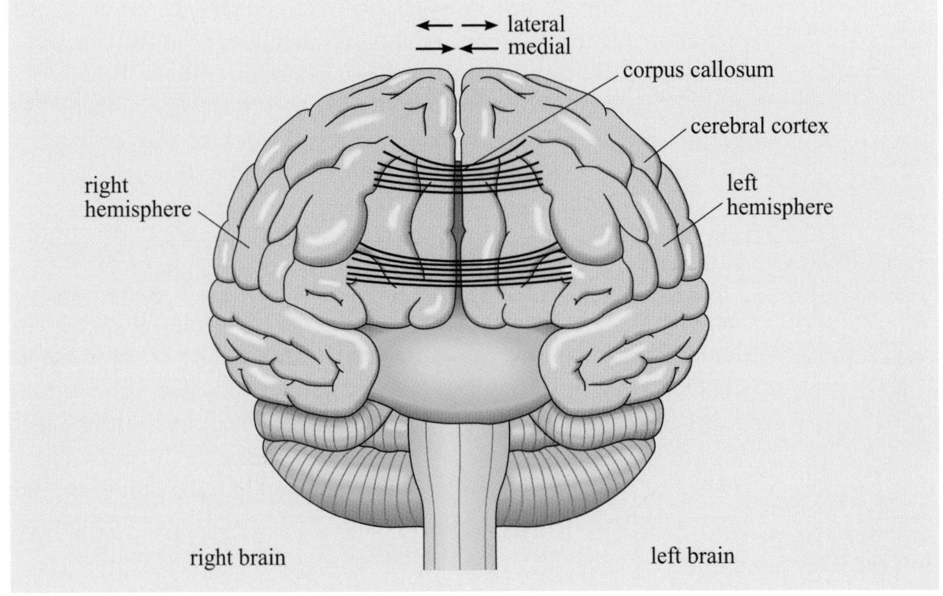

Figure 1.13 Anterior view of the human brain.

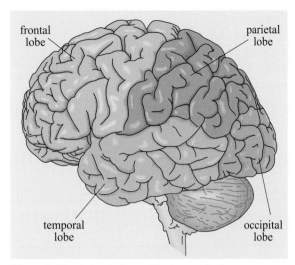

Figure 1.14 Lateral view of the human brain.

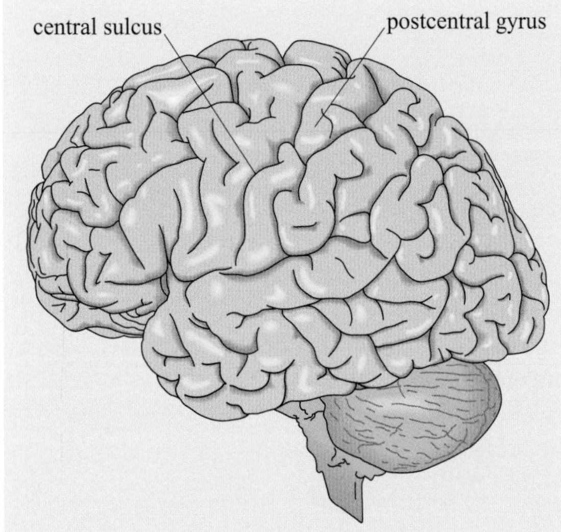

Figure 1.15 The brain indicating, in pale pink, the cortex.

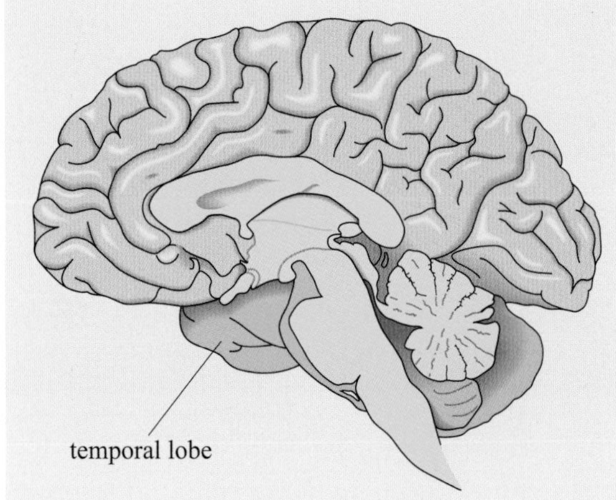

Figure 1.16 A view of the right hemisphere of the brain after the left hemisphere has been cut away.

- Which part of the brain of Phineas Gage (Figure 1.1) was damaged?
- The frontal lobe.

The outer layer of part of the brain, shown in pale pink in Figure 1.15, has a wrinkled appearance rather like a shelled walnut. This outer layer of the brain has the name of **cerebral cortex** and is made up of a series of ridges with grooves between them. A ridge is termed a **gyrus** (plural: gyri) and a groove is known as a **sulcus** (plural: sulci). These gyri and sulci are consistent when comparing different individuals and thereby they provide landmarks for mapping the brain. For example, Figure 1.15 indicates the central sulcus and the postcentral gyrus.

Figure 1.16 shows a sectional view of the right half of the brain after the left hemisphere has been cut away.

- This section involves a cut through which structure that has been introduced already?
- The corpus callosum (see Figure 1.13).

Sources of insight

There are a number of techniques for studying what nervous systems do and these are discussed in various chapters throughout the course, with a focus in Book 3, Chapter 2. This section gives a brief introduction to some of the more common techniques. Our understanding of how the nervous system works is tied closely to the techniques that are used for studying it. As these become more sophisticated, so we understand more.

Examining damaged brains – Historically, an important source of insight has been looking at the result of accidents (e.g. Phineas Gage) and damage due to injuries of war. Surgery on the brain has proven invaluable in understanding its function, as in the cases of H.M. and D.B., discussed earlier. For example, epilepsy based initially on abnormal neural activity in one hemisphere can tend to disturb the other, formerly intact, hemisphere. One way of trying to prevent this is by the drastic procedure of cutting through the corpus callosum, thereby disconnecting one hemisphere from the other. Patients can be tested before and after surgery and thereby any disturbance to behaviour and consciousness noted.

Imaging – These days an important source of insight into the brain is through what is termed **imaging** (discussed in more detail in Book 3, Chapter 2). A range of imaging techniques means that we can 'look' inside the brain and observe its structure and activity without the need to cut it open. In one such technique, 'labelled' glucose (or a substance with similar properties) is injected into the blood. By the term 'labelled', we mean that the glucose is radioactive and can be detected. As you saw earlier, glucose is used as a fuel by the neurons of the brain. At a time when a neuron is active and generating action potentials (as opposed to being relatively inactive), there is an increased demand for a supply of energy to the neuron. Therefore, particular bits of the brain that are most active at a given time take up more glucose from the blood than do relatively inactive regions. Since the glucose is labelled, the variation in the amount of radioactivity can be detected across the brain and hence the relationship between activity and brain region can be determined.

Using this technique, regions of damage can be identified in terms of their low activity and recovery of function can be monitored over time in terms of increasing activity. (See Figure 1.17.)

(a) 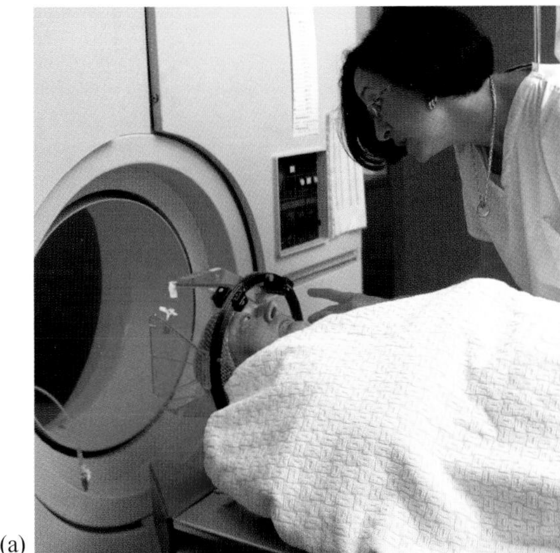

(b) 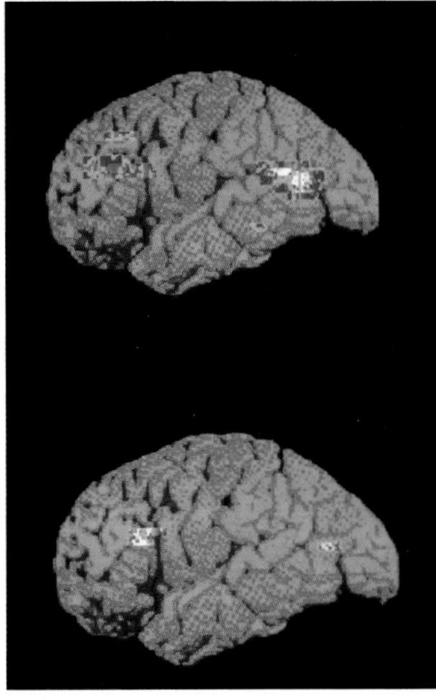

Figure 1.17 A PET scan (explained in Book 3, Chapter 2) showing images of the brain under different conditions. The different levels of activity are illustrated by the coloured regions. (a) Apparatus, (b) images.

The applications of this technology are wide. For example, the argument is sometimes made that violent psychopaths have an inability to inhibit impulsive behaviour, suggesting an underactivity in those front parts of the brain that were damaged in the case of Phineas Gage. Recording of glucose supply to different brain regions enables this to be assessed. Indeed, underactivity in parts of the brain of violent psychopaths has been found. The possible implications of this for the judgement made of violent criminals are vast.

Electrical recording – Another technique records the electrical activity of neurons. This technique, known as **electroencephalography** (EEG), involves attaching electrodes to the scalp and recording electrical activity (see Figure 1.18). (The recording is termed an **electroencephalogram**.) The electrodes pick up electrical signals that reflect the activity of groups of neurons, especially those nearest to the recording electrode, i.e. in the outer layer of the brain.

◆ What is the name of this outer layer of the brain?

◆ The cerebral cortex.

Amongst other areas of research, the EEG technique has proven very useful in the study of sleep. Sleep is not associated with a uniform pattern of electrical brain activity throughout the night but rather we go back and forth between a series of different phases. These are characterized by changes in such things as heart rate and, in certain phases, the appearance of small rapid movements of the eyes. Changes in the EEG are one way of identifying these phases (see Figure 1.18). EEG recording will be considered in more detail in Book 3, Chapter 2.

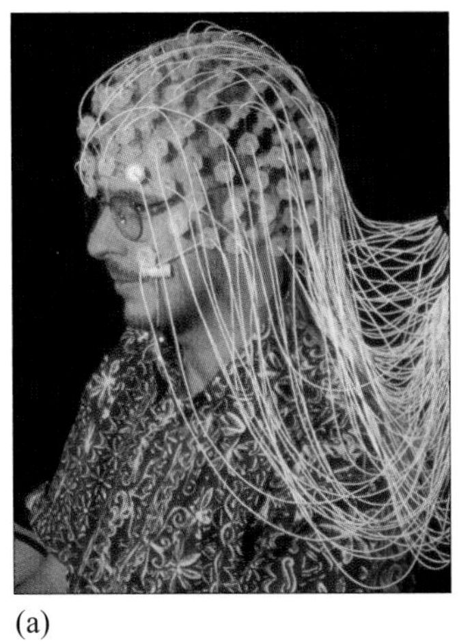

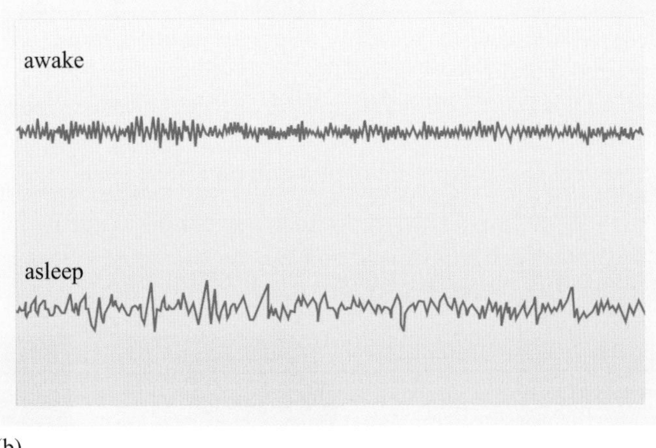

(a) (b)

Figure 1.18 Electroencephalography (EEG). (a) The apparatus used and (b) the trace of the electrical signal recorded.

Characterizing neurons and plotting pathways – It was noted in Section 1.3.2 that there are different types of neurotransmitter and that neurons can be characterized by the type of neurotransmitter that they contain and release. The study of the chemistry of neurons and their associated neurotransmitters is termed neurochemistry. By means of chemical analysis, researchers are able to establish the location of different types of neuron in different brain regions. Parts of the brains of laboratory animals can be analysed for their chemical content. Post-mortem analysis of human brains can be carried out and the chemicals located in different regions plotted. Comparisons between human and non-human brains can then be made. For example, consider Figure 1.19. It shows a section through a rat brain and a human brain. In the region known as the substantia nigra, there is a high density of dopaminergic neurons. These project to another brain region known as the striatum, conveying information from the one region to another. This exemplifies the point that particular pathways employing particular chemicals as neurotransmitters can be identified. The axons that form such pathways are bundled together.

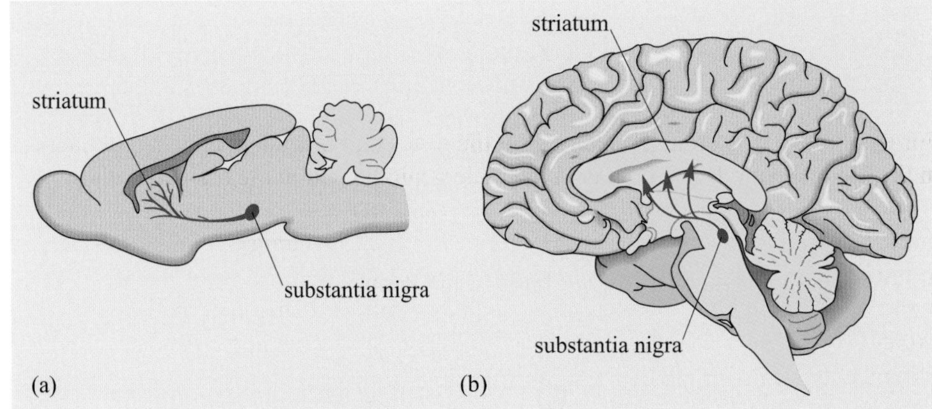

Figure 1.19 Substantia nigra and striatum, showing dopaminergic neurons that project between these regions in (a) a rat and (b) human brain.

1.3.3 The endocrine system

The endocrine system consists of the hormones of the body, their sites of release and their sites of action. A **hormone** is a substance that is secreted into the blood at one location and then transported in the blood to another location, where it exerts an effect on a target organ. The principal sources of hormones are the various **glands** that are situated throughout the body. (See Figure 1.20.)

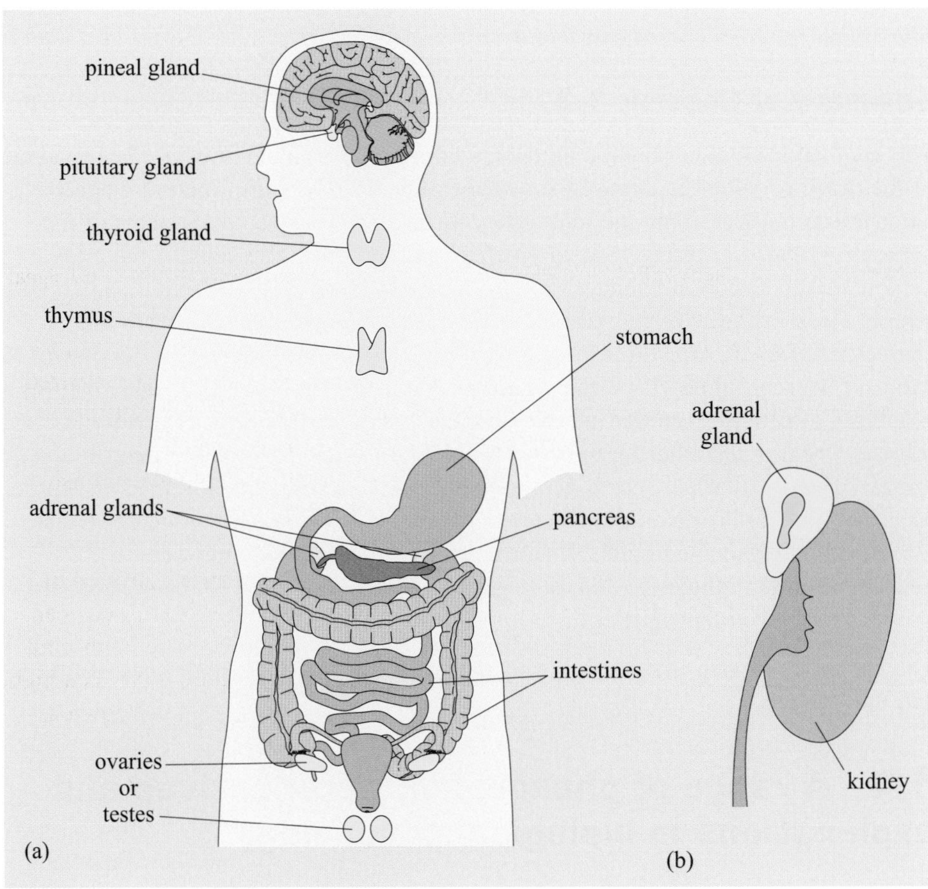

Figure 1.20 (a) Some of the principal glands from which hormones are secreted in relation to some of the body's organs. (b) The adrenal gland located above the kidney.

For example, testosterone is released by the testes and adrenal glands and circulates in the bloodstream. It has effects at the male genitalia and in the brain. Another hormone, arginine vasopressin, is secreted from a gland located at the base of the brain, the pituitary gland, in response to dehydration. It is transported in the blood to the kidney, where it slows up the production of urine. If the body is over-hydrated, secretion of the hormone is slowed or stopped altogether and the excretion rate of water is high. In this way, regulation of the body water level is achieved.

- ◆ What is the term given to this regulatory property of the body?
- ◆ Homeostasis (see Section 1.2.2).

Certain hormones will be a major interest in the present course because, via the brain, they both influence behaviour and are influenced by it. Thus, for example, a certain hormone influences the activity of parts of the brain underlying fear and thereby affects behaviour. Reciprocally, the brain influences the secretion of hormones. By its effects on the brain, the environment can influence levels of hormones.

So much for the basic biology, we shall now build on this by turning to a more detailed consideration of the nature of explanation in biological psychology and to some of the controversial issues that it raises.

Summary of Section 1.3

The brain and spinal cord make up the central nervous system (CNS). The remainder of the nervous system is termed the peripheral nervous system. There are agreed conventions for describing the relative location of the various components of the nervous system, e.g. terms such as 'ventral' and 'dorsal'. The cells of the body exhibit a small electrical voltage. Neurons are specialized cells that exhibit a particular type of electrical activity that takes the form of action potentials. Neurons are characterized by the neurotransmitter that they release. In some cases, bundles of the axons of neurons employing a particular neurotransmitter form identifiable pathways. Examples of neurotransmitter include acetylcholine and glutamate. Following its release, a neurotransmitter influences a neighbouring cell, i.e. another neuron or a muscle. The junction between a neuron and a neighbouring cell is termed a synapse. Means of gaining insight into the nervous system include examining the behaviour associated with damaged brains, imaging, electrical recording and tracing neurotransmitter pathways. A measure of the combined activity of many neurons is shown in the electroencephalogram.

The endocrine system is made up of the hormones of the body, their sites of release and their targets.

1.4 A range of phenomena, perspectives and explanations in biological psychology

1.4.1 Introduction

Earlier sections raised a number of issues in biological psychology such as the role of inheritance (exemplified by Huntington's disease) and the nature of explanation of behaviour based on single case reports. The last section considered the link between brain structure and behaviour. This section will build on earlier material by considering (a) the wide range of phenomena studied in biological psychology, (b) different perspectives taken in studying these phenomena and (c) the different *types of explanation* that relate to them. A challenge will come in the present chapter, and even more so later in the course, in trying to relate these types of phenomena, perspectives and the associated types of explanation.

Explanation, in essence, consists of trying to establish the existence of reliable relationships between different events. Sometimes these events are close in time, for example, a particular substance is injected and you immediately feel ill. In other cases, the effect of the events are reflected over a large part of a life-span, e.g. you were frightened of water when young and this is manifest as a fear of learning to swim when adult. In still other instances, we try to relate events over many generations, explanations that appeal to principles of genetics and evolution. This section will look at the range of these different types of explanation.

1.4.2 Describing and relating the phenomena

Introduction

Figure 1.21 shows something of the hierarchy of phenomena studied in biological psychology. As we go from bottom to top, so the scale of the phenomena becomes larger. At the lowest level, there are the chemicals that make up the nervous system. Just above this is the level of the activity of whole neurons and at the next layer up is the activity of collections of neurons making up the nervous system. Above this is the behaviour of the individual and, at the top, is the social behaviour of groups of individuals. Explanations within biological psychology usually cross these levels, as indicated by the arrows. For example, individual behaviour is often explained in terms of events within the nervous system (represented by an upward-pointing arrow). The approaches to explanation differ in where the focus of explanation is made. In the context of Figure 1.21, some examples of the sources of insight are now given.

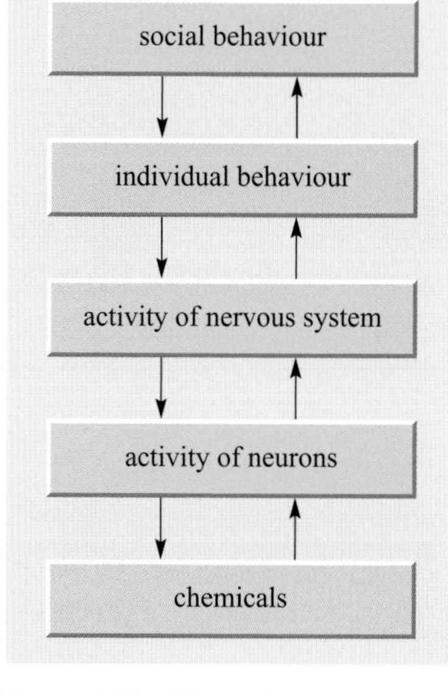

Figure 1.21 Hierarchy of phenomena studied in biological psychology.

Explaining behaviour – the neuroscience approach

An investigation of the properties of neurons and how they perform can give useful insights into behaviour. For example, it is possible to identify different neurotransmitters (e.g. dopamine), investigate their chemical properties and relate these to the role of dopaminergic neurons and the synapses that they form.

As another area of research, some investigators look at topics such as the speed of transmission of action potentials in different neurons. See Figure 1.22. There is a relationship between the diameter of the axon of a neuron and the speed with which it conducts action potentials (Figure 1.22a). As a classic example, the squid has one particular neuron with a relatively enormous axon diameter. This neuron has a high conduction speed and is involved in the animal's escape response from dangerous stimuli. Some species including humans (but not the squid) have an insulated coating around the axon (Figure 1.22b). This increases the speed with which action potentials are transmitted. In some disease states, this insulation is lost with an associated slowing of the speed of conduction of action potentials; this is manifest in such ways as disorders of the control of movement. There are some important properties of neurons that are common to different species, so looking at a neuron from, say, a squid can illuminate features of how the neurons of humans work.

Other researchers are primarily concerned with the investigation of behaviour, often with reference to the nervous system, as we shall now discover.

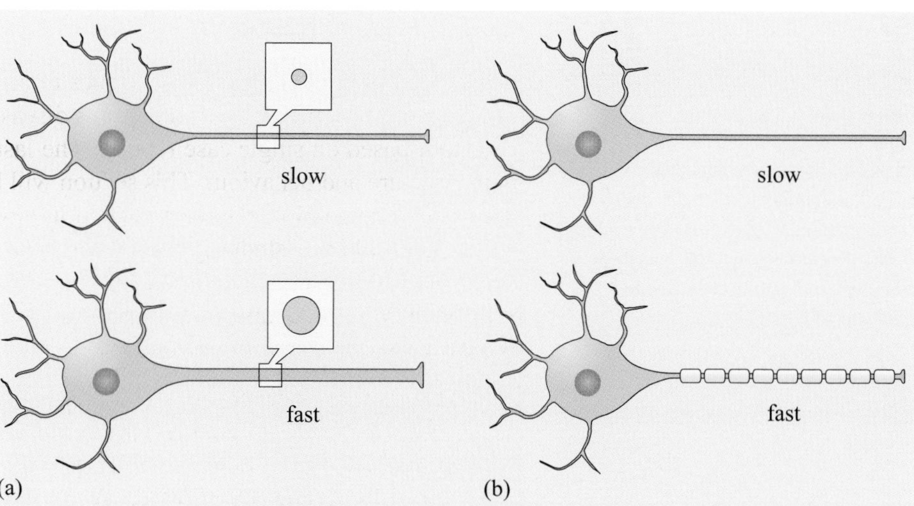

Figure 1.22 (a) Different neurons with different diameters of axon conduct action potentials at different speeds and (b) the presence of insulation speeds up the action potential.

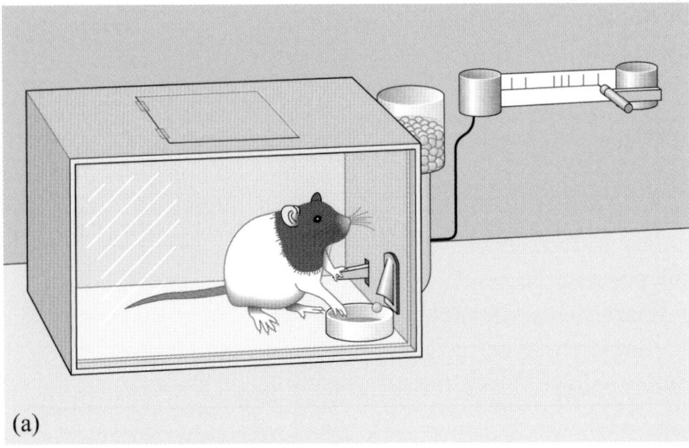

Figure 1.23 Skinner box (a) for a rat and (b) for a pigeon.

Explaining behaviour – the psychological approach

Traditionally, psychologists have attempted to derive general principles of behaviour from their observations of rather few species, namely rats, pigeons and humans. Psychologists have studied behaviour in simple well-controlled environments, often focusing on individual animals. In this way, a single variable can be altered and the effect on behaviour observed. For example, the effect of a prior period of food deprivation on feeding behaviour can be investigated.

To achieve control over the experiment, psychologists use various pieces of apparatus such as the maze and the **Skinner box**. (See Figure 1.23.) In the Skinner box, a hungry rat presses a lever and is rewarded with a pellet of food. Using this apparatus, such questions as, what factors influence how rapidly the rat learns to press the lever can be investigated. For example, increasing the length of time a rat has been deprived of food before the experiment decreases the amount of time it takes it to learn the task of pressing the lever. Also, as shown in Figure 1.24, once a rat is trained (has learned to press the lever), prior deprivation has the effect of increasing the rate of lever-pressing for food.

Figure 1.24 The results of an experiment in which rats earned food pellets by pressing a lever in a Skinner box. The graph shows responses (lever-presses) per minute for a group of rats plotted against the length of time they had previously been deprived of food.

Another use of the Skinner box is in assessing the perceptual capabilities of animals. For example, suppose that a pigeon is rewarded with food for pecking when a green light is shone on a screen in the box. It is not rewarded when a blue light of the same intensity is shone. The pigeon will come to peck only in the presence of the green light and refrain from pecking when the blue light is present. That is to say, the animal forms a 'discrimination'. Two colours very similar to each other can be tested under these conditions to see whether the pigeon can discriminate between them. Thereby, the limits of a pigeon's perceptual abilities can be measured.

Within this tradition, moving between levels to seek explanations commonly takes the form of trying to explain behaviour in terms of events in the nervous system (represented by an upward-pointing arrow in Figure 1.21). For example, injection of a particular chemical into a brain region might stimulate drinking. Another chemical in a different region might boost or reduce appetite, as measured by the rate of lever-pressing for food in a Skinner box.

Another application of the Skinner box is to investigate emotion (discussed in Book 6, Chapter 1). For example, a rat can be trained to fear a particular audible tone following its pairing with a mild electric shock. The tone's fear-evoking capacity is measured by the degree to which it suppresses responding for food by a hungry animal. The effect of drugs that alter mental state in humans (psychoactive drugs, e.g. anti-anxiety drugs) can then be investigated, as measured by their effect on reducing the suppressive power of the tone. The Skinner box has proven valuable in testing psychoactive drugs for human use. Whether an experimental species such as a rat or pigeon really experiences a subjective state of conscious emotion is a topic of speculation but their behaviour shows some important similarities with that of humans.

The accusation has often been made that looking at species performing simple tasks within a piece of laboratory apparatus fails to capture the full richness of a species' potential. In other words, pose an over-simple question and you might expect an over-simple answer. However, the value of the Skinner box in drug testing is without doubt.

Explaining behaviour – the ethological approach

The science of **ethology** is a branch of zoology where a wide range of species are studied and their behaviour is looked at mainly in natural environments. When animals are brought into the laboratory for study, attempts are made to create something of the natural lifestyle of the species. A broad range of different behaviours are studied. However, ethologists tend to focus on what is common within a given species. Ethologists seek insight into how particular species achieve particular feats of behaviour. For example, how are the visual and auditory systems of the owl geared to hunting at night?

Seen in these terms, different species can find very different 'solutions' to problems of survival depending upon such things as the habitat in which they evolved. Thus, scientists might compare the behaviour of two closely related species living in two different habitats. For example, consider the two species of gull, the kittiwake, which nests on cliffs, and the herring gull, which nests on the ground. The herring gull camouflages its nest, whereas the kittiwake does not. Ethological studies have revealed that the nest of the herring gull is commonly prone to predation, whereas that of the kittiwake is not.

The ethological tradition of looking at (often subtle) differences in behaviour between related species and linking this to function has strongly influenced a number of biological psychologists. Indeed, these days, the disciplines of ethology and biological psychology often tend to merge. In some cases, closely related species can be compared not only in behaviour but also in nervous systems and this can be linked to function.

As an example, consider two North American species of vole with very different lifestyles in one important regard: the monogamous prairie vole and a species that does not form social bonds, the montane vole. After mating the prairie vole normally forms a pair-bond. Evidence suggests that two hormones, oxytocin and vasopressin, are implicated in the forming of pair-bonds. Both are released at the time of copulation in voles. In prarie voles, injection of these substances into the brain facilitates pair-bonding, whereas substances that impair the action of these natural hormones inhibit pair-bonding. Neither substance has an effect on the social behaviour of the non-pair-bonding montane vole, even though they are naturally present. This has led to the identification of areas of the brain rich in receptors to these substances in prairie voles but lacking them in montane voles. This suggests that such areas are implicated in forming pair-bonds.

1.4.3 Some implications of moving up and down the hierarchy of phenomena

Introduction

The relationship between the phenomena shown in Figure 1.21 is of a two-way nature, as indicated by the two directions of arrows. An upward-pointing arrow represents lower-level events being used to explain higher-level phenomena. For example, as just noted, the study of behaviour can be illuminated by considering the activity of neurons. Thus, injecting a particular chemical that mimics the action of dopamine might change the behaviour of an animal. This could give us insight into the way in which this chemical affects the activity of specific neurons and thereby systems of neurons and ultimately behaviour. Also in terms of upward-pointing arrows, the explanation of social phenomena sometimes appeals to biological principles. For example, examining the causes of human aggression involves asking questions of the kind – what is the role of the hormone testosterone?

However, as indicated by the downward-pointing arrows, events at a lower level can sometimes be explained by events at a higher level in Figure 1.21. For example, there is a growing realization that social relationships between animals can affect the biology of the body. In a study of the effect of the drug amphetamine (a drug that triggers activation of dopamine) on the social behaviour of monkeys, no consistent result was found. However, when the researchers looked at the social status of the animals, order could be extracted from the data: for animals high in the social hierarchy, dominance was increased by the drug, whereas for those low in the hierarchy, the tendency to submission was increased. The role of the drug made sense when viewed in a social context. This example illustrates particularly well how (a) influences arise at different levels and (b) why scientific explanation necessarily crosses different levels of phenomena.

Studying phenomena located at a top position does, of course, not mean a better perspective on behaviour. Rather, it refers simply to the scale of the phenomena described.

Reductionism

With reference to Figure 1.21, the process of providing an explanation of a higher-level phenomenon in terms of events at a lower level is sometimes termed **reductionism**. For example, an understanding of the behaviour of an animal might be sought by looking at the properties of the neurons that make up the nervous system or levels of activity of a particular hormone.

A caution needs to be sounded in the use of reductionism. First, although insights can be gained by reduction, in general the process of explanation is not *simply* one of looking to lower levels. Let us consider again the effect of the drug amphetamine. Useful understanding of its effects on behaviour can be found by looking at how it influences specific types of neurons, e.g. dopaminergic neurons in particular brain regions. There is a very good understanding at this level. However, the *whole brain* is involved in producing behaviour and a drug's effect cannot be understood solely in terms of what happens at the particular neurons that form the target of a drug intervention. By its effects on behaviour of an individual, the social dynamics of the group are influenced and such social behaviour, in turn, influences the individual. Via perception of the world, the nervous system is influenced by the behaviour of other animals.

For an example that makes a similar point, consider the role of the hormone testosterone. This hormone has a number of influences on sexual motivation and aggression. Thus, to understand behaviour we would need to look at the role of this hormone within the body, e.g. its action on neurons in the brain. However, in addition, the social dynamics within which the individual exists, also affect the activity of the hormone. In monkeys, winning a fight increases testosterone levels and defeat is associated with a reduction. In human males, when their favourite football team wins there is an increase in the level of testosterone.

Emergent properties

As one feature of explanation, the term **emergent property** is sometimes used. This term conveys the sense that, at each level of organization, new properties appear that are not evident by studying the components, i.e. at a lower level.

For an example, consider that water is made up of a mixture of two gases: oxygen and hydrogen. At one level of analysis, that of chemical constituents, water is *nothing but* this combination. However, it is obvious that the combination yields new properties that are not present in the components. For example, the property of liquidity emerges from the components; it is not possessed by the individual gases. Any study of the properties of water, as in looking at its flow in pipes and rivers, would need to consider this emergent property of liquidity.

◆ In what way can social behaviour be used to exemplify the notion of emergent property?

◆ Obviously, the complexity of social behaviour depends upon the properties of the individuals who are interacting socially. However, looking at each individual in isolation does not enable us to predict the behaviour of these individuals when put together in a social group. New principles of organization *emerge* at the social level and new types of explanation are needed. For example, crowd violence at a football match usually occurs when rival supporters clash. It cannot be understood in terms of the behaviour of an individual *viewed in isolation* even though, of course, individual behaviour is involved.

The existence of properties that emerge at one level serves as a caution against the unwarranted excesses of reductionism.

1.4.4 Causation and correlation

A study of the structure and function of the nervous system and its relation to behaviour and the mind, as introduced in the last three sections, is the major perspective within biological psychology. This type of investigation most usually corresponds to an upward-pointing arrow in Figure 1.21. In large part, this approach is characterized by considering questions of a *causal* nature and which lead to a **causal explanation**. Suppose that one event appears to *cause* another to occur. Did it really cause the second event to occur or is their relationship in time mere coincidence? If we are able to establish a causal link between two events, a further question is *how* did one event cause an influence to be exerted on another event?

However, care is needed when establishing a link – imagine a series of observations on two church clocks. It is noted that every time that the clock on one church chimes so, half a minute later, that on a neighbouring church also chimes. Here we have a close and reliable association between two events but we would not suggest that the first event causes the second to occur. Rather, we would say that they are 'correlated'. It is important to distinguish between what is nothing more than correlation and what is truly causation. You met this kind of consideration in one of the case reports (Section 1.1.2): the brain regions concerned with control of the fingers in violinists tend to be asymmetric. Did the asymmetry *cause* them to choose the violin or, as seems more likely, did playing the violin *cause* the asymmetry. It is also possible that neither of these is true and there is nothing more than a correlation present. Some third factor might have led both to changes in the brain and to this choice of career.

In order to establish that one event causes another to occur, as experimenter, we need to manipulate one event and see whether this is followed by changes in the other event (discussed in detail in Book 2). For example, we might manipulate the level of alcohol in someone's body by giving them standard doses of alcohol and see whether their performance on a simulated driving task is impaired.

Suppose that alcohol is ingested and shortly afterwards the person behaves in a more extrovert fashion and shows some lack of motor coordination. We might ask – what happened to cause this change in behaviour? Was the nervous system affected by the chemical content of the drink or did the participants act according to an expectation of the role of alcohol?

- ◆ What would the latter effect be termed?
- ◆ A placebo effect.

Here we formulate precise hypotheses of what causes what, e.g. that alcohol makes a person more extravert or it causes a slowing of reaction time. We might also hypothesize that it does so by means of its direct chemical effects on the nervous system and even in the absence of any expectation on the part of the participants. It is possible to perform experiments to test such hypotheses, the topic of Book 2.

As discussed here, causal questions often relate to events rather close together in time, such as the effect of alcohol on performance. The following section is devoted to examining events over rather longer periods of time, including sometimes a whole lifetime, and here occasionally questions of a causal nature are also asked.

1.4.5 Within-lifetime explanations

This section considers two classes of change that occur within the lifetime of a given individual but over relatively long periods of time. It asks the question – how do differences among individuals arise? Close scrutiny reveals that the distinction between the two phenomena described in this section, development and learning, is not an absolute one but one which is made for initial convenience of explanation.

Development

We start our lives as one fertilized egg, a single cell. This cell then divides into two, a process termed **cell division**. In turn, these also divide, and so on, until we end up with the astronomically large number of different cells that make up the adult. Amongst the cells that arise in this way are those that make up the nervous system.

- What is the type of such cells that we have described so far called?
- Neurons.

The term **development** refers to the emergence of the adult form from what was initially a single cell. Development can be investigated from both a biological perspective (e.g. development of new neurons and the changes in their structure and interconnections with age) and from a psychological perspective (e.g. the child's acquisition of language). The challenge for biological psychology is to try to form links between these perspectives, e.g. how does the emergence of new psychological characteristics relate to development of the nervous system? (Development of the nervous system will form the central theme of Book 3, Chapter 3.)

Role of genes and environment – In order to understand development, we need to know something of **genes** which contain the hereditary information of the body. So what are genes? Genes are complex molecular structures that are contained within the cells of the body. Genes are joined one to another to form longer molecules called **chromosomes**. See Figure 1.25 for a very simplified representation. Chromosomes are paired structures, as can be seen in the diagram.

Genes are responsible for the accurate construction (termed 'synthesis') of a type of molecule called a **protein**. Proteins are a particular kind of molecule that form an important part of the structure of cells and therefore of the body. Thereby, genes are involved in the construction of the body.

As shown in Figure 1.25a, genes exist within a cellular environment. In turn, each cell exists within an environment in the body. The whole animal exists within a physical and social environment. This gives several layers of interaction as shown in Figure 1.25b. Genes play a role in the developing animal, human or other, but they do not do so in isolation. Genes are said to be 'turned on', or expressed, at particular times, i.e. when they exert their effect on protein synthesis. When they are turned on depends in part upon events surrounding the genes within the cell and these in turn depend upon events outside the cell.

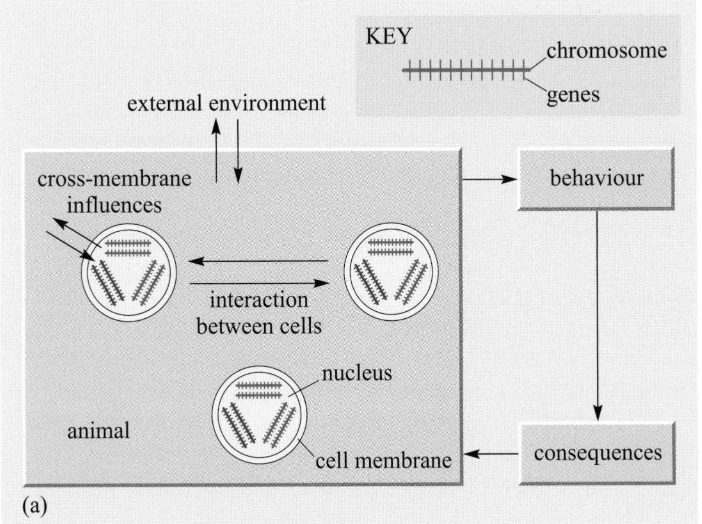

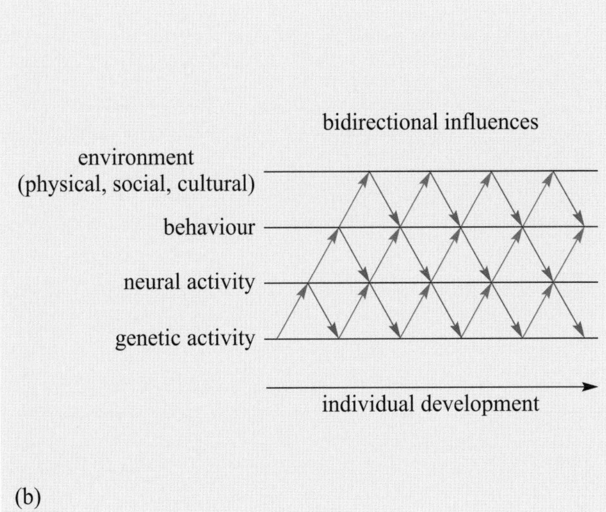

Figure 1.25 The interactive nature of development. (a) Representation of the animal showing some of its cells. (b) Representation of the dynamics of interactions across levels.

Consider, for example, the social environment provided by human parents. The behaviour of the baby would normally solicit smiles from the parents and these would in turn alter the behaviour of the baby. Evidence suggests that the development of parts of the baby's brain concerned with emotion (i.e. changes in connections between neurons) depends upon such dynamic social interactions. Hence, we need to see the developing body as acting in dynamic interaction with the environment having both physical (e.g. warmth, nutrition) and social dimensions.

Figure 1.26 shows that there is no simple direct link between genes and behaviour. Rather, the link is mediated by the nervous system, but modulated by various levels of environmental influence (Figure 1.25). The genes are required to construct the proteins needed by the developing nervous system which in turn determines behaviour. However, it's important to understand that gene expression, nervous system development and behaviour are significantly affected by the levels of environmental influence and so to argue which of two factors, genes or environment, is the most important in determining behaviour would be naive and misleading. Rather, we need to consider that *differences* in genes between people can manifest in *differences* in their nervous systems and thereby contribute towards *differences* in their behaviour.

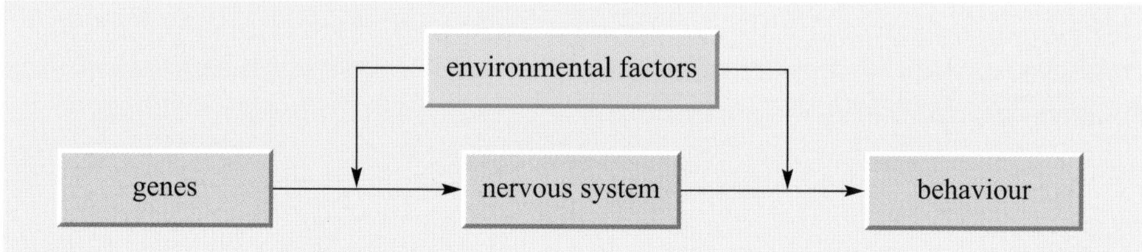

Figure 1.26 The link between genes, nervous system and behaviour is modulated by environmental factors.

Learning and memory

Not all of the changes that occur over a lifetime are described as development. Behaviour can also change in the light of experience, this being an instance of **learning**. The information storage in the brain that is manifest as learning is termed **memory**. In some cases, distinguishing between development and learning can be a formidable task.

Consider the following example of learning and memory. An animal eats food of a particular flavour and then experiences gastric upset shortly afterwards. A wide range of species, including humans, react in such a situation by avoiding food of this particular flavour in the future. Thus, the animal experiencing gastric upset forms a memory of the food and its negative association. (Learning and memory form the topic of Book 5, Chapter 1.) Again a challenge comes in trying to relate the psychological level (as manifest in behaviour) to changes in the brain that form the biological basis of learning and memory.

Although learning is usually only manifest over rather long time periods (e.g. hours, days or weeks), it is still appropriate occasionally to pose questions that seek a causal explanation. Thus, we might ask whether injecting a drug changes the speed of learning a maze. To answer this, two groups of rats would be investigated: one injected with the chemical in question and another injected with a neutral substance. Their speeds of learning to solve the maze would then be compared.

- What do you call the group injected with the neutral substance?
- The control group.

We have looked at events that occur within the lifetime of a given individual. We now need to turn to consider events that occur over generations.

1.4.6 Genetics and sexual reproduction

Genes were introduced in the last section in the context of their role in development. We now need to reconsider the topic of genes in the context of the process of transmitting information from one generation to another. Such characteristics as hair and eye colour are known to be inherited, but here our primary concern is with the relevance of inheritance to the nervous system and thereby to a link with behaviour. (This subject is explored in greater detail in Book 3, Chapter 3.) Genes are inherited through reproduction. At fertilization, the genetic material contained within the sperm cell of the male combines with that contained within the egg cell of the female to form a fertilized egg, termed a **zygote**. In this way, we all start out as a single cell. (See Figure 1.27.)

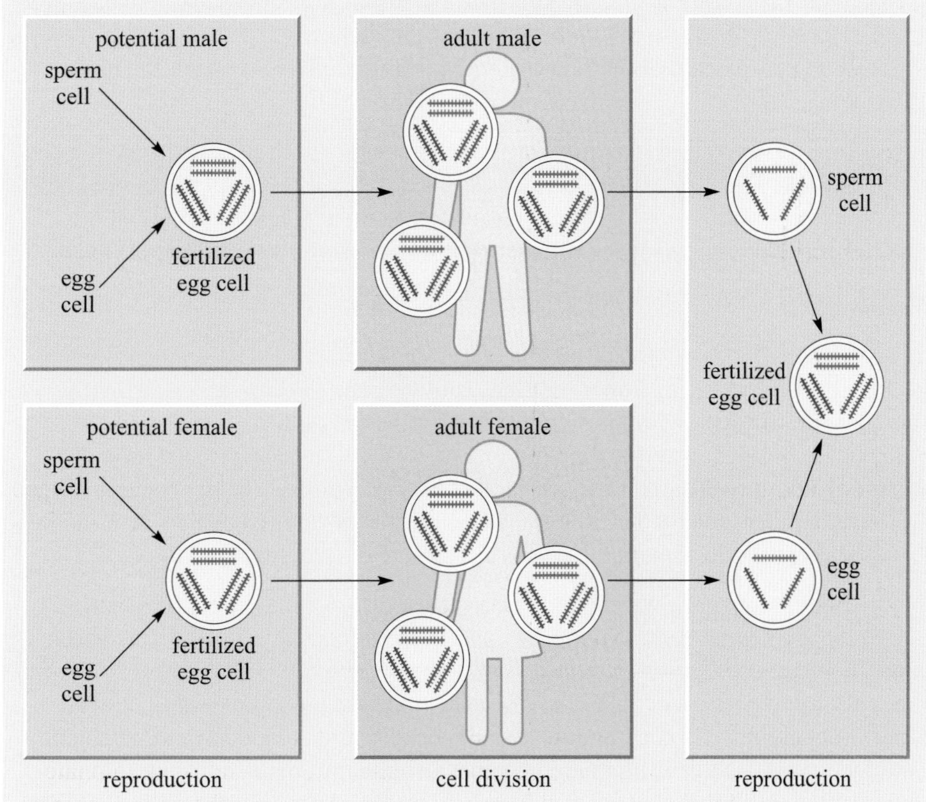

Figure 1.27 The processes of sexual reproduction and cell division. Note the paired chromosomes with some of their associated genes indicated and also the unpaired chromosomes within the sperm and egg cells.

An understanding of genetics can help us to understand some of the differences that exist between individuals.

Huntington's disease

- ◆ Can you recall from Section 1.1.3 the example of Huntington's disease (HD), which is manifest in abnormalities of behaviour in later life? What is the relevance of genetics to this disease?
- ◆ It was noted that this disease is transmitted genetically from one generation to another.

A given gene can come in different *variants*. The role of genetics in the transmission of HD (i.e. the nature of the genes in question and how the particular variants are passed from one generation to another) is well established. If someone carries the variant of the gene which leads to this disorder, it is inevitable that they will develop HD. This emergence of the disorder occurs over the whole range of different environments in which the individual might live.

- What is the site of the abnormality in HD?
- Regions of the brain concerned with, amongst other things, the control of movement.

How do particular variants of genes determine that this disorder will emerge? As noted, genes play a role in the construction of proteins (sometimes termed 'coding for' proteins). In the case of a genetic disorder such as this, the variant of the gene responsible for the disease codes for an abnormal protein such that parts of the brain are abnormal. With reference to Figure 1.26, the particular link between genes, nervous system (in this case the brain) and behaviour that characterizes HD will appear, irrespective of the range of viable environments in which the person grows and lives.

Apart from a few well-established cases such as that of HD, genetic influences on brain and behaviour are not easily predicted. That is, it is not possible to see a direct one-to-one link between genes and an aspect of brain and behaviour. However, genetics still has an important explanatory role. We turn to an example of this next.

Personality

It is often said that behavioural characteristics described as 'temperament' or 'personality' are prone to 'run in families' but we need to consider critically the evidence for this and any interpretation that can be put on it.

- If behavioural characteristics do indeed 'run in families', is this because of genetic inheritance or because of what is termed a 'familial effect', i.e. that offspring tend to imitate the characteristics of the parents?
- It could be because of either a genetic effect or a familial effect. Perhaps more likely, it could be both.

When we use a phrase like 'because of genetic inheritance' what exactly do we mean? Suppose that we compare individuals that differ in a dimension of personality. Could it be that there are differences in genes between these individuals and these genetic differences are reflected in differences in personality? Such questions might be simple to state but they are anything but simple to investigate in a way that yields clear answers. Indeed, even the questions themselves reveal a host of ambiguities and problems, and these will be pursued in later chapters of the course.

How in principle might genes contribute to a personality characteristic such as impulsiveness or neuroticism? It is obvious that the structure of the brain underlies the behaviour that someone exhibits. It is also clear that genes play a role in determining the structure of the brain. Again we need to consider that *differences* in genes between people can be manifest in *differences* in their nervous systems and thereby possible *differences* in their behaviour.

Tendencies to, say, neuroticism or conversely emotional stability are associated with differences in particular levels of chemicals in certain brain regions. Suppose that differences in genes between individuals underlie such differences in their brains. In this way, we might be able to identify how acting through their role in a personality characteristic, such as neuroticism, particular genes may be associated with a tendency to depression. However, any such links are still not fully understood and there is by no means such a clear (gene) → (brain) → (behaviour) relationship as for Huntington's disease.

A particular combination of genes might give a tendency towards depression. However, this does not mean that the individual in question necessarily suffers from the condition or will suffer from it. Life events and social support might be such as to cushion them from this or, conversely, the person's experience might also give a tendency towards depression. Thus, although Figure 1.26 still applies, the vagaries of different environments interact in such a way that gene effects are not so readily isolated as in the case of Huntington's disease.

Suppose that a combination of genes exerts an influence such that there is a tendency towards sensation-seeking and impulsive behaviour. This might then bias the individual towards finding a certain type of environment, e.g. one in which there is a ready availability of illegal drugs and where it is considered fun to steal cars and race them at high speed.

- So, is the genetics or the environment responsible for the person's behaviour?
- There is no 'either/or' gene–environment dichotomy. Rather, 'interaction' between gene and environment is the crucial word to describe what is happening.

We now deal with another topic closely connected with genetics and a closely related means of explanation.

1.4.7 Evolution and functional explanations

Basics of evolution

The animals that we see around us today, including ourselves, are the product of a very long history of **evolution**, a process of gradual change over time in both body and corresponding behaviour. By looking at such things as fossil records, we can try to construct a profile of this history and understand the changes in body structure that have taken place over evolutionary time. As with all of the body's other systems, nervous systems have undergone a process of evolution and the behaviour with which they are associated has changed over evolutionary time.

Important insight into brain and behaviour can be gained by considering evolutionary roots. Suppose that we are able to associate a particular part of the brain with serving a particular function. It is then interesting to compare different species in terms of this brain region and to see how their behaviour differs. For example, evidence suggests that a particular brain region known as the *hippocampus* is involved in spatial skills and the exploitation of spatial memory for what is located where in the environment. A comparison of bird species has found that species that hoard a large number of food items have a relatively large hippocampus compared to those that don't hoard food.

How does evolutionary change occur? Characteristics are inherited from one generation to another by means of the genes. According to the theory of evolution, evolutionary change occurs by means of small changes in genetic material. In the study of brain and behaviour, evolution is associated with a particular kind of explanation, described in the next section.

Functional explanations

The word 'function' can take on different meanings and a question often raised is – 'what is the function of behaviour?' In other words, what advantage does it serve in terms of survival? To take a simple example, what is the functional advantage of everyone in Britain subscribing to the convention of driving on the left? Clearly, this is a social, cultural and legal convention that serves the function of minimizing accidents. One imagines that biology has little to offer by way of explanation for why Britain differs in this regard from the rest of Europe! In this course, we are concerned with a particular use of the term 'functional', a rather different kind to that exemplified by the conventions of driving and for which biology is at centre-stage in the explanation.

As a particular type of explanation that draws on insight from principles of evolution, we speak of the **functional explanation** of behaviour. For example, consider the question of why animals, including humans, sleep. That is to say, how is it to an animal's advantage, in evolutionary terms (i.e. in terms of its survival), to sleep? You might feel that the answer is obvious. In fact, however, detailed study of humans and other species has revealed that there is no simple answer to the question of the function served by sleep.

One question posed from a functional perspective is – does sleep serve some kind of recuperative function within the brain? Alternatively, or in addition, does it serve to keep an animal out of harm's way at a time when it is most vulnerable? This is the level of the functional explanation. Here one might imagine that comparisons of different species would be able to yield useful insights. Unfortunately, despite a rich variety of data and some suggestive theories, there is still no entirely convincing functional explanation of sleep.

Another question raised by a functional perspective is – what is the function served by consciousness? In other words, what is the advantage conferred upon an animal by the possession of consciousness? This leads to other related questions, such as – which species possess consciousness? (A topic raised in Chapter 4.) What is special about the kind of information processing that engages conscious processes, in terms of giving a functional advantage to behaviour?

Summary of Section 1.4

Biological psychology involves a range of phenomena, perspectives and explanatory techniques. Within a hierarchy of phenomena, explanations can be provided by going from a low level to a higher level (e.g. explaining behaviour in terms of events within the nervous system) and by going from a high level to a lower level (e.g. explaining a change in hormone level in terms of social context). Seeking an explanation at a lower level is termed reductionism. There are pitfalls in its uncritical pursuit. An emergent property is one that emerges at a certain level of complexity. The property is not evident in the performance at a lower level.

Psychologists have typically looked at rather few species in tightly controlled environments, for example the Skinner box.

The relationship between events can be studied over various lengths of time. Commonly, the effects of an intervention (e.g. injection) are observed within a few seconds or so of the intervention. In considering the phenomena of development and learning, events are observed over long periods, e.g. a lifetime. A causal explanation is concerned with explaining how one event causes another to happen.

The study of genetics has an important role in aiding our understanding of the link between brain and behaviour. Genes are complex molecules that code for the construction of proteins. Huntington's disease is an example of a genetically transmitted disorder where specific genes have directed the manufacture of faulty proteins and hence abnormal brain properties. Differences in personality can be associated with genetic differences but there is not such a straightforward relationship as in Huntington's disease. Small changes in genetic material form the basis of evolutionary change. A functional explanation is concerned with explaining the function of behaviour in terms of evolution.

1.5 Final word – bringing things together

1.5.1 Introduction

The last section considered the different types of explanation used in biological psychology and some of the controversial issues that this raises. How might we use these principles to start to draw an integrative picture that shows the workings of brain and behaviour? How do we relate the material in Sections 1.1–1.4? This section will give some pointers in this direction. It will do so with the help of the case reports that were described in Section 1.1. The examples of bringing the parts of the story together are presented here so as to give some intellectual 'tools of the trade' when it comes to thinking about similar issues in the later chapters.

1.5.2 Differences in brains

Section 1.1 considered some actual differences and, more speculatively, some possible differences between brains. We looked at the results of accidental brain damage and genetically determined abnormalities of parts of the brain. Based on Sections 1.2–1.4, what can we now say to illuminate this discussion?

Exceptional abilities

We considered the possibility that exceptional individuals might have rather different structures in parts of the brain (Section 1.1.2). Of necessity, this discussion was left somewhat unresolved. From the subsequent discussion of analogies with computers, you might logically extrapolate that differences in performance between individuals do not necessarily map onto obvious differences in the structure of their brains. For example, to exploit the analogy, the difference between a good essay and a bad one does not reside in differences in the computers on which they are written. These issues are very much open to investigation.

Brain damage and disease

You will recall the topic of causal explanations (Section 1.4.4) and, in this light, it is interesting to return briefly to a consideration of brain damage. Ideally, we would like to be able to pose questions of a causal nature, i.e. did brain damage *cause* the change in behaviour? This is extremely difficult to ascertain for certain since so much else changes between brain damage and its evaluation. Using humans for research in this area, of course, makes controlled experimentation impossible. However, the effects seen in patients such as H.M. and D.B. are so striking that psychologists try to gain as much understanding from them as possible.

Under some conditions, brains go wrong in ways that are characterized by a malfunction of a particular group of neurons employing a particular type of neurotransmitter and located in identifiable regions of the brain.

One of the case reports concerned Huntington's disease (Section 1.1.3) and its genetic basis was described (Section 1.4.6). There is a clear link between variants of particular genes and the emergence of the disorder. The disease consists of the death of neurons that employ the neurotransmitter known as γ-aminobutyric acid (usually termed GABA) in the striatum. See Figure 1.28, which compares the brain of a patient with Huntington's disease and an unaffected brain. Note the loss of brain tissue in a particular region of the brain.

For another example, a disorder of movement control known as Parkinson's disease (PD) arises because of a loss of dopaminergic neurons that project from the substantia nigra to the striatum (see Figure 1.19). Post-mortem analysis of the brains of people with PD reveals such a deficiency. One treatment consists of trying to boost the rate of production of dopamine by those dopaminergic neurons that remain intact.

As another type of explanation, can insight be gained from looking at the role of genetics in PD? There is some evidence to suggest that particular genes exert a tendency to the disorder. The notion of a *tendency* mediated by genes was described in Section 1.4.6 in the context of personality. So, PD is not a genetic disease as such, though we need to consider the role of genes in it.

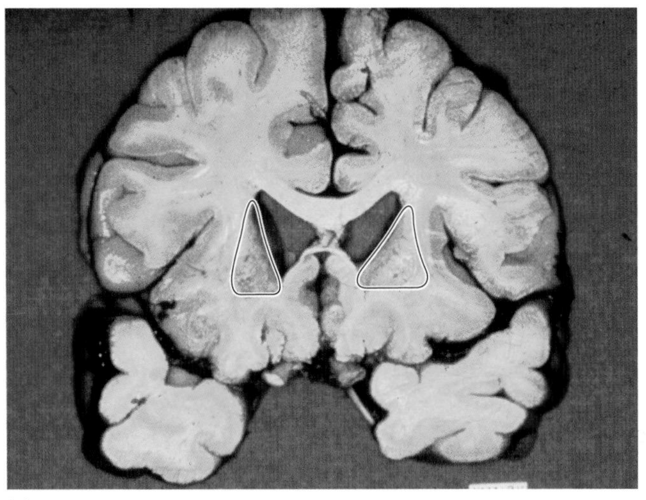

(a)

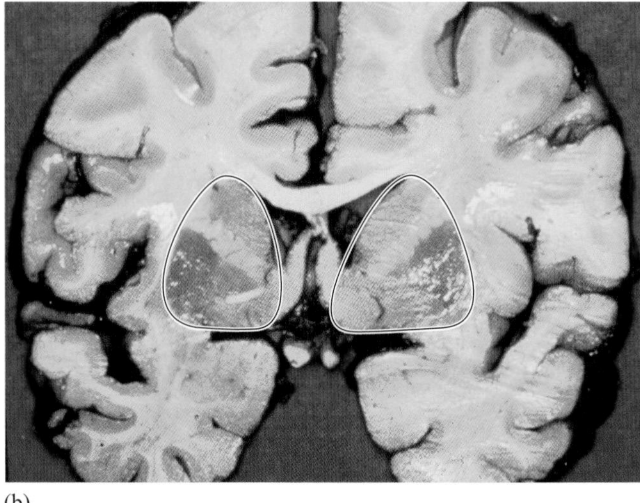

(b)

Figure 1.28 (a) The brain of a patient with Huntington's disease and (b) an unaffected brain. Note the overall brain shrinkage in the affected brain and more specifically the shrinkage in the regions outlined that underlie movement control.

1.5.3 Causal and functional explanations

As an example of integrating different types of explanation, it can be useful to consider the links between causal and functional types. This section gives two examples of where causal and functional types of explanation are considered in parallel.

Homeostasis

Dehydration of the body tends to promote the *motivation* to seek water and drink it. Drinking plays a crucial role in the homeostasis of the body (Section 1.2.2). The dehydrated animal is said to be highly motivated to seek water and, once trained, would press a lever in a Skinner box at a high rate for the reward of water. At a causal level, this guides investigators in their search for a process of detection of body-fluid level and a link between this and behaviour. In the case of humans, introspection reveals powerful *conscious* experiences of distress associated with dehydration and pleasure associated with the restoration of homeostasis. This exemplifies links between events in the body and mental events.

The principle of homeostasis is also illustrated by the fact that the hormone arginine vasopressin is released in response to dehydration and thereby the kidney conserves water. Both of these processes, the extrinsic (i.e. behavioural) and the intrinsic (involving the kidney), act in the same direction. If a disease state disrupts the production of the hormone arginine vasopressin, relatively enormous amounts of urine are produced with a corresponding thirst and a high level of ingestion of water. Taking a synthetic form of the chemical can restore the situation to near normal. This example illustrates how insights can be gained by studying what happens when things go wrong.

At a functional level, it is clear that dehydration is a threat to the functioning of the body, and mechanisms that give a high priority to its correction will favour the survival of their possessor. Of course, considering the state of the tissues of the body and their hydrational levels will not give a reliable guide to all aspects of human drinking! Rather, social context is also a powerful determinant of what we drink and when, e.g. we occasionally drink almost anything to be sociable. This exemplifies the point (Section 1.4.3) that we need to consider events at different levels in gaining a more complete picture of brain and behaviour.

An interesting problem: sleep

We mentioned sleep in Sections 1.3.2 and 1.4.7. In trying to understand sleep, some researchers investigate the brain mechanisms that are involved in producing it. They ask questions of the kind – activity in which parts of the brain trigger sleep? Here it is possible to pose experimental hypotheses and to test them (see Book 2). For example, are there particular chemicals in the blood, which, when they rise (or fall) to a certain level, play a role in triggering sleep?

◆ Is such a question correctly described as 'causal'?

◆ Yes. It concerns what (internal event) *causes* what (behaviour).

Do these chemical events really *cause* sleep to occur? There is an issue to be aware of here.

◆ What is this issue?

◆ The issue is whether the relationship is one of causation or only of correlation.

Can sleep be reduced or increased by disrupting these chemicals, e.g. by taking medicine? This is where careful experimentation is needed. The consideration of such questions can be illuminated by the further question – what function does sleep serve? It might be to maintain the level of a certain chemical within safe bounds. Considering this issue leads to causal questions such as – does a toxic chemical appear in the blood during waking and does sleep serve to reduce this level? Alternatively, sleep might serve the function of keeping an animal inactive at a time when it would be risky to move around. Both of these functional explanations might be true; sleep can serve more than one function.

1.5.4 Brain, mind and understanding the placebo effect

Earlier sections of this chapter introduced some of the vexed issues that surround our consideration of brain and mind. For example, the notion that consciousness is a subset of the mental operations of the mind was introduced (Section 1.2.3). The discussion of the placebo effect (Section 1.1.7) drew attention to the important role played by the patient's conscious insight and expectation.

Section 1.1.7 raised the issue – does the placebo effect really provide evidence that something can be 'all in the mind'? That is to say, is it really an example of 'mind over matter'? Such a notion causes profound problems for the science of biological psychology because it suggests that something that is outside the body (in the mind) can nonetheless have an influence on the physical body.

◆ What is the name for such a belief?

◆ Dualism.

An interpretation of the placebo effect within the traditions of biological psychology would generally appeal to the idea expressed earlier that the mind is 'what the brain does' or that 'the mind is an aspect of the brain'.

◆ Suppose we were to try to relate the notion of 'emergent property' (Section 1.4.3) to discussions of the relationship between brain and mind. How might this notion be applied?

◆ We can speculate that the mind is an emergent property of the activity of the brain. It depends upon the brain but takes on new properties (e.g. conscious awareness) that *emerge* from the whole collection of neurons put together.

When we take a drug for a medical condition, there is a mental world of ideas and expectations concerning its efficacy. However, the mental world does not exist in a domain that is independent of the brain. Rather, mental processes correspond to a pattern of activity within the brain. For each mental state there is a corresponding brain state. In other words, hearing an expression such as 'Here is a drug that should bring you some relief' will have an effect on the brain. Indeed, we can only hear these words because they trigger activity in the ear and thereby in the neurons that convey information from the ear to the brain. This effect within the brain has a corresponding mind state described in such terms as 'expectation', 'hope' or 'relief'.

What then is the actual biological basis of the placebo effect? A placebo is usually described as a 'non-specific substance', meaning that almost any *substance* such as pure water or a salty solution can serve as a placebo. However, the placebo *effect* can be highly specific. Thus, a placebo taken in expectation of a stimulant drug will typically increase heart rate whereas one taken in expectation of a tranquillizer will reduce it.

A team at the University of British Columbia, Canada investigated the means by which a placebo can have an effect. They looked at the treatment of patients with Parkinson's disease (PD), where placebo drugs can produce anything up to 59% of the beneficial effect of a specific drug. As was noted earlier, the biological basis of PD is a loss of dopamine-containing neurons with cell bodies in the substantia nigra. The specific medication used in the treatment of PD is such as to target dopaminergic transmission. Could it be that a placebo substance taken by PD patients also exerts its effect through activating a dopaminergic pathway? It was found that PD patients show significant amounts of activation of dopaminergic pathways in response to placebo treatment. This result is important in that it shows that placebo effects are represented by specific activity within the physical brain. Further research will indicate whether other equally specific placebo effects occur in other conditions.

◆ Might such a result relate to the ethical issue surrounding the placebo effect raised in Section 1.1.7?

◆ At least in the case just described, the doctor could state in all honesty that the treatment has a known specific effect in relation to the condition being treated.

Another phenomenon that raises a similar set of issues on brain and mind is that termed **psychosomatic illness**. Generally speaking this is interpreted to mean that a psychological disturbance, i.e. something involving the 'psyche' or mind, can have an influence on the 'soma', or body. At the one level, the existence of a psychosomatic disorder is not theoretically problematic. It is widely recognized that such psychological events as hostility and the stress of bereavement or divorce can have a harmful effect on the body. Gastric ulcers and the irritable bowel syndrome bear all-too adequate witness to this. However, when we dissect the expression 'psychosomatic' more closely, it is sometimes taken to imply that events within the psyche, something *outside* the physical body, can, nonetheless, exert an effect on the physical body. If this were true, it would be problematic for the kind of integrative biological psychology that is being advanced in this course.

The notion that psyche and soma are two *distinct entities* that nonetheless are able to interact is not one that is popular in science these days. It suggests that the mind can exist even in the absence of the body. It is more popular to suggest that the mind is an *aspect* of the brain (or 'emergent property' of the brain) that cannot exist in the absence of the brain. In such terms, explanations are sought for the nature of the relationship between the two. Psychosomatic illness, although challenging, does not present a mystery that undermines biological psychology, since mental events correspond to activity within a part of the body, i.e. the brain.

Summary of Section 1.5

The section has exemplified how our understanding of a given phenomenon can be enriched by bringing different kinds of explanation and levels of description to it. We showed how explanations of Huntington's disease and Parkinson's disease draw on the biology of genetics, neurotransmitters and brain structures, as well as psychology, as illustrated by the role of a placebo effect. Explanation is often able to build on both causal and functional aspects of behaviour. For example, an explanation of the homeostasis of body fluids and drinking can be given in terms of such things as the role of dehydration in triggering drinking and the role of the kidney in urination. In functional terms, an explanatory insight can be given in terms of the advantage to survival of homeostasis and action that restores body fluid level following a disturbance. An understanding of the placebo effect and psychosomatic illness also needs to draw on various sources of input. Thus, insight into the biological consequences of a placebo treatment as well as the issue of the relationship between brain and mind are central to its consideration. A current understanding of the relationship between brain and mind is to describe the mind as 'an emergent property' of the brain.

Learning outcomes for Chapter 1

After studying this chapter you should be able to:

1.1 Recognize definitions and applications of each of the terms printed in **bold** in the text.

1.2 Present the evidence for the existence of conscious and unconscious determinants of behaviour.

1.3 State the nature of the problems associated with trying to study the mind.

1.4 Explain what is meant by the terms placebo effect, homeostasis, emergent property and reductionism and how they relate to each other.

1.5 Describe the functioning of neurons and nervous systems in relation to the techniques used for studying them.

1.6 Distinguish between causal and functional levels of explanation.

1.7 Explain why the dichotomy of genes versus environment is misleading.

1.8 Take a more critical stance towards claims made in the area of brain, mind and behaviour.

Questions for Chapter 1

Question 1.1 *(Learning outcomes 1.2 and 1.3)*

Consider the sayings, 'Seeing is believing' and 'The eye doesn't deceive'. In what way might the behaviour of the patient D.B. be related to such claims?

Question 1.2 *(Learning outcomes 1.3, 1.4 and 1.8)*

'It is important for a new medicine to be tested in order to see that it has an effect 'greater than that of a placebo''. What is meant by such a claim? How might it be tested?

Question 1.3 *(Learning outcomes 1.1 and 1.2)*

Do the terms 'mind' and 'conscious awareness' mean the same thing?

Question 1.4 *(Learning outcomes 1.1 and 1.5)*

What is the technical name for a type of cell that forms a major part of the nervous system?

Question 1.5 *(Learning outcome 1.5)*

What might be meant by the claim that transmission of information in the nervous system is partly electrical and partly chemical?

Question 1.6 *(Learning outcomes 1.1 and 1.5)*

Distinguish between a neurotransmitter and a hormone.

Question 1.7 *(Learning outcome 1.6)*

An animal that has been deprived of food gives a particularly high priority to searching for food. What are the functional and causal explanations for this?

Question 1.8 *(Learning outcome 1.1)*

Distinguish between sexual reproduction and cell division.

Question 1.9 *(Learning outcomes 1.7 and 1.8)*

With reference to Figure 1.25, in what different scales can the term 'environment' be employed?

CHAPTER 2

THE BUILDING BLOCKS OF THE BRAIN

2.1 Exploring nervous systems

All animals can sense changes in the environment and are able to react to these changes in some way by, for instance, controlling their movements. They possess specialized structures, called sense organs, which contain receptors that respond selectively to specific types of energy – the eyes respond to light energy and the ears respond to sound energy, for example. Energy that is received from outside the body is converted into electrical signals that can be processed by the nervous system. An appropriate response is generated, mainly by controlling the activity of cells in other organs or tissues that bring about action outside the nervous system. These cells are known as **effectors**, for example the cells that form muscle or the secretory cells of salivary glands.

Information about an animal's internal environment, such as heart rate and body temperature, is also being generated and constantly monitored by the nervous system so that, as we saw in Chapter 1, homeostasis is always maintained. The information processed and integrated by the nervous system is also being stored – this is called learning. Information storage adds a further aspect to the behavioural response as it may modify the outcome even when the same stimulus is applied on a later occasion. The processes of learning and memory will be dealt with in more detail in Book 5, Chapter 1. Figure 2.1 shows a block diagram representing an example of a behavioural response, i.e. the flow of information from the sensory system that detects the stimulus (by way of a sense organ) to the behavioural response generated by effectors (for example muscles of the motor system), a process coordinated by the nervous system. This is obviously a simplified diagram as it leaves out a number of key pathways that are necessary for the fine-tuning of the response, such as information on the state of the muscle. However, it provides a good starting point as an example of a particular behaviour pattern and its underlying neural pathways.

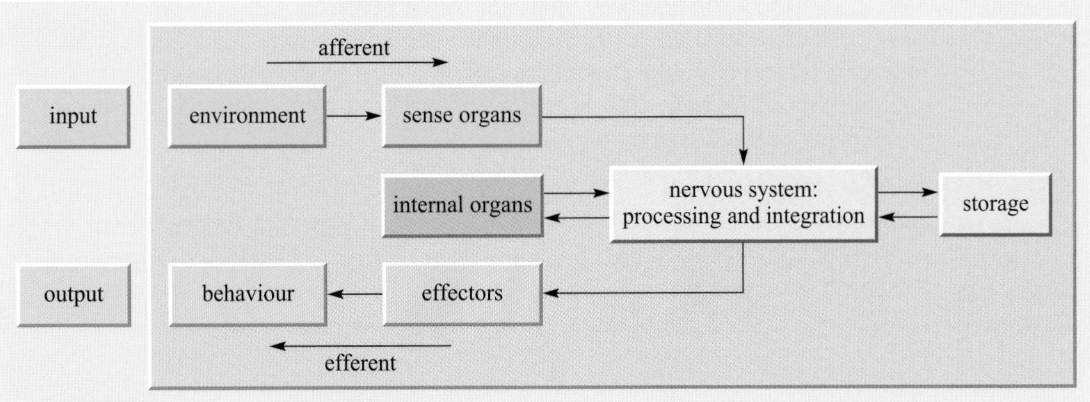

Figure 2.1 Block diagram of a behavioural response. Notice that the terms afferent and efferent refer in this case to the flow of information into and out of the nervous system, respectively.

Behavioural responses to information flowing into and out of nervous systems may range from deliberate, coordinated movements to reflex, automatic responses. For example, if you are suddenly awakened by a loud noise, you may perceive a situation of danger which may entail both automatic responses (pupil dilation, sweating, increased heart rate) and willed behavioural responses, such as escaping from the source of danger. Human behaviour depends upon the integrative properties of the nervous system as a whole and, in order to achieve such integration, nervous systems must have extensive interconnections within them. The basic elements of nervous systems are the neurons, previously introduced in Chapter 1 (Figure 1.6). These are specialized cells that form interconnected networks that convey information throughout the body in the form of electrical and chemical signals. It is worth reiterating here the difference between a nerve and a neuron, two concepts you already encountered in Chapter 1. The term 'nerve' refers to bundles of specific, long, thin structures of neurons called **axons** that are located together, whereas the term 'neuron' refers to a single electrically excitable cell.

This chapter describes how nervous systems are organized, from the more obvious structural features such as the brain and spinal cord to the ways in which neurons are grouped together to form specialized areas that contribute to specific functions. However, although much is known about nervous systems, *exactly* how they operate to produce a particular pattern of behaviour is often not completely understood. From the point of view of an investigator, it is more straightforward to study relatively simple nervous systems that contain just a few neurons whose activities can be associated with distinct patterns of behaviour than to study more complex animals. Indeed, many fundamental discoveries on how nervous systems function have been made using somewhat simple invertebrate nervous systems. It will be useful to begin this chapter by comparing the features of nervous systems that are common to many species. This study will be followed by a description of neurons and other cell types within nervous systems – the basic units that form the building blocks of the brain.

2.2 From nerve nets to centralized nervous systems

There is a striking diversity of animal life – estimates range from 10–30 million different species. Those multicellular animals that do not have a backbone (such as worms, snails and insects) form a group called **invertebrates**. In fact, if you consider their relative abundance within the animal kingdom (Figure 2.2), most multicellular animals belong to this category as they greatly outnumber those animals with a backbone. The latter are called **vertebrates** and include fish, amphibians, reptiles, birds and mammals.

Neurons similar to those in humans occur in almost all the multicellular animals shown in Figure 2.2 (the exception being sponges). However, the *number* of neurons and the *complexity* of the connections between them differ between species. It is the communications between neurons that allow relatively simple

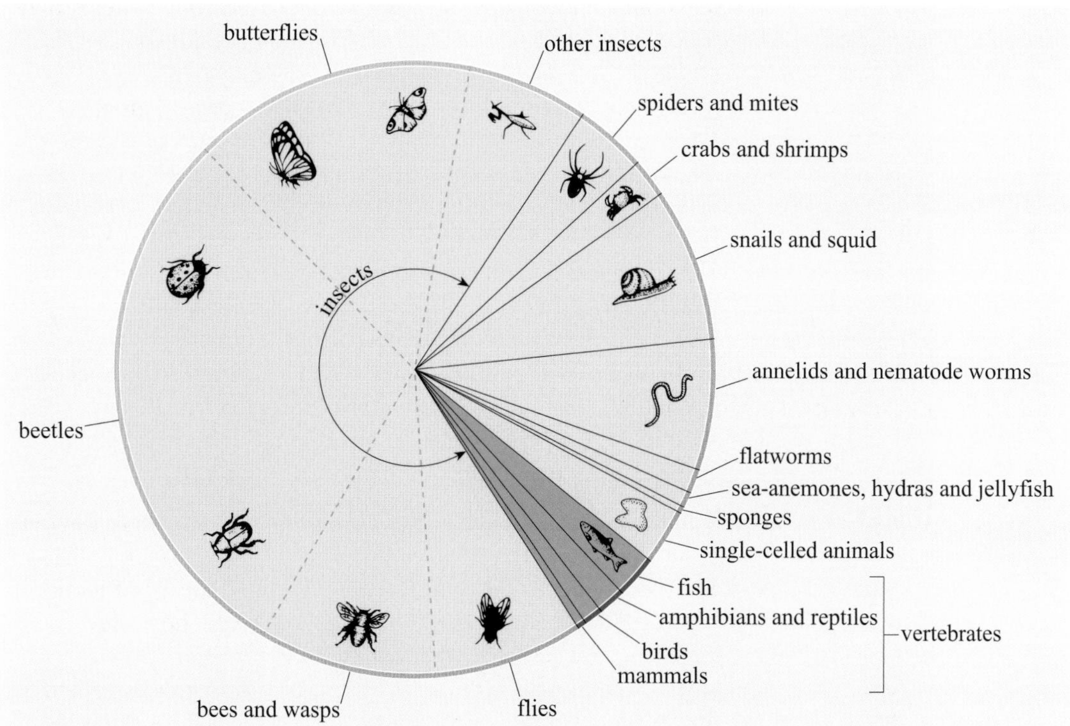

Figure 2.2 The relative abundances of known species of living animals. Notice the small proportion taken up by vertebrates (green) compared to invertebrates (yellow).

multicellular animals such as corals, sea-anemones, jellyfish (Figure 2.3a) and hydras (Figure 2.3b) a wide range of behavioural responses, including the capture of prey, digestion, orientation to light and gravity, and escape. These responses are regulated by one or more sets of neurons that are interconnected, forming what is termed a **nerve net** (Figures 2.3c and d). If neurons are stained with a dye, a fine 'net' can be seen scattered throughout the whole animal. However, this seemingly random distribution of neuronal connections generates circuits with specific aims, for example around the mouth there are slightly more neurons, presumably because feeding requires a greater amount of control. The nerve net receives information from the outside world by means of specialized types of neurons termed **sensory receptors**. Sensory receptors may be diverse in the stimuli to which they respond; some may be sensitive to touch whereas others may be sensitive to different types of chemical. In the case of the hydra, if prey such as a small shrimp touches a tentacle, an electrical signal is generated by sensory receptors located on the tentacles that then spreads in all directions over the nerve net. The behavioural response to this stimulus is the movement of other tentacles to enclose the shrimp, conveying it to the mouth to be ingested (Figure 2.3b). The tentacles constitute an effector system, but their response may be completely different, depending on the activation of different types of sensory receptors on their surface. For instance, a gentle tap with the tip of your finger would make the hydra swiftly retract its tentacles – the withdrawal reflex response – instead of it attempting to trap the prey.

Many of the illustrations include a scale bar. This is included to give you an idea of the actual size of the object.

10 cm

(a)

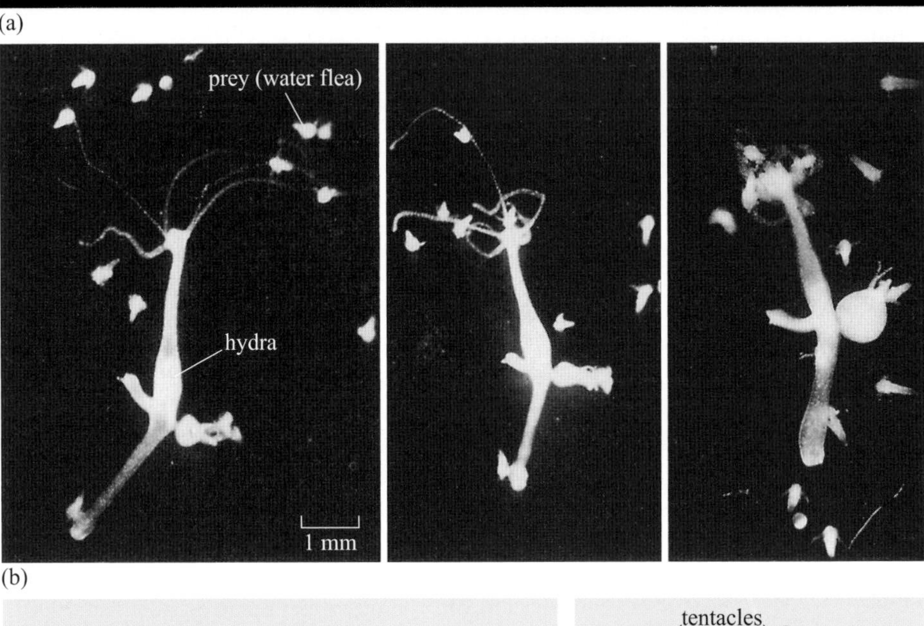

(b)

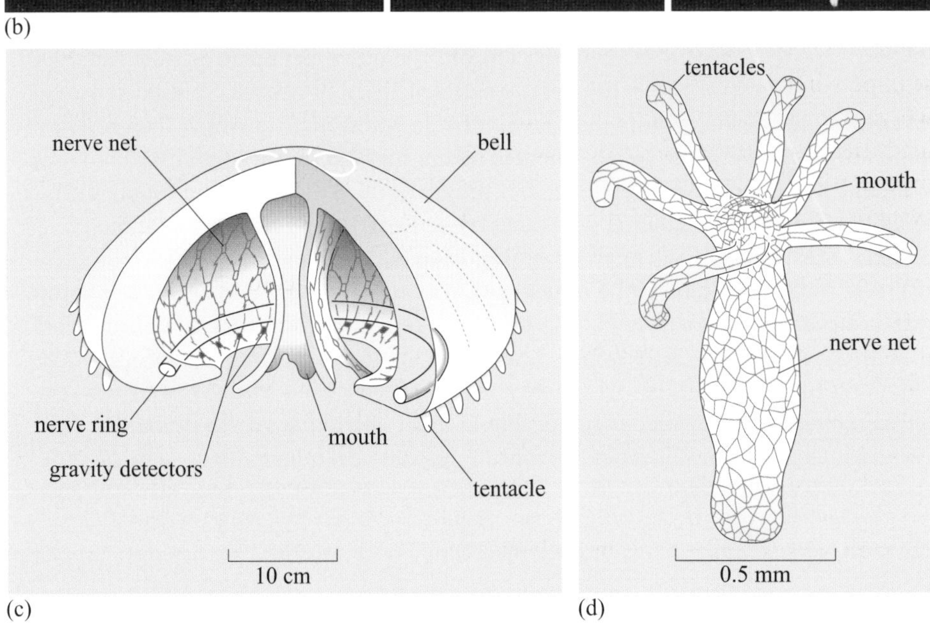

(c) (d)

Figure 2.3 Invertebrate animals such as (a) the common or moon jellyfish, *Aurelia*, and (b) *Hydra*, a small freshwater relative of the sea-anemone, contain simple nervous systems. The nervous system consists of a 'net' of interconnected neurons called a nerve net. The internal structure and distribution of the nerve net of a jellyfish is shown in (c) and of a hydra in (d).

- Why is the hydra's reaction following a gentle finger tap on a tentacle different from that induced by a small shrimp?

- The difference in the two responses is due to the activation of different types of sensory receptors, arising from the fact that the two stimuli are different in nature – the tactile stimulus induced by the prey is more continuous and rhythmical as the shrimp tries to free itself from the hydra's tentacles whereas the sudden touch by a finger tip usually represents danger. The shrimp will also release chemicals that will activate additional sensory receptors on the hydra's tentacles which are sensitive to the chemicals.

Jellyfish have sensory neurons that effectively coordinate muscle contractions, resulting in efficient swimming. The stimulation of different types of sensory neurons that respond to light, orientation, touch and chemicals generates appropriate movements suitable for diverse situations. For example, sensory neurons that detect gravity are distributed around the bell and are used to keep the jellyfish upright. If one side tips down, the gravity detectors on that side are stimulated, electrical signals are conveyed to nearby muscle cells which then contract faster and the jellyfish 'rights' itself. The rate of contraction of a jellyfish's muscle cells, that is its behavioural response, is proportional to the strength of the stimulus. In other words, the stronger the stimulus (the more the jellyfish is tilted to one side), the larger the response (the faster the rate of muscle contraction) will be.

Nerve nets are one of the earliest and simplest forms of nervous system in animal evolution. However, these simple networks of neurons are not restricted to just a few invertebrates – they are also found forming part of the nervous systems of many other animals. In vertebrates with more complex nervous systems, nerve nets are found scattered along the gut where they control smooth muscle contraction and the movement of food.

Many invertebrates and all vertebrates show bilateral symmetry, meaning that they can be roughly divided into two 'mirror-image' halves by a line, called the midline, running from head to tail (Figure 2.4). (In radially symmetrical animals, such as the hydra, the organism can be divided into two similar halves by any one of several planes that include the central line.) In addition, most animals consist of a series of repeated units or segments – in other words, their bodies show **segmentation**. The segments in the earthworm, leech and lobster are obvious to the naked eye, whereas in vertebrates each individual bone or vertebra that makes up the spine identifies a segment. This anatomical arrangement is reflected in the basic organization of nervous systems in both invertebrates and vertebrates. In segmental systems, neurons are not evenly distributed as we saw in nerve nets, rather they group together to form distinct structures within the nervous system. In invertebrates, one such structure is the **nerve cord**. This cord consists of a double series of repeated swellings termed ganglia (singular: **ganglion**) and runs along the midline (Figure 2.5). A ganglion is a functional unit that contains groups of neurons which may be specialized to perform particular tasks. For example, there may be ganglia that are involved in controlling locomotion whereas others may operate mouthparts. Nerves, formed by bundles of neurons' axons, join each pair of ganglia with those in their vicinity. These nerves are termed **connectives**. Transverse nerves, another type of nerve, connect ganglia with sensory neurons and motor effectors (e.g. muscles) within each segment.

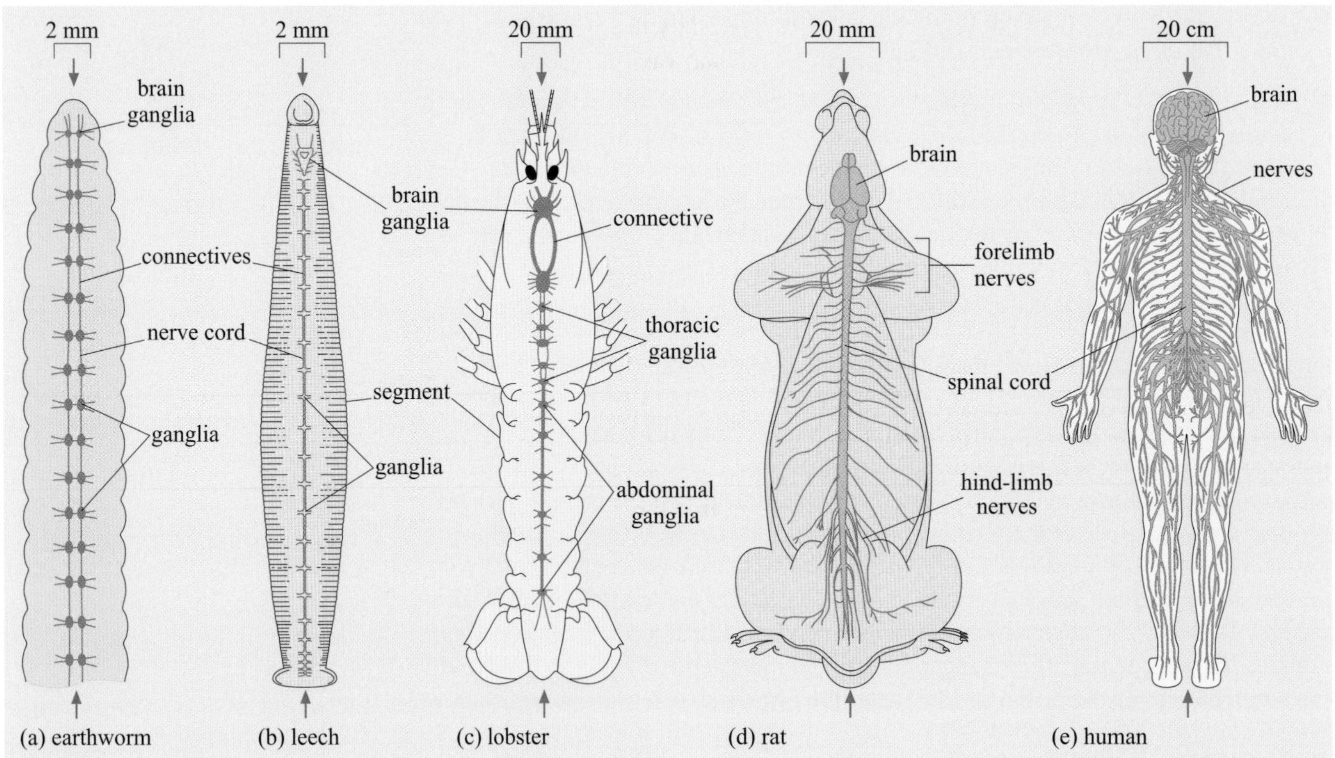

Figure 2.4 Diagram of the nervous system of (a) an earthworm, (b) a leech, (c) a lobster, (d) a rat and (e) a human. Notice their bilateral symmetry. The red arrows indicate the midline of each organism.

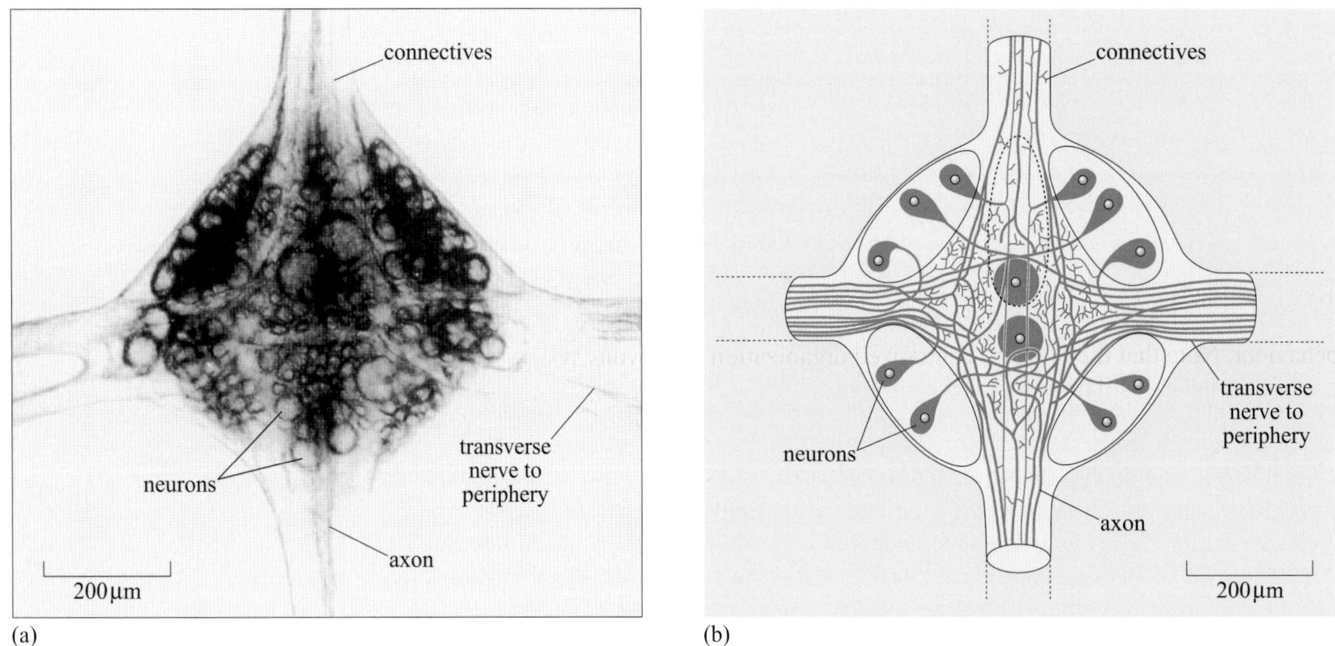

Figure 2.5 (a) Photograph of a ganglion in a leech. The ganglia have been dissected out of the animal and the cells inside are clearly visible through the protective layer even though they have not been stained. It is possible to identify neurons that occupy the same position in each ganglion in different individuals of the same species. (b) Drawing of (a) showing the arrangement of neurons and their axons within the ganglion. Note: 1000 μm = 1 mm

In vertebrates, the equivalent of the nerve cord is encased by the bones of the vertebral column and is called the spinal cord. In a similar way to those in invertebrates, bundles of axons that form nerves connect the spinal cord to sensory receptors and effector organs (Figure 2.4). This important feature of nervous systems is termed **centralization**. It separates the nervous systems in vertebrates, and most invertebrates, into two distinct parts: the central nervous system (CNS) and the peripheral nervous system (PNS), already introduced in Section 1.3.2.

- The different groups of neurons along the midline constitute the CNS.
- The network of nerves that stems from the CNS, responsible for receiving sensory inputs (afferent) and sending motor outputs (efferent), forms the PNS.

However, there is a major difference between the vertebrate CNS and the invertebrate CNS. In vertebrates the spinal cord is situated at the back of the animal whereas the nerve cord of invertebrates such as molluscs (e.g. snails) and arthropods (flies, lobsters, spiders, etc.) is situated towards the animal's stomach. The invertebrate CNS is said to be in a ventral position and the vertebrate CNS in a dorsal position (Figure 2.6).

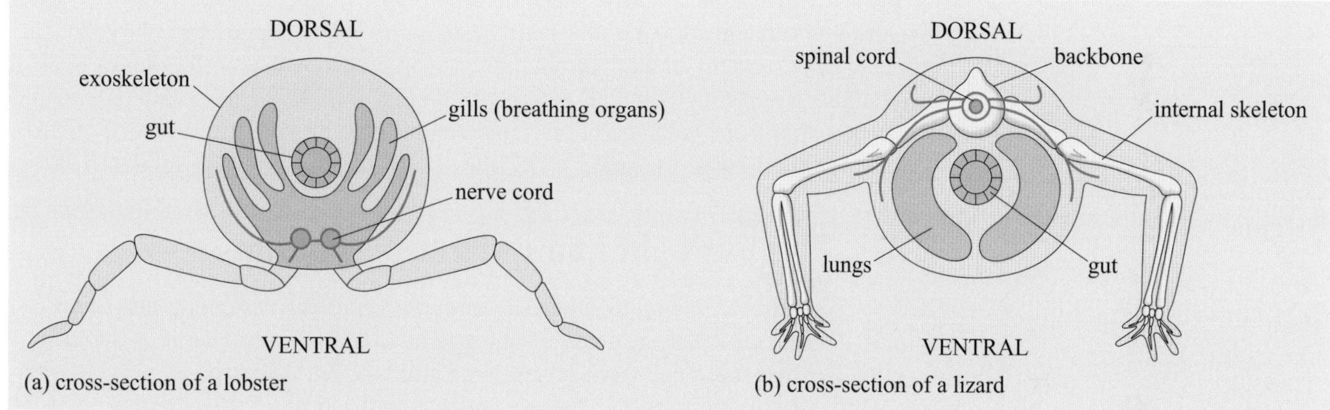

Figure 2.6 Cross-sections showing the position of (a) the nerve cord in an invertebrate (lobster) and (b) the spinal cord in a vertebrate (lizard). Notice that the skeleton of the invertebrate lobster is an external structure called the exoskeleton (*exo* is the Greek for outside and in this case refers to the shell) whereas the skeleton is internal in vertebrates.

The organization into more complex neural networks allows a far greater interchange of information and hence the coordination and control of even more complex behaviour. Note that the bilateral centralized organization of nervous systems contrasts with the radially symmetrical jellyfish and hydra where the neurons in nerve nets are uniformly distributed.

Most animals have a tail end and a head end and move predominantly in one direction. This is also reflected in the organization of the CNS. In invertebrates, ganglia in the head end are noticeably enlarged compared to those in other parts of the body. This is because ganglia within the head contain large numbers of neurons. This is called **cephalization** (from the Greek *cephalus*, meaning head). In vertebrates, the concentration of neurons in the head is known as the brain. Although the pair of enlarged ganglia at the head end may also be referred to as the brain in invertebrates, strictly speaking the brain should only be used to describe the enlargement of the CNS contained within the skull of vertebrates. The position of the brain and enlarged ganglia is said to be rostral (meaning close to the face or *rostrum*, see Section 1.3.2). By contrast, an area within the CNS away from the face or front end of the organism is in a caudal position. As animals move they need to be aware of the surrounding environment, so it makes sense to put the sensory organs and neurons close together in the leading end. This arrangement makes the distance for the transmission of information between some major sense organs (e.g. eyes, ears) and the brain fairly short and decreases the time taken to generate rapid, appropriate responses. Whatever its position, an organ can be serviced more efficiently if it is compact – hence the high demand for oxygen and nutrients by the brain can be effectively met by a few major blood vessels. As you will see throughout the course, this concentration of neurons plays an important role in coordinating the behaviour of the whole animal.

Summary of Section 2.2

This brief look at relatively simple invertebrate animals has illustrated some basic rules of how nervous systems are organized. Sensory receptors are specialized neurons that respond to particular external stimuli and transmit information from the external world to the rest of the nervous system. The nervous system is then responsible for coordinating a response by activating effector systems such as muscles. Centralization, i.e. the anatomical and functional division of nervous systems into central and peripheral systems, and cephalization, i.e. the anatomical feature characterized by enlarged grouping(s) of neurons in the head end, are important properties of nervous systems in many higher invertebrates and all vertebrates. In this section, we have also reiterated the concepts rostral and caudal, and dorsal and ventral, to help you, the observer, orientate yourself within nervous systems.

2.3 The vertebrate nervous system

This section introduces you to the basic organization of the vertebrate nervous system. As indicated earlier, much of the information about how nervous systems function has been obtained from invertebrate animals, but the range of behavioural responses that can be studied in these animals is rather limited. Non-human vertebrates not only more closely resemble humans but are also much more useful when we wish to study a wide range of behavioural and even cognitive responses.

2.3.1 Vertebrate nervous systems versus invertebrate nervous systems

For the purpose of interpreting laboratory results and extrapolating them to human behaviour, it is important to describe not only the common features that are shared by invertebrates and vertebrates, including humans, but also their differences.

Similarities

With the exception of radially symmetrical animals, both vertebrates and invertebrates show:

- bilateral symmetry: both nervous systems can be divided into two similar halves by the midline.
- centralization: the nervous system of both vertebrates and many invertebrates is divided into central and peripheral systems. The CNS in vertebrates consists of the brain and the spinal cord. In invertebrates, the ganglia that form the nerve cord constitute the CNS. Sensory input and motor output connections to the CNS are mediated by nerves of the PNS in both vertebrates and invertebrates.

- cephalization: there is a concentration of neurons at the leading end of the animal represented by the brain in vertebrates and the brain ganglia in invertebrates.
- segmentation: the vertebrate spinal cord has a segmental arrangement, as does the nerve cord in invertebrates.

Another similarity concerns neurons. Although neurons are more numerous and generally smaller in vertebrate nervous systems, they function in much the same way in both vertebrates and invertebrates. These similarities have proven extremely useful to elucidate how neurons transmit electrical signals, for example in the 20th century most of the initial work on electrical activity in neurons was carried out using squid nerve cells.

Differences

You already know that the vertebrate CNS is in the dorsal position whereas in invertebrates the CNS is in the ventral position (Section 2.2).

Vertebrates and invertebrates differ in size. With an internal skeleton (as opposed to an external one or no skeleton at all in invertebrates), most vertebrates have larger bodies than invertebrates and therefore their control of movement becomes a much more complex process as many more muscle fibres need to be monitored and controlled. The increased surface area of the body also entails an increased number of sensory receptors. These differences demand more neurons in the CNS of vertebrates – just compare the 300 billion cells that form the human CNS with the tiny 302-neuron central nervous system of the much studied nematode worm, *Caenorhabditis elegans*.

In vertebrates, the PNS can be further classified into two functional divisions, the **somatic nervous system (SNS)** and the **autonomic nervous system (ANS)** (Figure 2.7).

- The somatic nervous system comprises the sensory neurons that innervate the skin, muscle and joints. It provides information essential for interacting with the external environment such as information referring to muscle and limb position, touch and pressure, or whether tissue damage has occurred. It is important to note here that the cell bodies of output motor neurons reside in the CNS, although their axons which project onto effector cells form part of the peripheral nerves.
- The autonomic nervous system is responsible for maintaining the activity of systems that control normal body functions (e.g. cardiovascular system and digestive system) and together guarantee a stable internal environment.

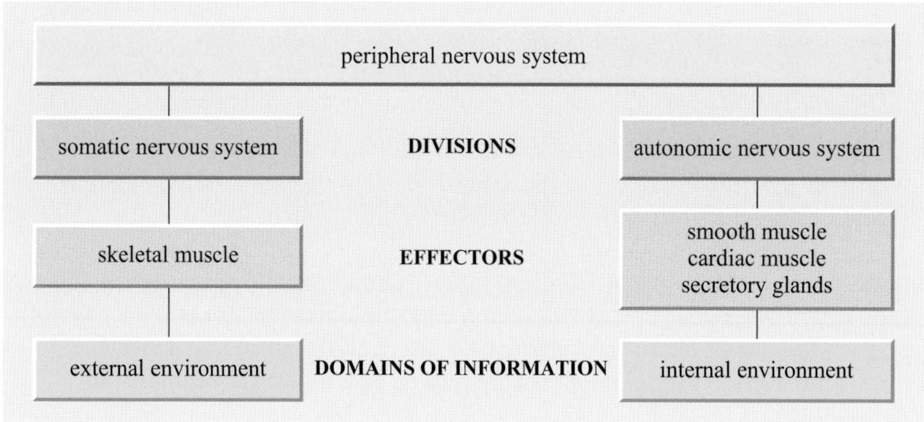

Figure 2.7 Domains of information processed and controlled by different effectors via the somatic and autonomic nervous systems in a vertebrate.

- ◆ What do you call the process by which action is taken to restore internal physiological parameters within the body that may have deviated from their normal values?
- ◆ Homeostasis (see Section 1.2.2), which is mostly maintained by the ANS.

The ANS is responsible for obtaining information about the state of internal organs (a process called visceral sensation) and for taking action to maintain their activity, ensuring homeostasis.

The basic difference between the autonomic and somatic divisions is the type of effector cells to which their neurons are connected. Whereas the effectors in the somatic division of the PNS consist mainly of skeletal muscle fibres (i.e. the muscles that move arms and legs), the ANS neurons innervate muscles of the internal organs (e.g. the heart and the gut), blood vessels and various glands (e.g. sweat and salivary glands).

- ◆ What type of muscle regulates the functions of internal organs such as the heart and the gut?
- ◆ The heart is made up of cardiac muscle that continuously contracts and relaxes causing it to beat. Smooth muscle surrounds structures such as the gut and blood vessels; its contraction regulates the movement of food in the gut and of blood in blood vessels. Both cardiac muscle and smooth muscle are inherently different in structure to skeletal muscle, the type of muscle that mediates interaction with the external world.

2.3.2 Basic plan of the central nervous system of vertebrates

We begin this section with a brief introduction to the general organization of vertebrate nervous systems. This is because an appreciation of the anatomy of the nervous system is the first step towards understanding how the brain functions. As you know, nervous systems can be divided into peripheral (somatic and autonomic) and central nervous systems. Vertebrate nervous systems can be further subdivided both anatomically and functionally. As you shall see later, this organization is based on the fact that groups of interconnected neurons that form separate anatomical areas within the vertebrate nervous system also share functional properties. This is called the *principle of localization*, which states that discrete parts of the nervous system are concerned with different functions. So there are different areas within the brain that participate in visual processes, memory formation, motor responses and, in the case of humans, language.

- ◆ Do similar functional groupings of neurons occur in invertebrates?
- ◆ Yes, in the form of ganglia. As you may recall, a ganglion contains a group of neurons that often performs a specialized function or functions (e.g. ganglia that control the activity of a group of muscles in the mouth).

However, it is worth noting at this stage that it is impossible to assign a particular component of behaviour in vertebrates to a single region of the brain – for example, we cannot talk about the brain centre for vision, but rather the brain's visual centres. In other words, different sensory, motor and cognitive responses are mediated by several structures distributed over large areas of the brain as a whole. Even the simplest task requires the coordinated activity of many regions in the nervous system (this is discussed further in Chapter 3).

As described in Chapter 1, the most obvious structures in the vertebrate CNS are the brain and spinal cord, which are connected to skin and muscles by the peripheral nerves (see Figures 1.8, 2.4d and e). The spinal cord is the most caudal structure in the CNS. To the naked eye, the spinal cord looks like a long, thin cylinder of nervous tissue contained within the spinal column or backbone. The major function of the spinal cord is to receive and process sensory information from the skin, joints and muscles of the limbs and trunk and to control the movement of these same muscles. (Note that the activity of the spinal cord is modulated by the brain, as you will see in Chapter 3.) This is the case in all vertebrates and therefore the structure of the spinal cord has remained fundamentally similar in all of them. (We will study the structure of the human spinal cord in more detail in Chapter 3.)

Looking at the variety of brain sizes and shapes shown in Figure 2.8, it is not immediately apparent that brain structure is maintained across different vertebrate species. However, the brains of all vertebrates are organized in roughly the same way and can be divided into three major anatomical regions: the **forebrain**, the **midbrain** and the **hindbrain**. This division is particularly evident during the early development of all vertebrates (Book 3, Chapter 3). A human embryonic brain of three weeks is shown in Figure 2.9a, and a slightly more developed brain of six weeks in Figure 2.9b. The forebrain, midbrain and hindbrain areas can already be identified by the location of swellings in the embryonic brain. Each of these areas can be further subdivided into different structures, which in turn contain different groups of neurons associated with particular functions. Some important anatomical structures are described below to help you compare the brains of different vertebrate species. (Different areas of the CNS in humans are covered in more detail in the next chapter and as the course progresses.)

The forebrain contains the **telencephalon** and the **diencephalon**, divisions that can already be observed in the 6-week embryonic brain (Figure 2.9b). The diencephalon acts as a gateway for sensory information transmitted from the spinal cord to the telencephalon and also participates in many functions that regulate the internal environment. The telencephalon is the most rostral brain structure and is dominated by the large pair of **cerebral hemispheres**. In mammals, the outer layer of the cerebral hemispheres (which in humans is highly folded and has a large surface area) is a highly organized structure called the **cerebral cortex**. It includes areas that regulate both sensory and motor functions. Strictly speaking, the highly organized cerebral cortex (also called the neocortex) is found exclusively in mammals, but the term cerebral cortex is sometimes also used to designate the outer area of the cerebral hemispheres in non-mammalian vertebrates. In the context of sensory input, the forebrain receives information about chemical stimuli from the nose via the olfactory nerves and associated **olfactory bulbs**, which are located rostrally in relation to the cerebral hemispheres of most vertebrates (ventrally in primates). Note in Figure 2.8 how the relative size of the olfactory bulbs is larger in species where the dominant sense to detect the external environment is olfaction rather than vision, compared to those which have a poor sense of smell such as birds and primates. Indeed, primates, and humans in particular, have relatively small olfactory bulbs, indicating that olfaction is not often used by humans as a means of sensing the external world.

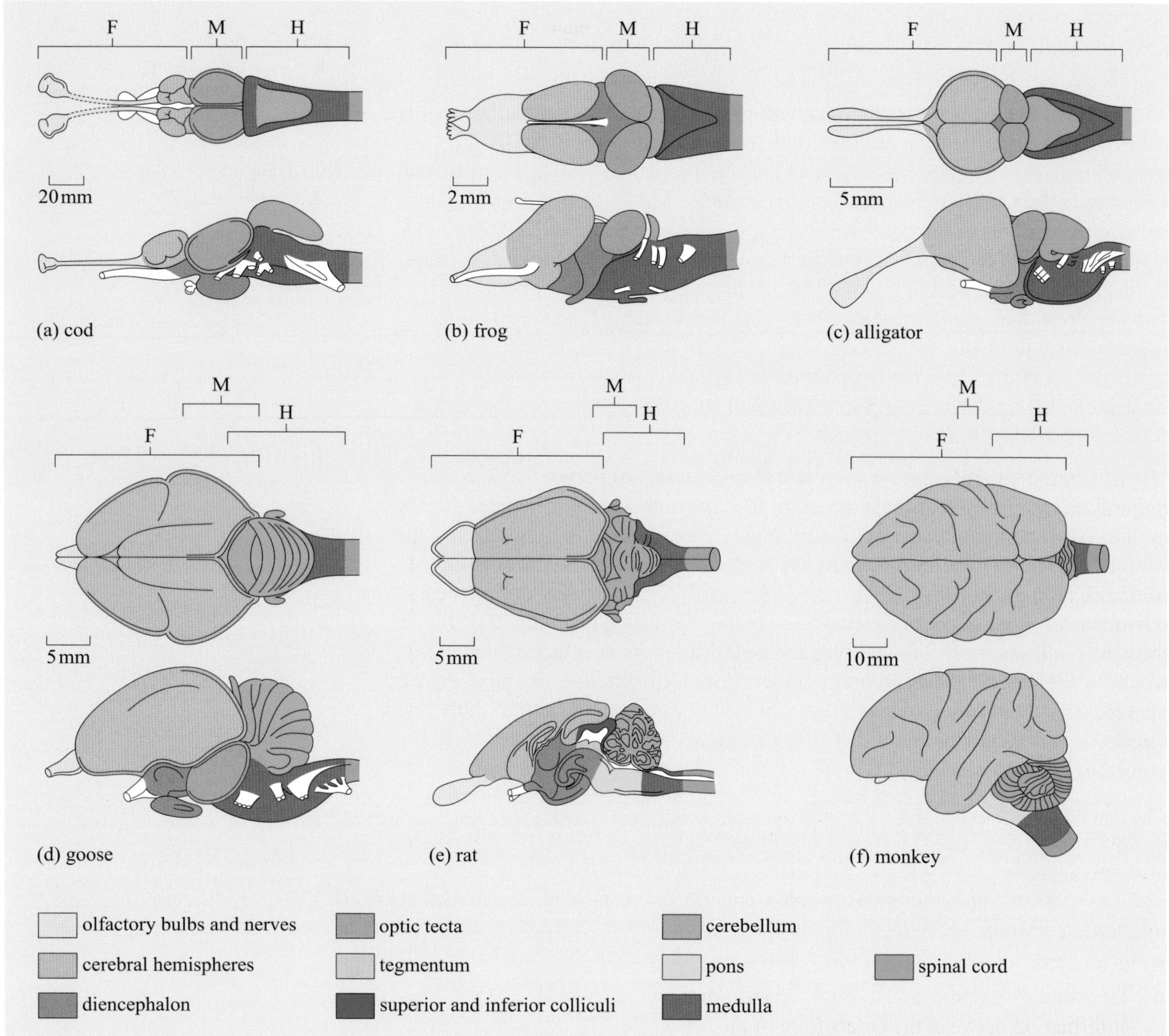

Figure 2.8 Dorsal and side views of some vertebrate brains (notice the different scales), showing the major brain divisions and structures within them. F, M and H stand for forebrain, midbrain and hindbrain. Rostral is towards the left; caudal is towards the right. (a) A cod brain, (b) a frog brain, (c) an alligator brain, (d) a goose brain, (e) a rat brain, (f) a monkey brain. The side view of the rat brain has been substituted by a section of the brain through the midline (known as a sagittal section) to show the position of the superior and inferior colliculi and the diencephalon.

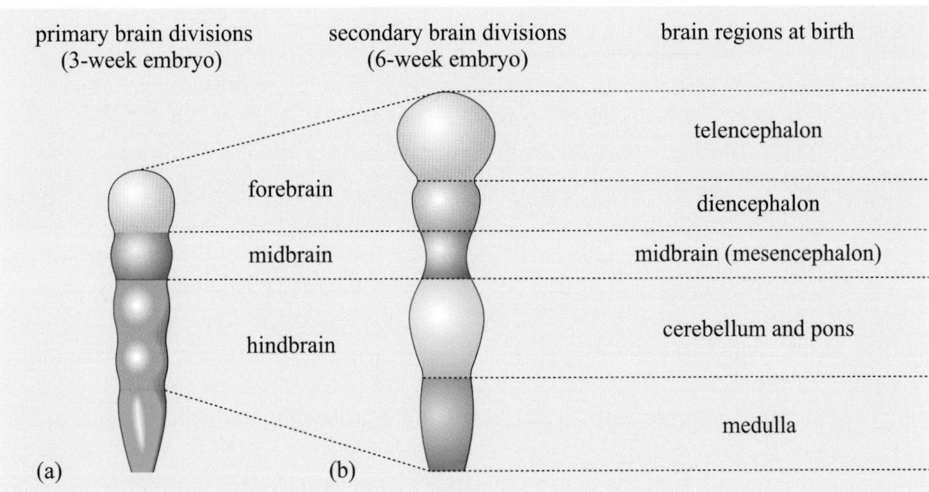

Figure 2.9 The embryonic human brain showing the major divisions at different stages of development: (a) primary brain divisions in a 3-week embryo, (b) secondary brain divisions in a 6-week embryo. The column on the right shows the equivalent brain regions already formed at birth.

The midbrain (also called **mesencephalon**) has a specialized role in controlling orientation to sensory information, especially visual and auditory information. The midbrain receives information about visual stimuli from the eyes via the optic nerve and initiates motor activities in response to this information. The roof of the midbrain forms a paired structure containing layers of neurons called the optic **tecta** (singular: tectum), which in mammals is divided into the **superior colliculi** and **inferior colliculi** (singular: colliculus). The word 'optic' is usually inserted in front of 'tecta' because they receive a large sensory input from the eyes, although they also receive important information about tactile and auditory stimuli. The floor of the midbrain is the **tegmentum** which is involved, amongst other things, in some aspects of motor control.

The hindbrain receives information about vibration and orientation from the ear and balance organs via the auditory and vestibular nerves, respectively. The hindbrain also contains a cauliflower-like structure called the **cerebellum**. This is concerned with coordinating body movements and learning motor skills. The structures in the forebrain, midbrain and hindbrain have extensive neuronal connections, not only within themselves but also with other areas in the CNS. For example:

- the **pons**, a protuberance in the hindbrain of mammals, acts as a relay point for information between the cerebellum in the hindbrain and the cerebral cortex in the forebrain;
- the **medulla**, the most caudal part of the hindbrain, connects the brain and the spinal cord. The medulla performs many vital roles such as controlling digestion, breathing and heart rate.

An additional common theme amongst vertebrates is the existence of paired sets of sensory organs – two olfactory sensory systems, two eyes, two ears that, together with the head and face, are connected to the CNS via paired sets of **cranial nerves**. Similarly, the rest of the body is innervated by paired sets of **spinal nerves**. The peripheral nerves forming the PNS can then be divided into cranial nerves (connecting the brain and the sensory and motor organs in the head) and spinal nerves (connecting the spinal cord and the rest of the body). Some cranial nerves are purely sensory (they convey information from receptors in the periphery to the CNS), some are purely motor (they innervate effector muscles), while the rest, along with the spinal nerves, have both sensory and motor components. We will study the structure and function of spinal and cranial nerves in more detail in Chapter 3.

You should now have an idea of the general organization of the CNS in vertebrates, but do all vertebrates follow this basic plan? The answer is yes, but there are obviously differences between species. The major difference in brain structure amongst vertebrates appears to be in the *size* of some of its parts, such as olfactory bulbs, rather than in their absence or presence. Learning about differences in the size of different brain regions can give an insight into the changes that have taken place during brain evolution. These variations in size also relate to the way of life of different vertebrate species. This is illustrated by the area within the cerebral cortex devoted to sensory input, which can be related to the relative role played by the sense organs in that animal's life. For example, rats and mice detect objects on their path by touch (with their whiskers) rather than by their vision, which is rather poor. Rodents, therefore, tend to have a large area in the cerebral cortex that integrates touch sensory information from the whiskers and a proportionately small visual area.

- ◆ Look at Figure 2.8. Is the size of the frog's optic tecta related to its lifestyle?
- ◆ The optic tecta are large relative to the other parts of the frog brain. They are responsible for processing sensory visual information. Frogs have generally a fine sense of vision as they need to detect rapidly moving prey such as insects.

- ◆ In Figure 2.8, the cerebellum of the fish is relatively large compared to that of the frog. How might this be related to the way of life of fish?
- ◆ The cerebellum coordinates movement. Fish swim in a liquid where they can move in any possible direction. This requires a much more refined tuning and control of muscle contraction than do movements performed by frogs, which are characterized by either hopping or crawling on the ground. By comparison, terrestrial movements are relatively simple to coordinate.

The relative size of the cerebral hemispheres is increased in mammals (especially primates) compared to other vertebrates, in birds compared with reptiles, in reptiles compared to amphibians, and in amphibians compared to fish. In effect, the evolution of vertebrates is characterized by the increase in size of the cerebral hemispheres and, more specifically, of the cerebral cortex. In mammals, the cerebral cortex dominates the initiation and control of behaviour. A relatively enlarged cerebral cortex allows a finer modulation in the function of other brain structures resulting in a more intricate pattern of neuronal interconnections between different areas. The consequence in behavioural terms is a more refined analysis and integration of sensory information and coordination of motor responses, together with a greater capability for information storage, i.e. learning and memory.

Summary of Section 2.3

Vertebrates and higher invertebrate nervous systems share various features, such as bilateral symmetry, segmentation, centralization and cephalization. There are also some differences and these include position, size and the divisions of the PNS into somatic and autonomic nervous systems in vertebrates.

An important message to take away from this section is that the organization of the CNS follows a basic plan in all vertebrates. The brain is organized at different levels: neurons are grouped together to form brain regions, which are contained within major brain compartments, and there are extensive connections between all the areas.

At this point, you may want to look at the flow diagram depicted in Figure 2.10 that contains the main terms covered in Section 2.3.2. You may also want to return to it later on in the course. Note that this diagram does not constitute an extensive list of the anatomical structures found in the vertebrate brain but is intended to summarize the concepts explained so far.

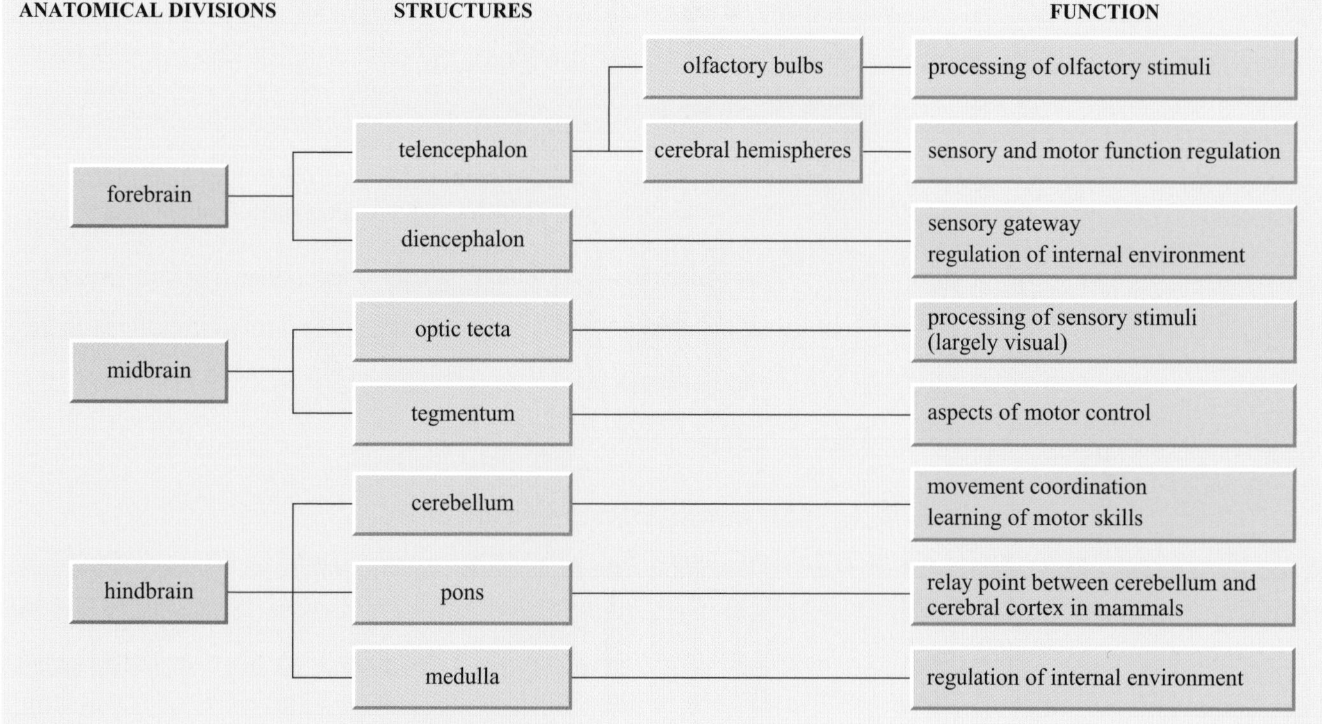

Figure 2.10 The basic plan of the vertebrate brain.

2.4 Cells of the nervous system

The complexity of a behavioural response is reflected by the intricate patterns of interconnections between different brain regions, as many parts of the brain are used simultaneously – whether it is a simple automatic reflex response or a complex mental act. Ultimately, particular behaviours can be traced to specific regions of the brain and understood in terms of the functioning of groups of neurons. As we shall see throughout the course, what distinguishes one brain region from another (and indeed the brain of one species from the next) is the number and types of its neurons, and how they are interconnected – the main theme of this section.

Section 2.4 explores the cellular architecture of nervous systems, that is, the structure and function of neurons and other cell types that constitute the building blocks of the brain. We begin by describing the basic structure of cells in the human body before moving on to the special properties of the cells in the nervous system that have developed from this basic cellular plan. If you are already familiar with the basic organization of a typical animal cell depicted in Figure 2.11, you can either go directly to Section 2.4.2 or read through the text to refresh your memory.

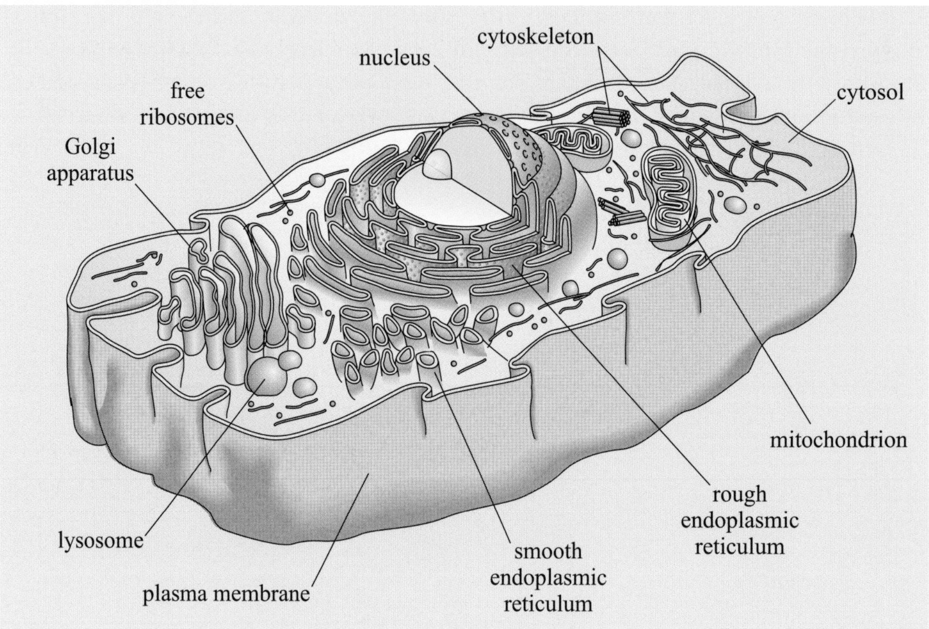

Figure 2.11 Schematic diagram of a 'typical' animal cell.

2.4.1 The basic structure of cells

The nervous system is just one of the many systems whose coordinated activities allow organisms to function normally. Systems are composed of groups of organs, for example the heart and blood vessels form the cardiovascular system in vertebrates. Organs consist of one or more different tissues (e.g. muscle tissue, connective tissue, nervous tissue), which are made up of groups of cells that have a similar function. Cells become specialized for different tasks depending on the tissue or organ they form, although their basic structure remains essentially the same.

1 μm (micrometre) is a unit of length that is a thousand times smaller than 1 mm. 1000 μm = 1 mm.

Cells vary in size depending on their specific function and the organism, organ or tissue they form. Most animal cells typically measure between 10–50 μm in diameter. The largest cells in the human body are egg cells, which can reach a diameter of several millimetres.

The shape (also called **morphology**) of cells reflects their specific function. For example, the morphology of neurons resembles a branching tree. This shape increases their surface area and allows them to receive information from many neighbouring cells. In contrast, immune cells circulating in the blood are essentially spherical, allowing them to circulate smoothly in the tubes formed by blood vessels.

So what are the key structural features shared by all living cells? We know that all cells are themselves organized into different compartments. The function of neurons cannot be understood without understanding the function of each of these cellular structures (Figure 2.11). Cells are delineated by an outer membrane which separates them from the external environment, also called the **extracellular** (outside the cell) space. Inside the cell, a central region or **nucleus** contains deoxyribonucleic acid (DNA), a nucleic acid that constitutes the hereditary or genetic material. The nucleus is surrounded by an **intracellular** (inside the cell) substance termed **cytoplasm** ('cyto' means cell, so cytoplasm could be described as 'cellular soup'). There are additional structures or **organelles** within the cytoplasm that are necessary for the biological processes of cellular life, such as making proteins or transforming nutrients into a utilizable energy source. An internal frame, termed the **cytoskeleton**, helps the cells to maintain their shape. Each structure within the cell performs particular tasks that are necessary to support the highly organized cellular machinery. We will now have a closer look at the specific functions of the different cellular structures illustrated in Figure 2.11.

The plasma membrane

The **plasma membrane** is the outer **cell membrane** that forms the interface between the intracellular and extracellular environments. It serves the function of holding the contents of a cell within a limited space. It also maintains the composition of the intracellular fluid, which is different from that outside the cell. Although the plasma membrane constitutes an effective barrier between the inside and outside of the cell, it does allow the selective passage of certain molecules and nutrients. You will learn in Book 4, Chapter 1 that the selectivity of cell membranes towards electrically charged particles (called **ions**) underlies the propagation of electrical signals from neuron to neuron. Cell membranes are essentially formed by fatty molecules (lipids) and, in the same way that oil forms a thin layer when poured over water, they actively separate the watery solutions that constitute both the internal cellular medium and the external surroundings. The main type of fatty molecules of cell membranes are called phospholipids. They are organized into two closely opposed layers (a 'bilayer') that have a water-soluble outer head and a water-impermeable inner tail (Figure 2.12a). Some form of mechanical support is given to cell membranes by cholesterol, which is another lipid that is commonly found in our diets and is interspersed amongst the chains of phospholipids. Carbohydrates that consist of chains of sugar molecules cover the outer surface of the plasma membrane. In addition, within the lipid bilayer are immersed a variety of proteins arranged in patterns that resemble a mosaic. Membrane proteins have the capacity to float and move laterally within the sea of lipids. Cell membranes are therefore considered to have a fluid character and are described as having a 'fluid mosaic' structure.

The functions of membrane proteins are mainly associated with biological processes that mediate the interactions of the cell with its environment and will be explained more fully in relation to neuronal function in Book 4, Chapter 1. For the moment, it is important to note that a group of membrane proteins called **receptors** respond to the presence of certain molecules in the extracellular fluid (the liquid medium that surrounds cells) by inducing a change in the activity of the cell. One such change is the opening of protein channels in the membrane (Figure 2.12b) which allows the selective entry of ions into the cell (Book 4, Chapter 1).

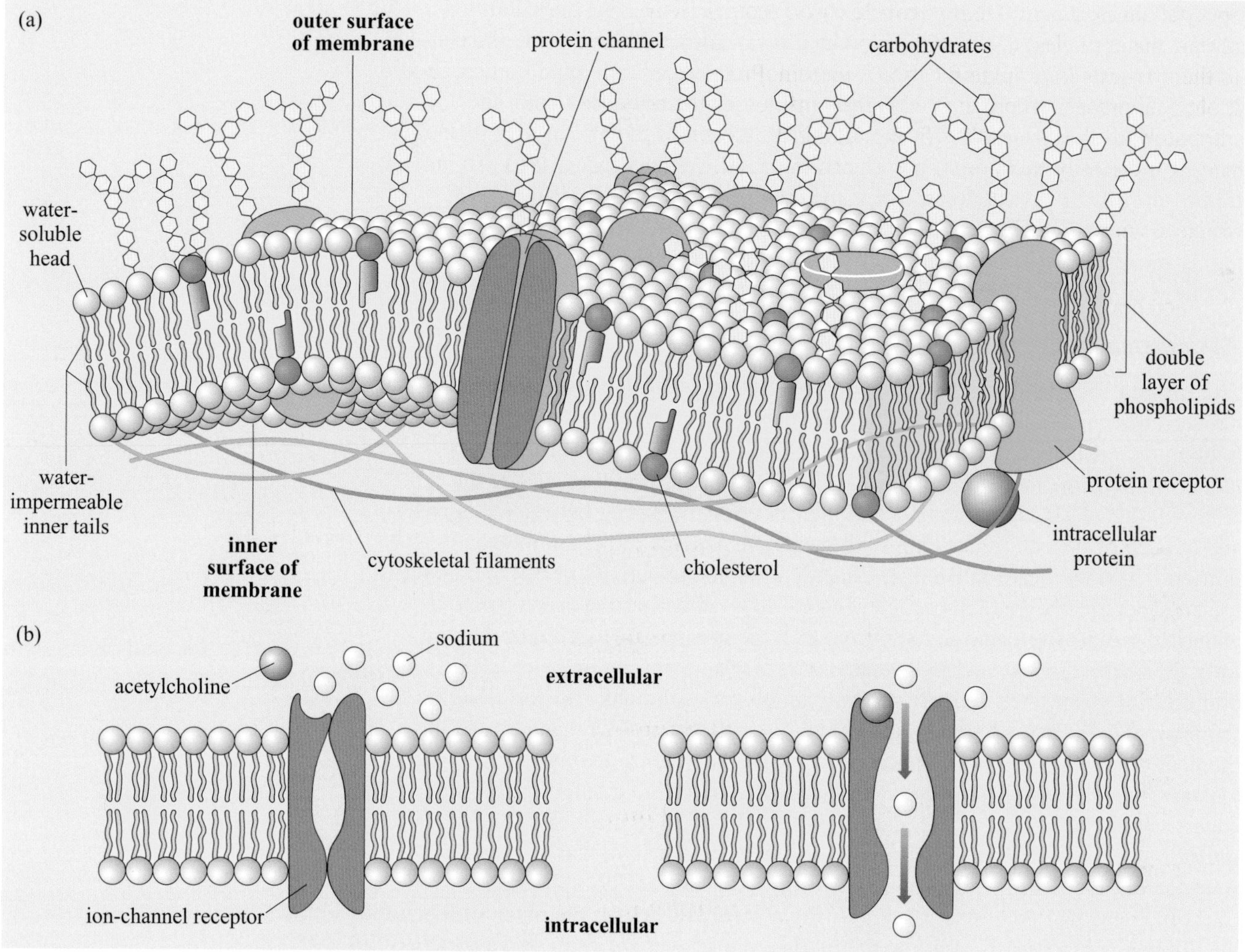

Figure 2.12 (a) Diagram of the basic structure of the plasma membrane of an animal cell. This structure is known as a 'fluid mosaic' (see text for explanation). Membranes surrounding intracellular organelles share the same basic plan. (b) Example of a protein channel inserted in the plasma membrane called an ion-channel receptor. When the ion-channel receptor is activated by the binding of a specific molecule, a change in the structure of the protein follows. This allows the entry (or exit, not shown) of ions (for example sodium) into the cell.

Intracellular organelles

How does a cell function as a living unit? As previously noted, the cytoplasm of animal cells contains all the different organelles, each with a different function required for cellular activity. Each organelle is surrounded by an intracellular bilayer membrane, assembled in much the same way as the plasma membrane (Figure 2.12).

Under the light microscope, the nucleus is the most prominent intracellular structure. It resembles a large, central sphere surrounded by a double nuclear membrane. The most important function of the nucleus is to contain the genetic material, DNA. It is estimated that two metres of DNA is tightly packaged within the nucleus of each cell. DNA molecules are organized into **genes** (Figure 2.13) which are functional units that carry the information that passes from one generation to the next. Genes are arranged into single, linear strings of DNA called **chromosomes** (Figure 2.13), whose number varies between species. In humans, there are 46 chromosomes: 22 pairs of identical chromosomes plus two sex-specific chromosomes – either two X chromosomes (females) or an X and a Y chromosome (males) (Figure 2.13b). The activation of a specific gene usually leads to the synthesis of a single functional protein. Protein synthesis is a highly regulated biological process whose control greatly influences the activity of cells and, ultimately, of the organs they form part of. How genes influence neuronal activity and, consequently, behaviour, is the central theme of Book 3, Chapter 3.

- Is the nucleus an intracellular organelle?
- Yes. The nucleus is separated from the rest of the cytoplasm by the nuclear membrane.

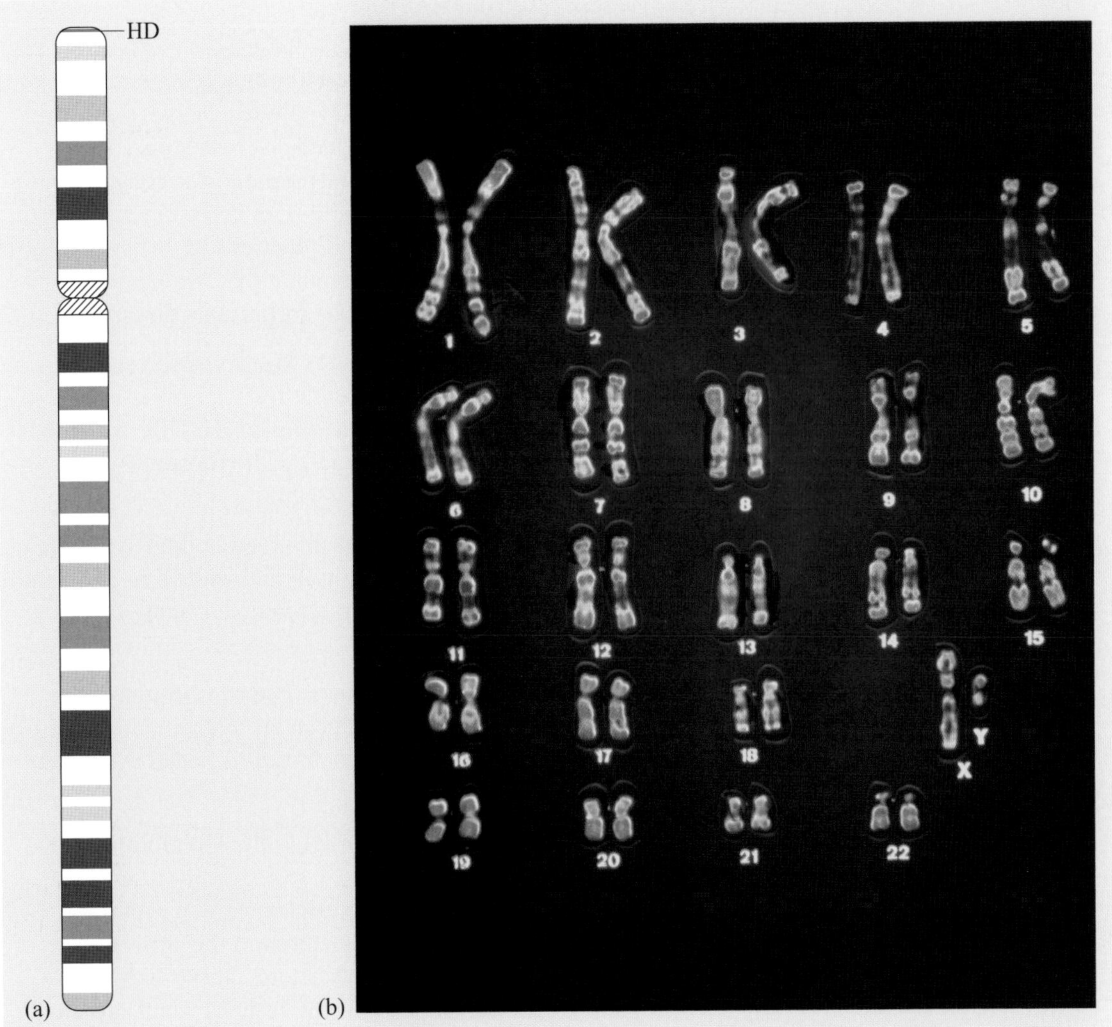

Figure 2.13 The human genome. (a) Diagram of human chromosome 4. Human chromosome 4 is a linear string of DNA which contains 1631 genes (the darker bands represent areas that can be stained with dyes – they are not individual genes). One example is the Huntington gene (HD in red) whose abnormal length is characteristic of patients with Huntington's disease, a disorder characterized by uncontrolled movements and dementia (Chapter 1). (b) The chromosomes of a human male magnified approximately 1000 times. The chromosomes were first stained and photographed with a digital camera. The image was then arranged in a conventional manner to show the 22 pairs of identical chromosomes plus the X and Y sex-specific chromosomes. The colours have been artificially added.

Before describing the other intracellular organelles, let us consider the part of the cytoplasm that lies outside the organelles but within the plasma membrane, known as the **cytosol**. Within the cytosol there are many molecules that have diverse functions, for example the concentration of ions and proteins in the cytosol is important in determining the electrical properties of a cell. Changes in the concentration of ions in the cytosol and in the activity of intracellular proteins may be the result of the binding of specific molecules to certain types of receptors on the plasma membrane. These changes are important in determining how cells respond to diverse stimuli.

- ◆ What is the difference between cytoplasm and cytosol?
- ◆ The cytoplasm lies within the plasma membrane. It includes the cytosol in which the organelles are suspended, but not the nucleus. The cytosol is the semi-fluid component of the cytoplasm.

The oval-shaped structures in Figure 2.11 are the **mitochondria** (singular: mitochondrion). These are responsible for producing a molecule called adenosine triphosphate (ATP) which captures energy from nutrients such as sugars (e.g. glucose) and fats. This process is known as cellular respiration as it consumes oxygen and releases CO_2 (not to be confused with respiration at the organism level, known as breathing, which also consumes oxygen and releases CO_2). The energy generated fuels the chemical reactions necessary to maintain life. Mitochondrial malfunction underlies many disease states, for example Parkinson's disease.

The network of membranes that forms tubes and sacs is known as the **endoplasmic reticulum (ER)**. This is mainly responsible for the synthesis of many molecules important for cellular life such as proteins and lipids. The ER is divided into two types, according to whether they are associated with **ribosomes** (molecules responsible for protein synthesis) or not.

- The smooth ER does not contain ribosomes and is involved in lipid synthesis. The smooth ER also contains stores of calcium ions which can be released into the cytosol. Calcium ions are thought to be important in determining the responses of the cell to extracellular stimuli.
- The endoplasmic reticulum containing dense globule-shaped ribosomes is known as the rough ER. It is involved in making proteins from another type of nucleic acid, called ribonucleic acid (RNA), which in turn is coded by nuclear DNA.

The proteins synthesized in the rough ER are transported to the **Golgi apparatus**. This consists of stacks of flat membrane-like sacs in close proximity to many round 'bags' of membranes of various sizes termed **vesicles**. Newly synthesized proteins are modified and sorted in the Golgi apparatus through this arrangement of sequential sacs to produce proteins with the correct structure. These fully functional intracellular proteins are ultimately packed into vesicles which are then directed to appropriate places within the cell. In a way, proteins are 'delivered' from the Golgi apparatus to where they are needed within the cell by use of this vesicular system.

Proteins within vesicles can also be exported out of the cell (a process termed **exocytosis**) (Figure 2.14a). The reverse process by which molecules outside the cell are taken into the cell is termed **endocytosis** (Figure 2.14b). Endocytosis is achieved by engulfing extracellular material into round vesicles formed by invaginations ('dimples') of the plasma membrane. Once inside the cell, these vesicles are directed to the Golgi area where their contents, if not required for cellular processes, are broken down by proteins located within small organelles known as **lysosomes**. Lysosomes are also responsible for degrading waste material or unwanted organelles in the cell.

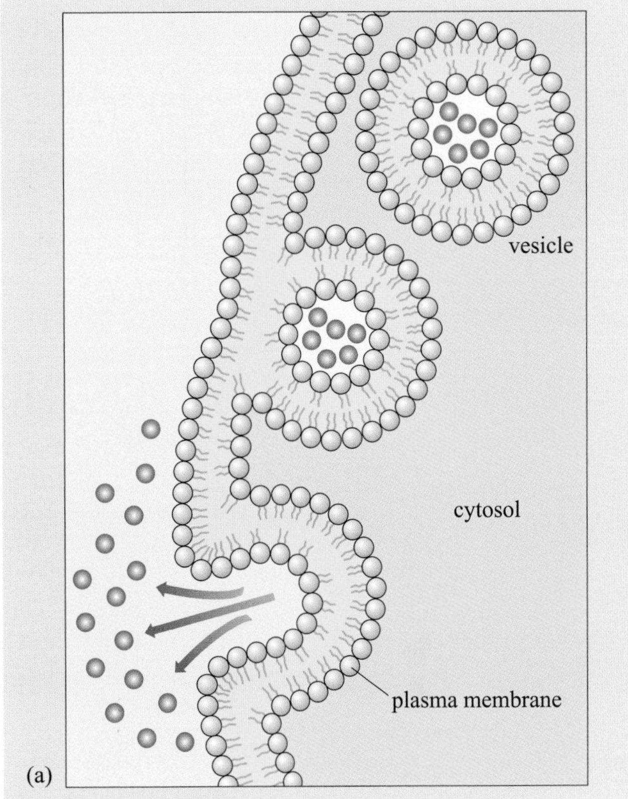

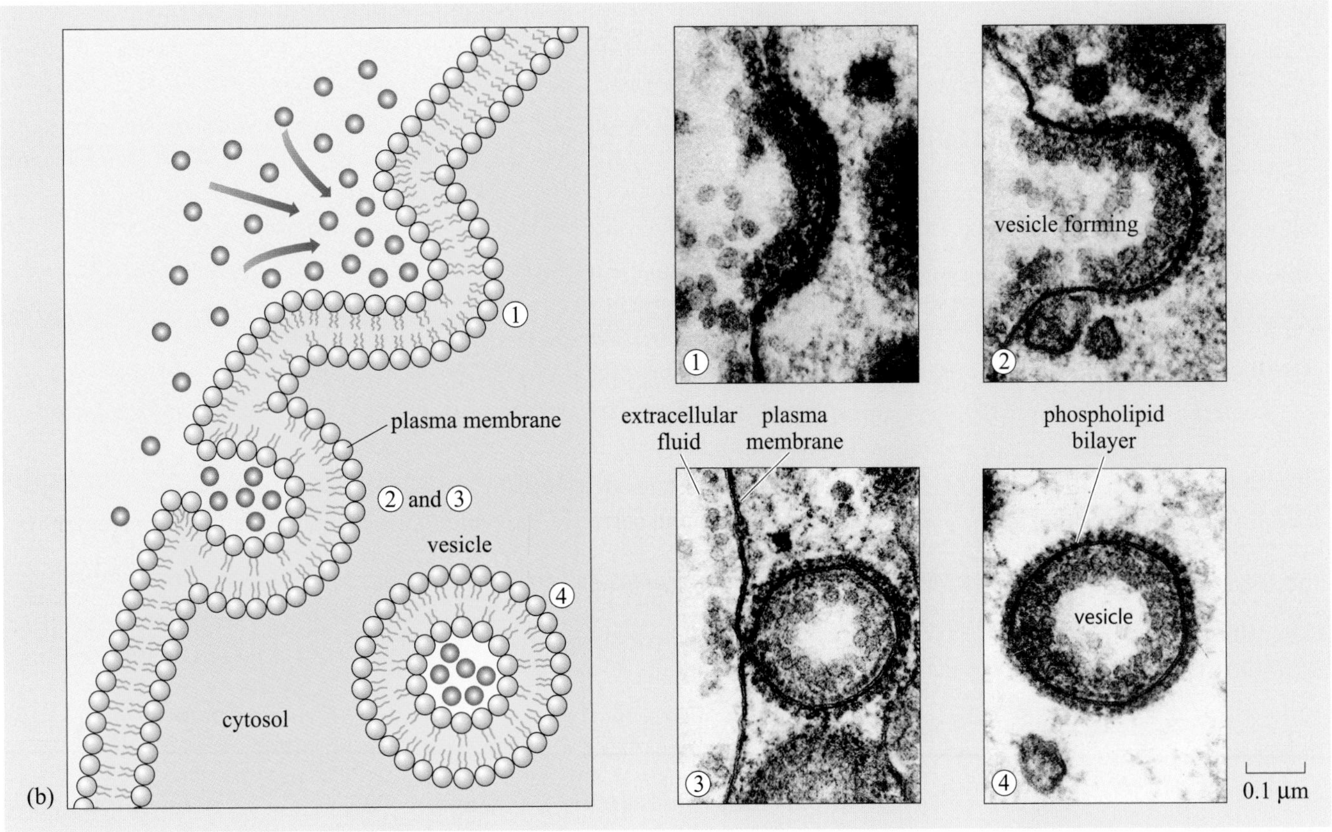

Figure 2.14 (a) The events in exocytosis by which intracellular material is secreted from the cell following fusion of a vesicle with the plasma membrane. (b) The basic sequence of events in endocytosis, the process by which material is taken into a vesicle formed by invagination of the plasma membrane. The electron micrographs 1–4 relate to the stages in endocytosis numbered on the diagram.

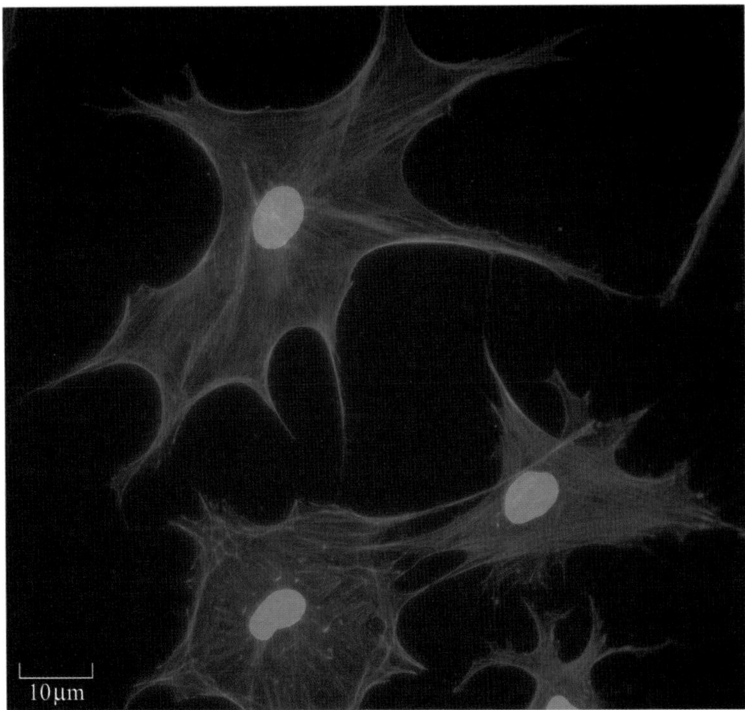

Figure 2.15 Photograph showing human cells which have been stained to show actin microfilaments (red). Cell nuclei have been stained with a blue dye. The cells shown here are called astrocytes (see next section) because of their star-like shape. They have been isolated from human brain tissue and cultured in Petri dishes. This staining technique is called immunofluorescence and uses antibodies to attach fluorescent dyes to specific molecules. (This is explained further in Book 3, Chapter 2.)

The cytoskeleton of cells

A network of bundles of filamentous proteins in the cytosol form the cytoskeleton, which is a form of cellular scaffolding that maintains the shape and structure of the cell. There are three types of filaments that make up the cytoskeleton, which have been classified according to their size, basic structure and specific functions:

- **microfilaments** (also known as actin microfilaments) are the thinnest (Figure 2.15);
- **microtubules** are tube-shaped and are the largest;
- **intermediate filaments** have a diameter which falls between those of microfilaments and microtubules, as their name indicates.

Collectively, these filaments are responsible for giving mechanical support and rigidity to the cells as well as being involved in cell movement and division, and the transport of organelles and molecules within the cell.

Table 2.1 summarizes the main cellular processes carried out by different cellular structures. You may also find this table useful later on in the course.

Table 2.1 The organelles of typical animal cells and their functions.

Organelle or structure	Function
cell membrane	separates cell from extracellular medium (also called the plasma membrane); separates organelles from cytosol
nucleus	contains DNA
ribosomes	assemble proteins from amino acids
endoplasmic reticulum (rough – contains ribosomes)	protein synthesis
endoplasmic reticulum (smooth)	lipid synthesis; calcium store
Golgi apparatus	protein modifications and targeting to intracellular sites
lysosomes	breakdown of molecules
vesicles	transport of molecules into and out of the cell
mitochondria	energy production
cytoskeleton	mechanical support; transport of molecules and organelles inside the cell

2.4.2 Overview of the major cell types in nervous systems

Nervous systems can be considered as communication networks whose integrated operation is ultimately responsible for a behavioural response. These complicated networks are made up of billions of interconnected cells that convey information between different parts of the body in the form of electrical and chemical signals (the human nervous system contains at least 300 billion cells in total). Although cells in nervous systems can be classified into thousands of different cell types according to their shape, function and location, there are three main cell types (see Table 2.2): neurons (Section 2.4.3), glial cells (Section 2.4.4) and endothelial cells (Chapter 3). One cell type that you have already met is the neuron which is supported by a mixed population of cells collectively known as **glial cells** (from the Greek for 'glue', as it was originally thought that they held nervous tissue together). The internal structure of cells in nervous systems is organized in essentially the same way as in all living cells in as much as they contain a plasma membrane separating the cytoplasm from the external medium, a nucleus and intracellular organelles. What makes cells in nervous systems, and neurons in particular, so unique and specialized in their function? Neurons constitute the fundamental communicating units within nervous systems and are said to be excitable cells (the term 'excitable' refers to their ability to propagate electrical signals). This property allows them to circulate information throughout the body, either from neuron to neuron (in the central nervous system) or from neuron to other cell types such as muscle cells (in the peripheral nervous system). Glial cells are more numerous than neurons by a proportion of at least ten to one and play key supporting roles for neuronal function. Their functions are extremely diverse and include maintaining a stable composition in the extracellular medium, insulating parts of neurons in order to accelerate signal propagation, and protecting neurons from damaging agents (glial cells are further subdivided according to their function and morphology – see Table 2.2 and Section 2.4.4). Another major cell population within nervous systems are **endothelial cells**. Endothelial cells wrap around themselves to form the blood vessel capillaries in which blood flows, securing in this way the supply of oxygen and nutrients to nervous systems. The functions of endothelial cells will be explained further in Section 3.5.2, when we look at blood circulation in the human CNS.

Table 2.2 The major populations of cells in nervous systems.

Cell type			Main function(s)
neurons			propagation of action potentials
glial cells	macroglia	astrocytes	regulation of potassium concentration; glucose and oxygen metabolism; structural scaffolding
		oligodendrocytes	formation of myelin in the CNS
		Schwann cells	formation of myelin in the PNS
	microglia		immune response to infection or injury
	ependymal cells		circulation of cerebrospinal fluid (CSF)
endothelial cells			formation of blood vessels in the brain

It is important to note at this point that different cell types within nervous systems do not function in isolation and that the activity of a particular cell or set of cells will influence the way other cells in their vicinity operate. It is the coordinated activity of all cell types that makes possible the normal functioning of nervous systems and which ultimately leads to a behavioural response. Figure 2.16 depicts the typical cellular organization found in the CNS.

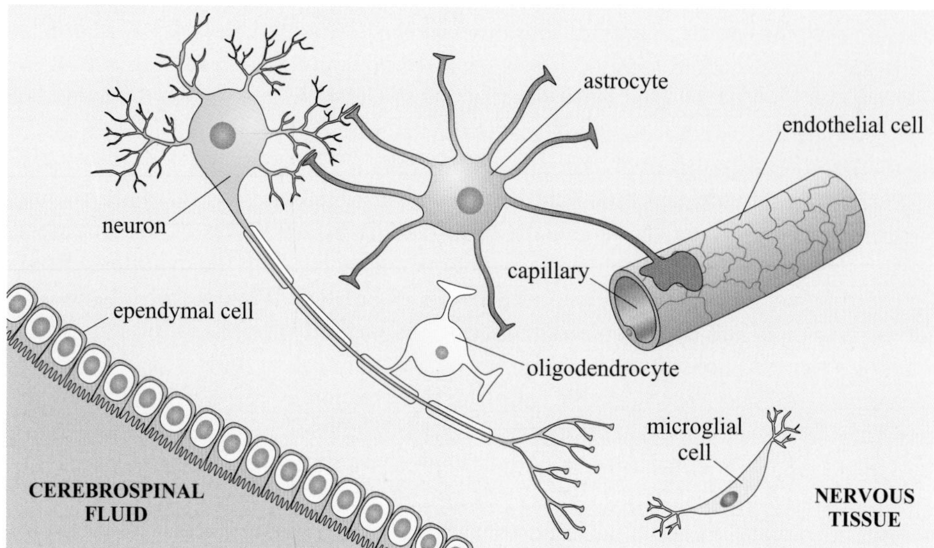

Figure 2.16 Organization of the different cell types in the central nervous system (only one neuron, astrocyte, oligodendrocyte and microglial cell are shown for convenience). Each cell type performs specific functions but its activity is influenced by nearby cells. For example, increased electrical activity by neurons is detected by surrounding astrocytes, which in turn send signals that regulate blood flow through blood vessels (Section 2.4.4).

2.4.3 Neurons

Neurons are extremely diverse in both shape and size (Figure 2.17), features that are affected by their location, their function, and the number of contacts they make with other neurons to establish neuronal circuits. In this sense, each neuron can be considered a unique entity. Despite differences, however, all neurons share the same basic structure (Figure 2.18). This consists of a central region called the **cell body** and a collection of processes that are specialized in carrying electrical signals, all bounded by a single, continuous cell membrane. From the cell body stem a collection of short, often highly branched extensions or **dendrites**, and an extremely long thin tube called the axon. Near its end, the axon divides into many branches to form contact points with the dendrites or the cell bodies of the next neurons along the communication network (Figure 2.19). The points of contact between neurons are the rather complex structures known as **synapses**. The cell body and dendrites receive the inputs to the cell, whereas the outputs are sent down the axon in the form of action potentials (see Section 1.3.2). It is important to note that the information flow generally occurs in only one direction, which is from the dendrites to the cell body and along the axon towards the axon terminals (Figure 2.18). At the synapse, the information is conveyed from one neuron to the dendrites or cell body of another neuron. A typical neuron on the receiving end has, on average, a hundred thousand synapses. It is this myriad of connections that form the complex neuronal networks of nervous systems.

'Processes' is a general biological term used to refer to the collection of structures (usually tube-like in shape) that stem from the main part of a cell, also called the cell body. So, axons are processes of neurons.

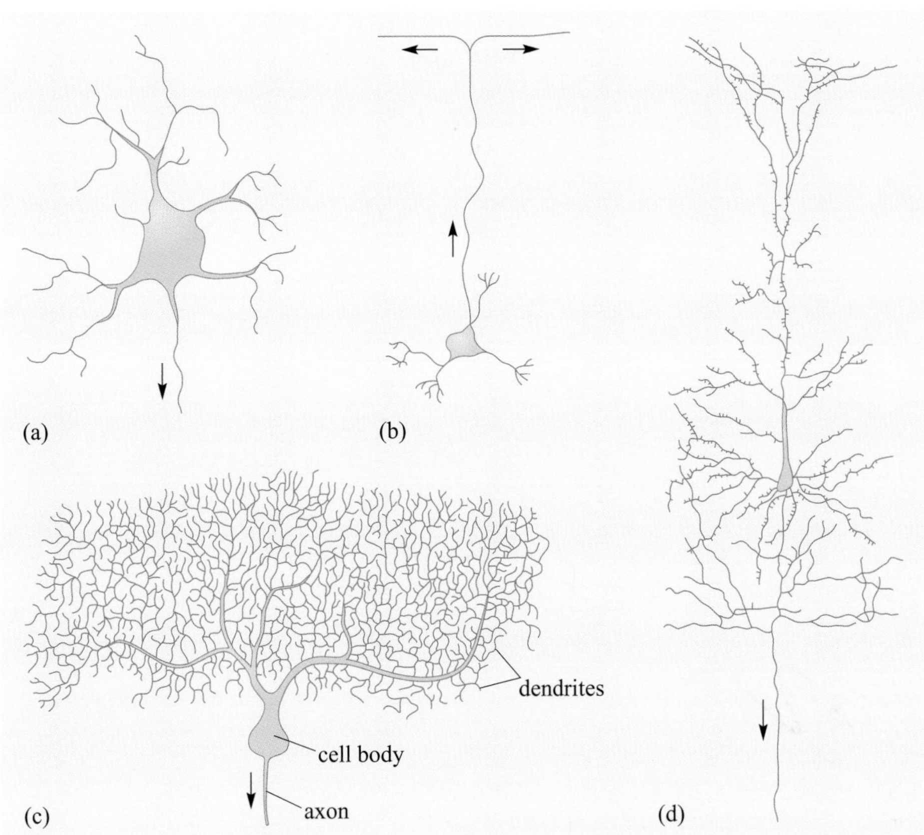

Figure 2.17 Some neurons from the mammalian nervous system showing variation in the shape of the cell body and dendritic tree as revealed by a Golgi staining method: (a) typical motor neuron found within the spinal cord; (b) granule cell found for example in the cerebellum and the olfactory bulbs; (c) Purkinje cell found in the cerebellum; (d) pyramidal cell found mainly in the cerebral cortex. Note the different names given to neurons depending on their shape, size and location. Arrows indicate the direction of propagation of action potentials.

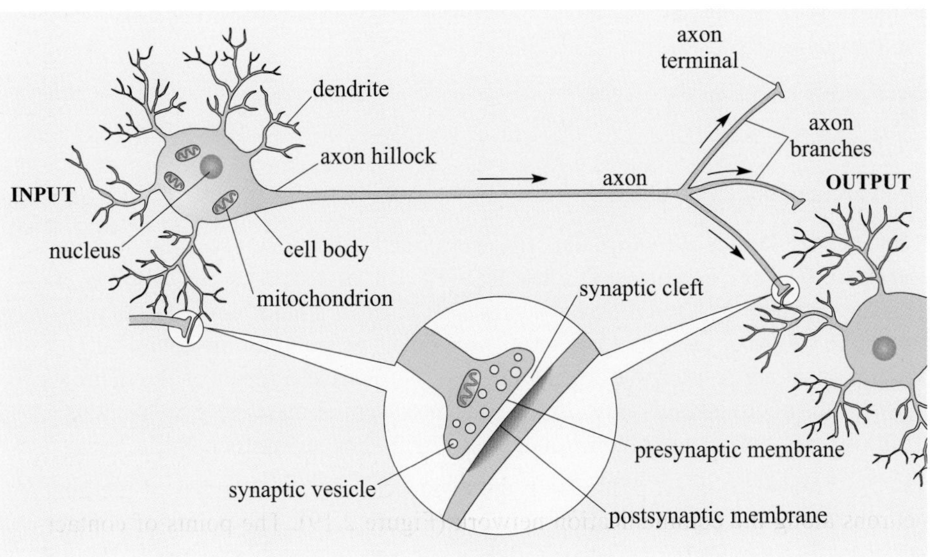

Figure 2.18 The main features of a typical vertebrate neuron. Arrows indicate the direction of propagation of action potentials. Input is received mainly via the dendrites and the cell body. Output in the form of an action potential travels down the axon to all the axon terminals. Information is then conveyed to the next neuron. Inset shows an axon terminal and the structure of the synapse.

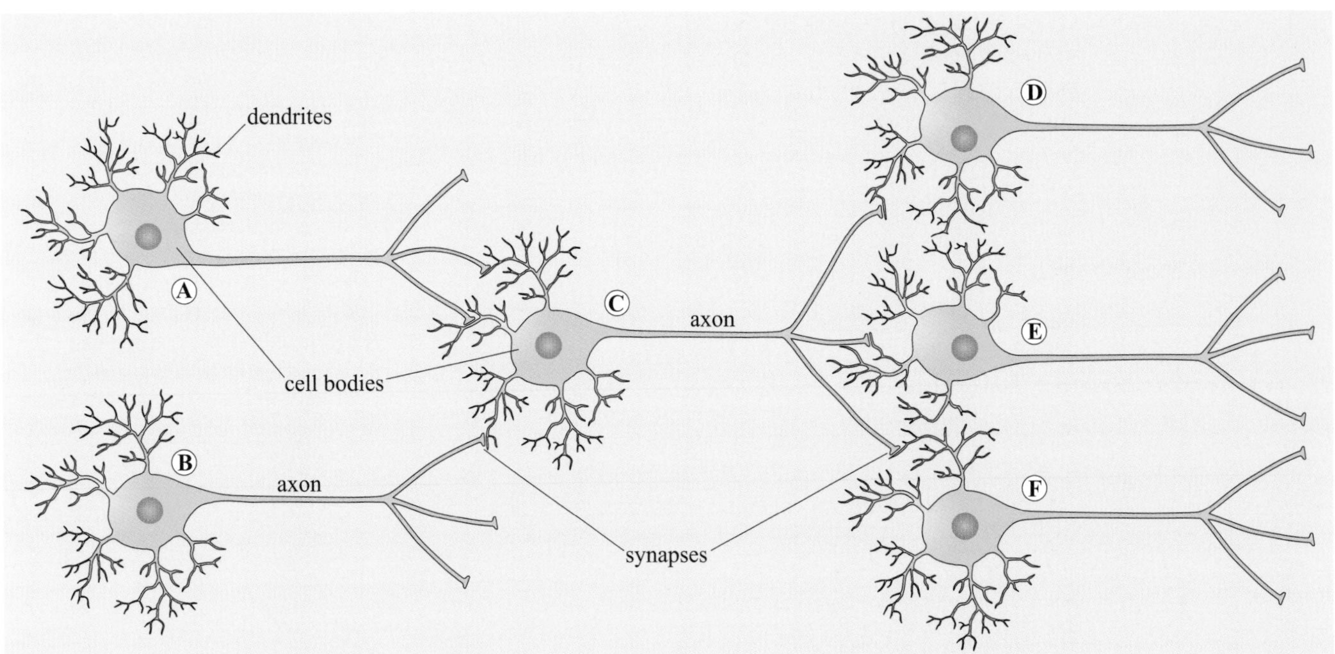

Figure 2.19 Diagram showing different arrangements of neurons connected by synapses. Neuron C receives inputs from many neurons and at the same time innervates (synapses onto) many other neurons. Neurons A and B are said to be presynaptic in relation to neuron C, which is termed postsynaptic. Note that neuron C is presynaptic in relation to neurons D, E and F.

Neuronal structure and function

In this sub-section we will consider:

(a) the neuronal cell body;

(b) dendrites and axons;

(c) the synapse.

(a) The neuronal cell body

Neuronal cell bodies are unusually large compared to other cell types within the human body. They can measure more than 100 μm across, which is 10 times more than the diameter of a red blood cell. The cell body of a neuron represents the metabolic centre of the cell. (The term 'metabolic' refers to all the chemical reactions that are responsible for the nutrition, growth and repair of the neuron.) In essence, the neuronal cell body contains all the essential machinery for cellular function, the nucleus and other intracellular organelles, the mitochondria, large quantities of ribosomes (either free or bound to rough endoplasmic reticulum), and a well-developed Golgi apparatus.

- ◆ What is the functional consequence of the expanded collection of ribosomes and rough ER, and the enlarged Golgi apparatus found in neurons?
- ◆ Ribosomes bound to rough ER are the centres for protein synthesis in the cell (see Section 2.4.1). The fact that they are especially prominent indicates higher levels of protein synthesis in neurons compared to other cell types. As neurons may extend over large distances, the extensive Golgi apparatus is necessary to transport molecules to distant parts of the neuron, i.e. the ends of axons and dendrites.

The high concentration of ribosomes in neuronal cell bodies has proved extremely useful for studying how neurons are arranged within the CNS. Ribosomes are intracellular organelles packed with RNA, which is a negatively charged molecule. Some histological techniques have taken advantage of this property to make cells more visible under the microscope. Substances used to stain neurons in this way have two characteristics:

Histology is the study of tissues. Different staining techniques are used to show how the cells are organized in different tissues.

1 They are positively charged molecules and therefore bind to the negatively charged RNA in the ribosomes.

2 They are dyes and therefore stained structures such as ribosomes show up as coloured intracellular areas under the light microscope (Figure 2.20a). In neurons, these stained ribosomes are called Nissl bodies.

These are by no means the only histological techniques used to study the cellular architecture of the brain. Other intracellular structures within neurons have been stained in the laboratory, including microtubules and neurofilaments that form the scaffolding of the cell or cytoskeleton (neurofilaments are the neuronal equivalent of intermediate filaments) (Figure 2.20b). Histological techniques that use dyes to stain the cytoskeleton were used to describe neuronal structure and location by the Italian Camillo Golgi and the Spaniard Santiago Ramón y Cajal at the end of the 19th century (see Box 2.1).

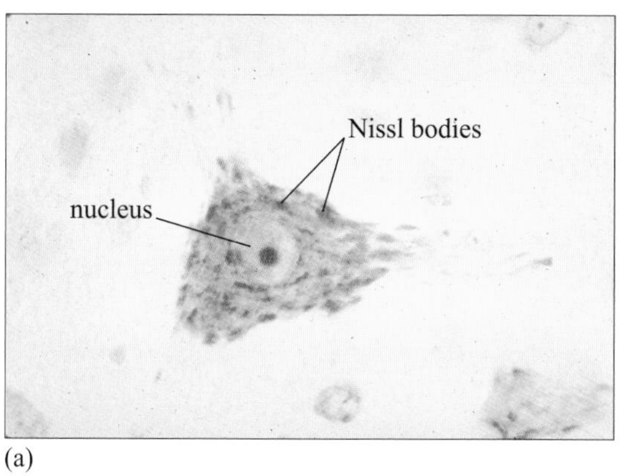

(a)

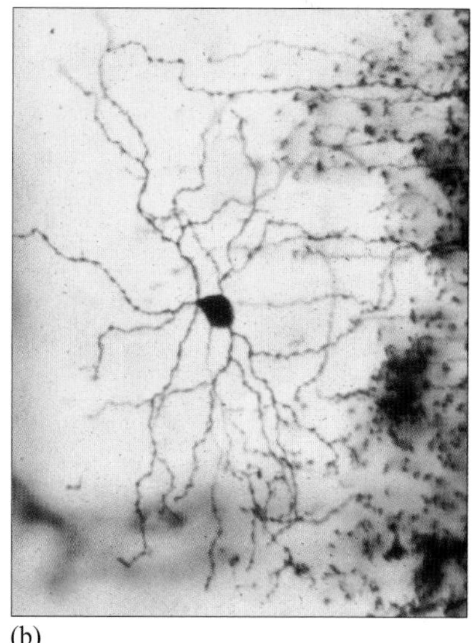
(b)

Figure 2.20 Two different histological techniques used to stain neurons: (a) the Nissl staining technique reveals Nissl bodies in the cell body of a motor neuron which appear as dark-red granules surrounding the nucleus; (b) the Golgi staining technique reveals the cytoskeleton in the cell body and processes of a motor neuron.

Box 2.1 The Nobel Prize in Physiology or Medicine, 1906

Camillo Golgi (Figure 2.21a), born in Italy in 1843, decided to concentrate on the experimental study of the structure of the nervous system soon after he started his scientific career in 1869. Although some histological techniques involving fixation (the treatment with chemicals to maintain the shape of cells), preservation (the chemical treatment to stop the tissue preparation from deteriorating) and different stains had already been developed for other tissues, they were inadequate for the complexity in the organization of the nervous system. In the 1870s, Golgi developed a revolutionary staining method, still in use today, which caused hardening of the nervous tissue. He used a chemical called potassium dichromate followed by metallic impregnations with silver salts that yielded what he described as a 'black reaction' in certain types of neuron. Although this method stains only a small proportion of cells, it allowed scientists to visualize cell bodies and processes of neurons in their entirety for the first time. In fact, Golgi's technique marked a milestone in the development of neuroscience although, much to his own chagrin, it was used by the Spaniard Santiago Ramón y Cajal (Figure 2.21b) to develop and confirm opposing neuroanatomical ideas that today constitute the basic principle of the organization of the nervous system. Camillo Golgi believed that the nervous system consisted of an uninterrupted mass of nervous fibres with no separation between them (the 'reticular theory'), in other words every neuron is connected to each other by dendrites whose cytoplasm is continuous, i.e. there is one large cell that takes the form of a net. By contrast, Ramón y Cajal correctly supported the notion that the nervous tissue is composed of billions of anatomically and functionally distinct cells. These cellular units were later called neurons by Wilhelm von Waldeyer in 1891, who officially enunciated the 'neuronal theory' on which modern neuroscience is based. Golgi, however, never conceded the point, and neither he nor Cajal would speak to each other when they finally met to receive jointly the Nobel Prize in Physiology or Medicine in 1906.

Figure 2.21 (a) Camillo Golgi; (b) Santiago Ramón y Cajal.

(b) Dendrites and axons

Dendrites are the main processes that receive inputs from other neurons and conduct these incoming electrical signals towards the cell body (although some connections occur directly on the cell body and on axons). Dendrites are extensions from the cell body that form a network of branches. They tend to be short and may divide a number of times forming complex structures that are capable of being contacted by many other neurons. As the pattern of dendrites resembles the branches of a tree (Figure 2.17), the collection of dendrites from a single neuron is also known as dendritic arborization or a dendritic tree. The whole dendritic tree receives information from many neurons by their contacts or synapses. The collection of cells from which input is received constitutes the **receptive field** of a neuron, the size of which varies markedly between different types of neurons.

Synapses occur on specialized protrusions on the dendrites called **dendritic spines**. The incoming signals generate local changes in the voltage of the dendritic spine plasma membrane, making it more likely (excitatory) or less likely (inhibitory) for an action potential to be fired by the neuron. All incoming electrical signals, whether inhibitory or excitatory, are carried from the dendrites into the cell body where they are integrated. Whether or not an action potential will be generated is then determined in the portion of the cell body called the **axon hillock**, which is located close to the boundary with the axon. If the excitation exceeds the inhibition by a certain amount, i.e. a threshold is reached, an action potential will be produced. For any one neuron, action potentials can be triggered at different rates (Figure 2.22). It is the firing rate (also called firing frequency) of a neuron that determines the nature of a response. For example, a low firing rate of action potentials in a motor neuron would cause a slight muscular contraction whereas a higher firing rate would cause a stronger muscular contraction.

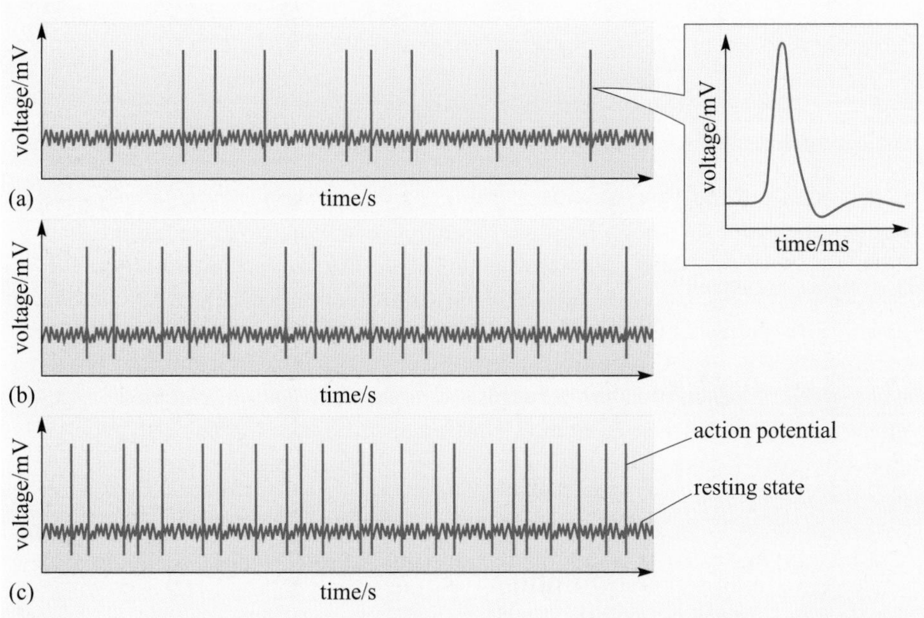

Figure 2.22 Record of activity in a neuron showing periods of resting and a number of action potentials. Firing rate of action potentials increases from (a) to (c). Inset shows a single action potential.

The axon is a tubular structure that stems from the cell body. Just as in dendrites, the axon is bound by a plasma membrane and contains cytoplasm but, in contrast, it is generally much thinner than dendrites (an axon may be less than 1 μm in diameter) and it only branches at its end to make contacts with numerous other neurons. The axon may be very short, especially within the brain, but it may also extend considerable distances, for example from the spinal cord in your lower back to a muscle in your foot! Once the action potential has been generated at the axon hillock, it is then conducted away from the cell body via the axon. The action potential is transmitted along the entire length of an axon and all its branches at speeds of up to $120\,\mathrm{m\,s^{-1}}$ (metres per second).

- ◆ Explain why neurons are said to be 'electrically active' or 'electrically excitable'.

- ◆ Neurons can suddenly change their voltage, resulting in the generation of action potentials that are carried along the axons. Note: inhibitory or excitatory electrical signals from other neurons make the production of action potentials either more or less likely. These inputs are received mainly by the dendrites and the cell body and are distinct from action potentials. Action potentials are only generated at the axon hillock.

The term 'fibre' can be used as a collective name for axons and dendrites; sometimes it is also used instead of either axons or dendrites.

Table 2.3 shows different types of axon or fibre. For any one axon, the speed of conduction of action potentials along its length is relatively constant, but different axons conduct action potentials at different speeds.

Table 2.3 Classification of mammalian nerve fibres.

Fibre type	Fibre diameter/μm	Conduction speed/m s^{-1}
Aα	8–20	50–120
Aβ	5–12	30–70
Aγ	2–8	10–50
Aδ	1–5	3–30
B	1–3	3–15
C	<1	<2

Note: it is not necessary to remember the details of these fibre types.

You may have noticed from looking at Table 2.3 that the larger the diameter of the axon then the faster the speed at which the action potential travels along it (its conduction speed). Another important feature that influences conduction speed is whether or not an axon is insulated, as electrical insulation will speed up conduction (this will be explained further in Book 4, Chapter 1). In fact, of the different fibres listed in Table 2.3, only C type fibres are not electrically insulated and they have the slowest speed of conduction. As we shall see in the next section, electrical insulation of axons is achieved in the CNS by a specific type of glial cell, called the oligodendrocyte (Figure 2.16).

- ◆ Look again at Figure 2.22. If the firing rate of a neuron increases as shown in (c), would the speed at which the action potential travels along the axon also increase?

- ◆ No. The rate of firing of action potentials by a neuron does not determine their conduction speed along the axon (which is constant). Their conduction speed is determined by the diameter of the axon and the presence or absence of electrical insulation.

When we discussed neuronal cell bodies, we noted that the internal cytoskeleton provides the scaffolding that maintains their shape. This is true not only for neuronal cell bodies but also for dendrites and axons. An important role of the cytoskeleton is to maintain axonal structure – axons can extend over long distances, which would be extremely difficult without some form of internal frame. However, this is not the only function provided by the different elements that form the neuronal cytoskeleton. The cell body contains most of the 'machinery', such as the rough ER, to synthesize proteins and other molecules. These molecules must be

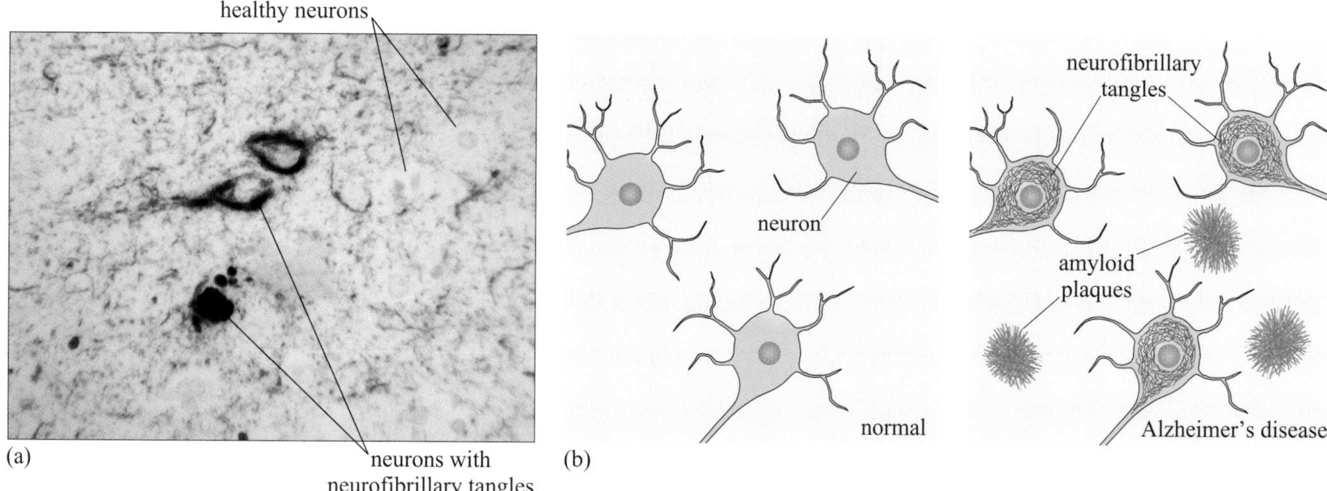

Figure 2.23 (a) Light micrograph showing tangles of intermediate filaments, called neurofibrillary tangles by pathologists, in the cell bodies of three neurons. Using an immunohistochemical staining technique, the diseased neurons appear dark brown whereas the healthy neurons appear unstained (colourless) under the light microscope. (b) Left: normal neurons; right: neurofibrillary tangles of intermediate filaments inside neurons together with deposits of substances that form aggregates in the extracellular space (called amyloid plaques). These are characteristic of Alzheimer's disease.

transported along axons and, to a lesser extent, dendrites when they are needed at the neuron's extremities. Microtubules and actin microfilaments running along the entire lengths of axons and dendrites provide a transport system to move proteins and organelles from the cell body to different parts of the neuron. The drug colchicine, obtained from the autumn crocus, causes microtubules to disassemble and has been extensively used by researchers to study axonal protein transport. (By inhibiting microtubule assembly, one can investigate the consequences of inhibiting protein transport along them.) It is important to reiterate here that the transfer of information as electrical signals towards the axon terminal does not involve the transport of proteins along axons. The role of intermediate-sized neurofilaments is at present unclear, but they may be involved in determining the diameters of the axons. However, we do know that their normal function is important for neuronal survival – it has been shown that in Alzheimer's disease and other neurodegenerative conditions they form 'tangles' of intracellular filaments that may be lethal to the diseased neuron (Figure 2.23).

(c) The synapse

The axon branches into many finer endings towards one end and forms synapses or contact points with other neurons. The synapse is formed by three structures (Figures 2.18 and 2.24):

- a swelling in the axon, called the **presynaptic terminal**, surrounded by the presynaptic membrane;
- the plasma membrane of the dendrite or cell body of another cell, called the **postsynaptic membrane**;
- the extracellular space between the terminal and the membrane, called the **synaptic cleft**.

When an electrical signal reaches the presynaptic terminal of a neuron, the information is then conveyed to another neuron via the synapse. The various mechanisms by which this information is communicated from one neuron to another will be dealt with in more detail in Book 4, Chapter 1. For the moment, you only need to know that in many neurons this process is brought about by the release of certain types of molecule called **neurotransmitters** that are stored in vesicles on the presynaptic terminal at the end of the neuronal axon. When an

1 nm (nanometre) = 10^{-9} m

action potential reaches the presynaptic terminal, the neurotransmitter is released by exocytosis and crosses the tiny gap (about 20–50 nm wide) that forms the synaptic cleft and, due to its specific chemical function, it activates receptors on the postsynaptic membrane. A sequence of very specific events then leads to a change in the electrical properties of the neuron on the receiving end by making it more or less likely to produce an action potential in the axon hillock. This type of synapse, by far the most numerous in vertebrate nervous systems, is called a **chemical synapse** because it uses molecules to transfer information between neurons (Figure 2.25a). In the other kind of synapse, the **electrical synapse**, electrical current flows directly from one cell to another (Figure 2.25b). The latter are much more widespread in invertebrates than in vertebrates, although recent research indicates that they are more common in vertebrates than previously thought.

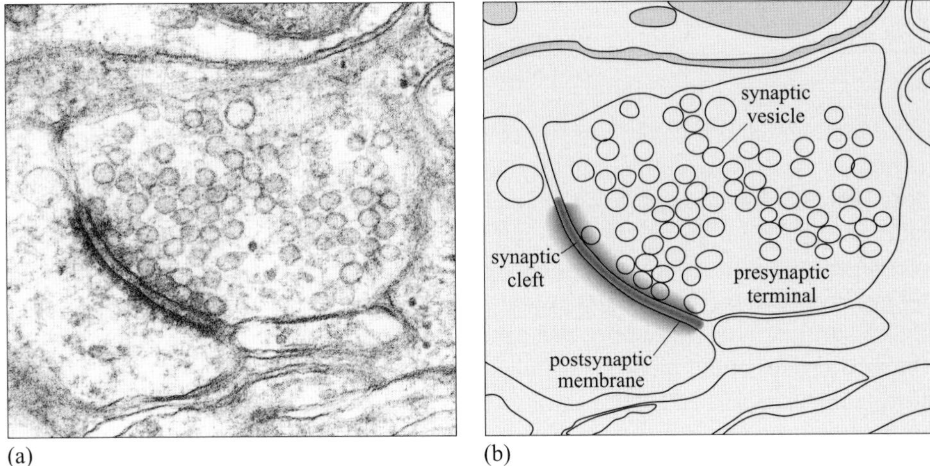

Figure 2.24 (a) Electron micrograph of an axon terminal synapsing with a dendrite. (b) Diagram showing the different parts of the same chemical synapse.

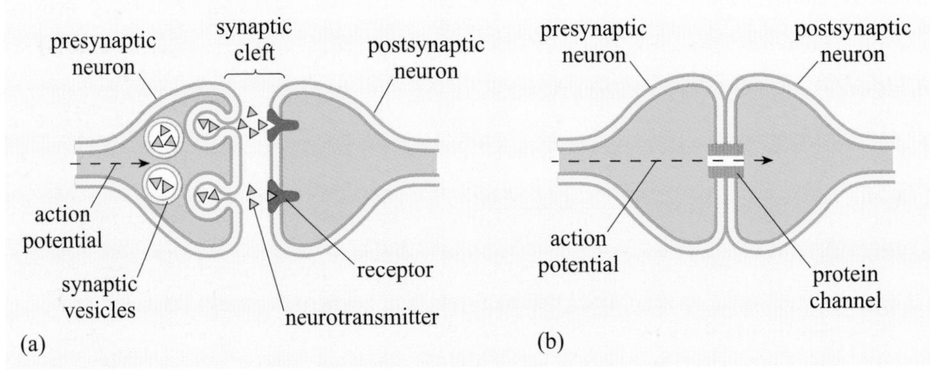

Figure 2.25 Chemical and electrical synaptic transmission. (a) At a chemical synapse, the arrival of an action potential at the presynaptic neuron terminal triggers the release of neurotransmitter molecules, which interact with receptor proteins on the postsynaptic neuron, causing excitation or inhibition. (b) At electrical synapses, the electrical current flows directly from one cell to another through protein channels located between the two neurons.

- Do you think the transfer of information between neurons will be faster via electrical synapses or chemical synapses?

- Electrical synapses are faster. Although very rapid, the diffusion of the neurotransmitter through the synaptic cleft of chemical synapses invariably creates a delay in the pathway of about 1 ms (millisecond) or longer.

Although electrical synapses may be slightly faster, chemical synapses modulate the activity of the postsynaptic neuron in a much more refined way. Chemical synapses may either inhibit or activate the postsynaptic neuron, depending on the neurotransmitter released, and the postsynaptic changes in electrical activity last for longer than with electrical synapses. These features allow a greater potential for the modulation of information transfer between neurons.

Synapses may occur between presynaptic axon terminals and dendrites, cell bodies and even axons in the postsynaptic neuron (Figure 2.18). The postsynaptic neuron then integrates the information transferred through all of its synapses and, as described earlier, determines whether or not an action potential is generated at the axon hillock. The pattern of connections or synapses each neuron makes with other neurons is unique and determines the path taken by signals as they travel along neuronal networks within nervous systems. Small changes in the pattern of connectivity of a neuron can occur, for example by increasing or decreasing the number of synapses or even changing the shape of a synapse. These differences in the arrangement of synapses distinctly influence the flow of information and the way it is processed by the nervous system. These small changes in connectivity, known as *synaptic plasticity*, play an important role in the mechanisms underlying learning and memory, as you will see in Book 5, Chapter 1.

Classification of neurons

So far we have described the general structure and function of a neuron, but nervous systems, especially those in vertebrates, are such complex systems that the neurons in them can become specialized for different tasks and can deviate slightly from this basic plan. In order to help with the study of the organization of nervous systems, neuroanatomists have devised several ways to classify neurons based on:

(a) their function;

(b) the type of response they generate in other neurons;

(c) their location;

(d) their morphology.

Although not exhaustive, you should find these methods of classification useful in understanding the diversity of neuronal function and structure within nervous systems.

(a) In terms of function, you have already come across the concept of sensory neurons and motor neurons:

- sensory neurons transmit information from the peripheral sensory organs, such as eyes, ears and skin, to the CNS;
- motor neurons connect the CNS to effector organs, such as muscle and glands, at the periphery.

Interneurons are the largest class of neurons. These neurons are neither sensory nor motor, but are exclusively connected to other neurons. Amongst these, there are local interneurons which make connections within the same area or structure (for example within the cerebellum) and projection neurons, which establish connections with relatively distant structures within the CNS, for example between the cerebral cortex and the spinal cord. In fact, when we say that brain region 1 projects to brain region 2, a phrase that you will often come across during the course, we mean that those neurons whose dendrites and cell bodies are located in brain region 1 extend their axons and synapse onto those neurons whose dendrites and cell bodies are located in brain region 2.

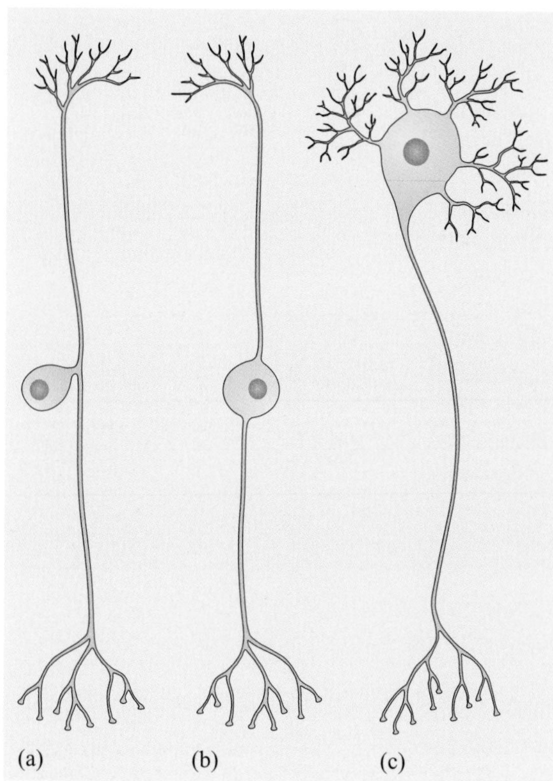

Figure 2.26 Different types of neuron classified according to their structure: (a) a pseudounipolar neuron; (b) a bipolar neuron; (c) a multipolar neuron.

(b) In terms of the type of response they generate, neurons can be classed as excitatory or inhibitory, according to whether they make it either more or less likely to induce an action potential in the neurons they contact. Projection neurons tend to be excitatory whereas local interneurons are usually inhibitory.

(c) According to their locations, the simplest classification divides neurons into either central neurons (their cell bodies are located within the brain and spinal cord) or peripheral neurons (their cell bodies are located outside the CNS).

(d) Classification of neurons according to their morphology simply depends on the number of processes that stem from the cell body. **Pseudounipolar** (Figure 2.26a) neurons have a single process coming off the cell body which then divides into two branches. (Unipolar neurons have just one undivided process serving both as axon and dendrites but are very rare in vertebrate nervous systems.) **Bipolar neurons** (Figure 2.26b) have two processes, an axon and a dendrite, whereas **multipolar neurons** (Figure 2.26c) have one axon and many dendrites. This classification is not just an arbitrary one as the shape of the cell and the number of processes reflect the function of each individual neuron.

◆ How would you classify the neurons shown in Figure 2.17 in terms of morphology?

◆ They are all multipolar (they have one axon and many dendrites).

2.4.4 Glial cells

The main difference between neurons and glial cells is that the latter do not generate or transmit action potentials. They are considered to be the 'housekeepers' of the CNS, as they have supporting roles that help neurons fulfil their role as information transmitters. In fact, without them, it would be very difficult for neurons to stay alive! This is illustrated by the variety of neurological conditions that result from the malfunctioning of glial cells (Box 2.2).

Glial cells are primarily divided into two major classes: **macroglia** and **microglia** (Table 2.2). Macroglia are further subdivided into three cell types: **astrocytes**, so called because of their star shape, **oligodendrocytes** and **Schwann cells**. An additional type of glial cell is the **ependymal cell** which will be further explained in Chapter 3, Section 3.5.2.

Astrocytes were originally thought to merely fill up the spaces between neurons to give them structural support, but this is far from the truth and their function has been found to be more complex. To start with, they twine around neurons, especially around synapses, thereby modulating the composition of the extracellular space (in particular, that in the synaptic cleft). These star-shaped cells play an essential role by regulating the concentration of potassium ions in the extracellular fluid. If the concentration of potassium ions increases in the extracellular space, astrocytes actively remove the excess potassium preventing deleterious effects. This is an extremely important role since fluctuations in extracellular levels of potassium may influence the electrical properties of neurons and the generation of action potentials (see Book 4, Chapter 1). Astrocytes also have an important role to play in mopping up leaked or released neurotransmitters within the synapses, as an excess of neurotransmitters may in itself be toxic to neurons. Some neurotransmitters even induce responses in astrocytes as they have similar receptors to those found in the postsynaptic membrane of neurons. The kind of responses that neurotransmitters generate in astrocytes strongly suggests that signals can be communicated between astrocytes and neurons. In addition, astrocytes are able to sense local metabolic requirements and regulate the transfer of materials, such as nutrients and oxygen, from the blood to the brain. As they are in close contact with the endothelial cells that form blood vessels (Figure 2.27), astrocytes are able to send signals to these cells that result in dilation of the blood capillaries. This effectively increases the blood flow and therefore the availability of oxygen and nutrients. This is a feature that is exploited in brain imaging, which was covered in Chapter 1 and that you will meet in Book 3, Chapter 2.

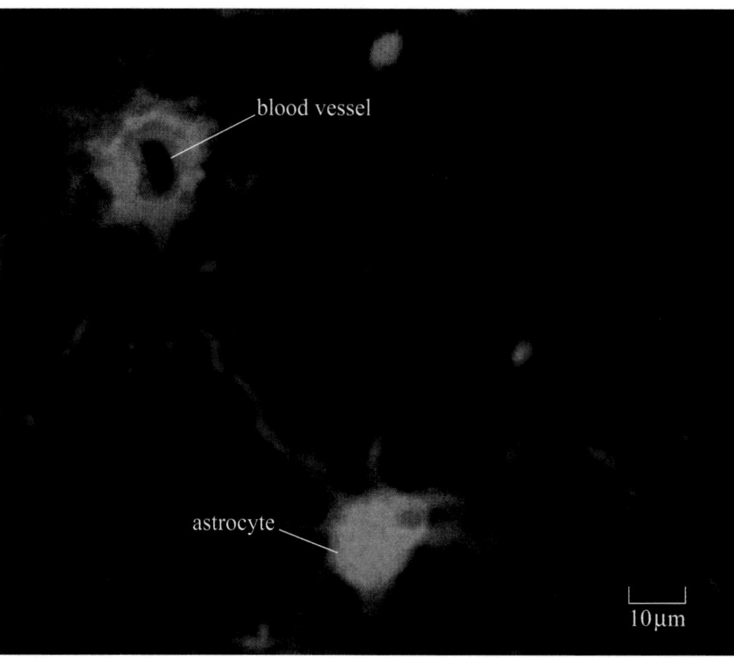

Figure 2.27 Immunofluorescence micrograph showing an astrocyte (green) and endothelial cells in a blood vessel (red) in a section of the human cerebral cortex. Note that the blood vessel is surrounded by a long, thin process that stems from the cell body of the astrocyte. This intimate contact between astrocytes and endothelial cells favours the exchange of signals between the two cell types.

In vertebrates, oligodendrocytes in the CNS wrap themselves several times around a number of axons in a manner not dissimilar to a Swiss roll around a creamy centre. As its hold on the axon tightens, all the cytoplasm is squeezed out of that part of the oligodendrocyte. This structure forms a thick, whitish, fatty layer called **myelin** (Figure 2.28). Because of its colour, areas within the brain that are abundant in myelin are referred to as **white matter**, contrasting with **grey matter** which comprises densely packed cell bodies. In the PNS, the myelin is packed tightly around individual axons by the Schwann cells, a type of glial cell serving similar functions to oligodendrocytes in the CNS. The main difference between Schwann cells and oligodendrocytes, apart from location, is that Schwann cells wrap themselves around just one axon. The role of myelin is to electrically insulate axons, greatly increasing the speed at which nerve impulses travel along them. In humans, the myelin sheath is synthesized during development and most of it is already laid down by two years of age. However, some of the nerves in the PNS continue this process well into the second decade of life. In adults, some diseases such as multiple sclerosis cause myelinated axons to become demyelinated (see Box 2.2).

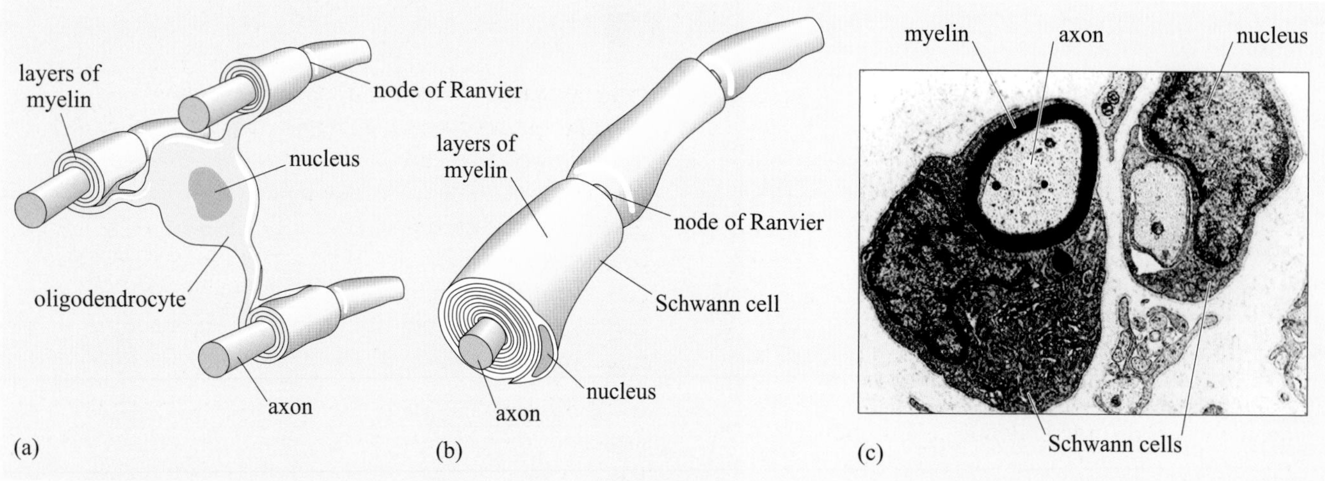

Figure 2.28 Diagram showing how axons are ensheathed by myelinating glial cells in (a) the CNS where an oligodendrocyte may wrap itself around several axons, and (b) the PNS where a Schwann cell wraps around just one axon. The nodes of Ranvier are the unmyelinated areas of the axon. (c) Electron micrograph of a myelinated axon (left) and a partially myelinated axon (right) in a peripheral nerve of the leg of a young rat; the centre of the axon is filled with neurofilaments and neurotubules. During development, myelin is still being synthesized and many axons are yet to be fully insulated by the protective myelin sheath.

- ◆ It has already been stated that type C fibres are the slowest in terms of conduction speed. Why are they the slowest?
- ◆ The two main structural properties that affect the speed of conduction are myelination and the diameter of the fibre. The diameters of type C fibres are the smallest of all the fibre types (see Table 2.3). They are also not electrically insulated – in other words they are unmyelinated.

- ◆ Myelin is only found in vertebrates. How might invertebrates compensate for the slower speed of conduction in unmyelinated fibres?
- ◆ They do this in two ways: (a) by increasing the diameters of axons and (b) by means of electrical synapses, which are faster than chemical synapses.

Axons may be quite long, so electrical signals may need to travel large distances. Along each axon's length, there are segments that are not insulated between one oligodendrocyte and the next. This feature results in the formation of gaps in the myelin sheath of around 1–2 μm every 0.5–2 mm. These gaps are called **nodes of Ranvier**. In Book 4, Chapter 1, we will discover why these breaks in the myelin sheath are extremely important for the transmission of electrical signals.

As their name indicates, microglial cells are smaller in size than other glial cells. Microglia are the immune cells of the CNS, but as such they are usually in a resting state in healthy nervous tissue. However, when infection or injury occurs, microglial cells become activated and direct the immune response (Box 2.2). They also act as brain scavengers, mopping up bacteria and cell debris, if the death of neurons or other glial cells occurs. Ependymal cells are a type of glial cell that help to circulate the liquid that flows within the cavities of the brain and spinal cord, called the **cerebrospinal fluid (CSF)** (Section 3.5.2).

Box 2.2 Glial cells and nervous system disease

Glial cells perform a variety of roles which are essential for neuronal function. This is demonstrated by the symptoms experienced by people who suffer from neurological conditions where the primary diseased cell type is not the neuron but glial cells. Multiple sclerosis is one such devastating condition. There are several forms of multiple sclerosis, but the most common one is characterized by periods of acute disease or relapse followed by partial remission. Common symptoms during periods of relapse are extremely varied and include visual disorders (double and/or blurred vision), 'pins and needles', fatigue, muscle pain and lack of coordination, partial paralysis, tinnitus (ringing in the ears), speech disorders, depression and anxiety. How can all these disparate symptoms occur due to just one form of a disease? The answer lies in one of its most prominent characteristics – the loss of myelin. In multiple sclerosis, axons become devoid of the insulating fatty layer of myelin produced by the oligodendrocytes. This process is called demyelination (see Figure 2.29). Demyelination invariably slows down the speed of conduction of the axons that become unmyelinated. Depending on where the neurons whose axons have been affected are located and what function they perform, the patient will suffer a myriad of different symptoms. It is believed that multiple sclerosis is an autoimmune disease in which the patient's immune system does not recognize myelin as belonging to their own body and destroys it as a result. Astrocytes and microglia also intervene in this process. Both cell types become activated and release mediators of the immune reaction. Why multiple sclerosis affects certain people and not others, that is, whether it has a genetic component or is triggered by a still unidentified infectious agent, is a hotly debated topic of research.

In other inflammatory diseases, microglia appear to have an extremely prominent role. An example of this is the dementia resulting from infection by the human immunodeficiency virus (HIV), known in medical terms as HIV encephalopathy. If HIV accesses the brain from the blood, microglia are the major cell type that becomes infected. (Astrocytes also get infected but to a lesser extent.) HIV-infected microglia allow replication of viruses which are then released to infect other cells. At the same time, microglia are activated and initiate an immune response directed against the viral infection. It is thought that products shredded from the virus and substances released by excessively activated microglia are toxic to neurons. This pathology results in a complicated neurological condition termed AIDS-dementia complex that primarily affects children infected with HIV.

Figure 2.29 Section of the brain showing a demyelinated lesion of a multiple sclerosis patient. The myelin has been stained with a blue dye. Notice the absence of myelin in the middle of the field.

Summary of Section 2.4

All cells consist of a plasma membrane surrounding intracellular organelles. The nucleus contains the genetic material, or DNA. Neurons are cells that are responsible for transmitting information in the form of electrical signals from one part of the nervous system to another. The flow of information is usually from dendrites and cell bodies towards the axon terminal. Neurons establish contact with each other via synapses, which may be electrical or chemical. Neuronal function is aided by other cells residing in nervous tissue, the most numerous being glial cells.

2.5 Summary of Chapter 2

By the end of this chapter you should have acquired a working knowledge of the general principles governing the functioning of nervous systems.

The first half of this chapter looked at the nervous systems of some invertebrates and compared and contrasted them with the nervous systems of vertebrates. We started by describing the most basic type of nervous system, the nerve net, characteristic of hydra, an aquatic invertebrate. A nerve net is a network of neurons, which respond to a variety of stimuli, located on the body wall of the animal. Although somewhat simple, the wide range of behavioural responses generated by nerve nets allows the organism to adapt to diverse situations in the external environment. Higher invertebrate nervous systems and vertebrate nervous systems are more complex in that they show centralization and cephalization, and as a result are closer in anatomy and physiology to the human nervous system, the main emphasis of this course. In vertebrates, including humans, the brain can be divided up into regions, each specialized for a particular function(s). The size of different brain structures can be related to an animal's lifestyle, a feature that also occurs in humans as you will see in the following chapter. In describing the roles of brain structures and brain systems, information has been gained from studying animals as diverse as worms, flies, squid, rats, cats and monkeys.

In the second half of this chapter, we turned our attention to the organization of nervous systems at the cellular level. Neurons, the cells that are responsible for communicating electrical signals, require supporting cells such as glial cells to sustain their function. In other words, the role of glial cells (together with endothelial cells) is to maintain the homeostasis of nervous systems. In the last century, we have gained an enormous knowledge of how all these cell types operate either as single cells (by tracing the molecular changes underlying their function) or as collections of cells (by studying electrical and metabolic events occurring within different brain structures). Yet the understanding of how the activity of cells within nervous systems ultimately generates a behavioural response still eludes us. As you will see in the next chapter, some simple behaviours such as reflex automated responses have been studied in detail and are well understood. Perhaps the greatest challenge of all for neuroscientists is to gain an insight into how collections of neurons and changes in their function at the molecular and cellular level can give rise to complex cognitive behaviours.

Having reviewed the components of nervous systems and studied some anatomy in this chapter, the next chapter describes how neurons in the human nervous system work together to enable us to sense our environment and react to it.

Learning outcomes for Chapter 2

At the end of this chapter you should be able to:

2.1 Recognize definitions and applications of each of the terms printed in **bold** in the text.

2.2 Show how the structure of nervous systems is related to the lifestyle and habitat of invertebrates and vertebrates.

2.3 Use the correct anatomical terms to describe relative directions and positions within vertebrate and invertebrate nervous systems.

2.4 Compare vertebrate and invertebrate nervous systems and explain the main differences and similarities in structure and function.

2.5 Describe the basic anatomical organization of vertebrate nervous systems.

2.6 Describe the intracellular structures and basic functions of a living cell.

2.7 Identify the main features of neurons and explain their function.

2.8 Describe the functions of glial cells.

Questions for Chapter 2

Question 2.1 *(Learning outcome 2.2)*

What general properties of nervous systems are illustrated by nerve nets?

Question 2.2 *(Learning outcome 2.2)*

What advantage(s) do centralization and cephalization confer on nervous systems in terms of animal behaviour?

Question 2.3 *(Learning outcomes 2.2 and 2.4)*

List five similarities and five differences between a vertebrate nervous system and a higher invertebrate nervous system, such as that of a lobster.

Question 2.4 *(Learning outcome 2.5)*

Label the following structures in the nervous systems of (a) a laboratory rat and (b) a Rhesus monkey depicted in Figure 2.30:

spinal cord, medulla, pons, cerebellum, cerebral hemispheres, olfactory bulb

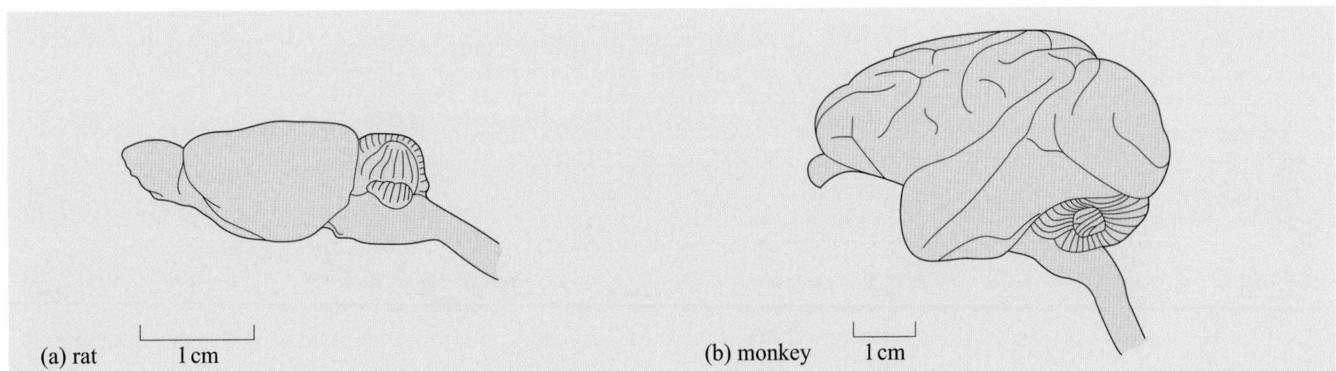

Figure 2.30 Structures in the central nervous system of (a) a rat and (b) a monkey, for use with Question 2.4.

Question 2.5 *(Learning outcomes 2.3 and 2.5)*

Look again at Figure 2.30. Which of the following statement(s) about the two vertebrate brains are true?

(a) Relative to the cerebral hemispheres, the cerebellum is in a rostral position in the laboratory rat.

(b) The pons lies ventrally in relation to the cerebellum in the Rhesus monkey.

(c) Rhesus monkeys rely more on olfaction than laboratory rats do to detect changes in the external environment.

(d) The relative size of the cerebral hemispheres is larger in laboratory rats than in Rhesus monkeys.

(e) The medulla of each animal connects the brain and the spinal cord.

Question 2.6 *(Learning outcome 2.6)*

Complete each of the phrases (a)–(g) with one of the answers selected from 1–7.

(a) Endocytosis…

(b) The mitochondria…

(c) The rough endoplasmic reticulum…

(d) A receptor…

(e) The nucleus…

(f) The cytoskeleton…

(g) The cytosol…

1 …contains ribosomes which are responsible for the synthesis of proteins within a cell.

2 …is the 'scaffolding' that provides the internal structure of a cell.

3 …is a type of protein which is inserted in the plasma membrane and responds to a variety of molecules in the extracellular space.

4 …is the process by which cells take up material from the extracellular medium into vesicles.

5 …are the 'powerhouses' of the cell.

6 …contains the genetic information of a cell.

7 …is the area of the cytoplasm that lies outside the intracellular organelles.

Question 2.7 *(Learning outcome 2.6)*

Why are cell membranes described as having a 'fluid mosaic' structure?

Question 2.8 *(Learning outcome 2.7)*

(a) Label the following structures on Figure 2.31:

dendrite, axon, cell body, axon hillock, myelin sheath, nodes of Ranvier, synapse(s)

(b) What is the function of each of these neuronal structures?

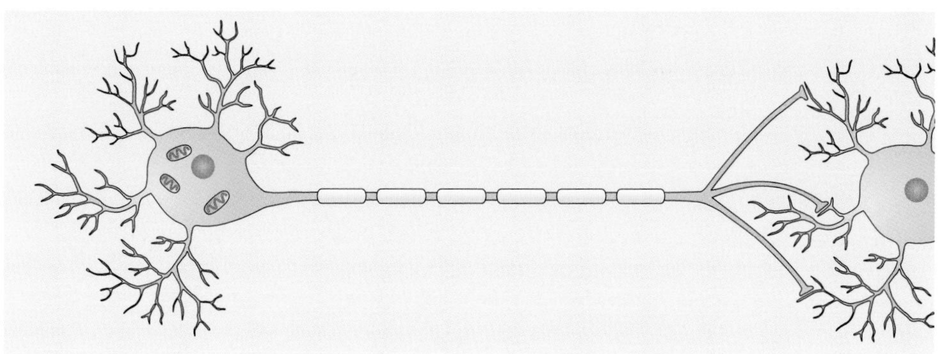

Figure 2.31 Main features of a typical vertebrate neuron for use with Question 2.8.

Question 2.9 *(Learning outcomes 2.4 and 2.7)*

What are the main features responsible for high conduction velocities in axons of (a) vertebrates and (b) invertebrates?

Question 2.10 *(Learning outcomes 2.6 and 2.7)*

In what ways are membrane receptors and sensory receptors similar?

Question 2.11 *(Learning outcome 2.8)*

What are glial cells and what is their role in nervous system function?

Question 2.12 *(Learning outcome 2.5)*

Look at Figure 2.32 and try to fill in the empty boxes with the name of a brain structure, its main function or the anatomical division to which it belongs.

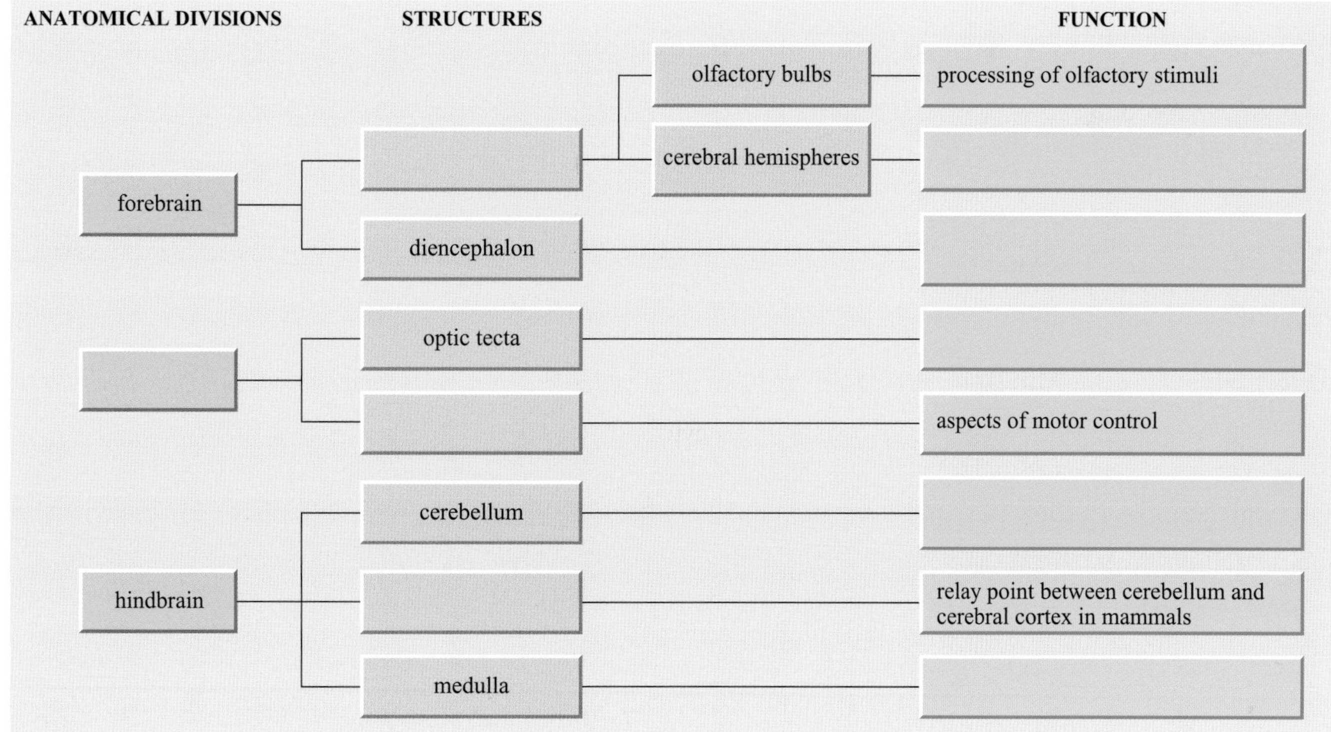

Figure 2.32 Brain plan of the vertebrate brain for use with Question 2.13.

THE HUMAN NERVOUS SYSTEM

CHAPTER 3

3.1 Introduction

We humans pride ourselves on being the most sophisticated species on the planet. Some of our distinctive features such as walking upright have been determined largely by our evolutionary origin, others arise primarily as a result of our social interactions. In fact, humans exhibit extremely complex patterns of behaviour and are able to adapt remarkably well to new situations, and this most probably accounts for our success in colonizing extremely diverse ecological niches all over the planet. But is the human nervous system really exceptional in any way? Or does it fall into patterns of organization similar to those of other animals? The answer to both questions is yes. As you read through this chapter you will learn that our nervous system is remarkably similar in structure to those of other animals, in particular other mammals, which you read about in Chapter 2. You may want to revisit Section 2.3, where the vertebrate nervous system was discussed, in particular, the basic plan illustrated in Figure 2.10. This plan will be expanded in this chapter. We should stress, however, that different species show characteristics that are specific to them, and humans are no exception in this respect. One of the most evident features of the human nervous system is the large size of the brain relative to the body, a subject that will be discussed in some detail at the end of this chapter (Section 3.6). Not only does the size of our brains influence the way we process sensory information and react to the external world, it also has far wider implications. For example, a large brain size has resulted in a large skull size and this has meant that the size and the shape of the female pelvis have evolved to accommodate the passage of a large head at birth. It is this interplay of a variety of interrelated anatomical and physiological evolutionary factors that has determined the way we modern humans look and behave.

In this chapter, we are mainly concerned with the unique characteristics of the human nervous system. The aim of this chapter is also to provide a guide to the structure of the human nervous system and introduce you to its basic anatomy, with the intention that you refer back to it in later parts of the course. Use the multimedia package *The Human Brain* to help you find your way around the various structures of the human nervous system explained in Sections 3.2 to 3.4. Sections 3.3 and 3.4 explain the different structures comprising the central nervous system (CNS) and how they are organized functionally. In Chapter 2, you learnt that the peripheral nervous system (PNS) consists of the somatic and autonomic nervous systems in vertebrates. The latter is discussed in Section 3.5.1 with reference to humans. The somatic nervous system, which comprises the spinal and cranial nerves, will be studied with reference to the CNS structures to which they connect; the spinal cord for the spinal nerves and the medulla, pons and midbrain for the cranial nerves. We will then learn in Section 3.5, how the exceptionally sophisticated human nervous system maintains the normal physiology of many different organs in our body. Finally, as indicated above, we will discuss in Section 3.6 the significance of having an enlarged brain.

3.2 Orientation within the human nervous system

In Sections 2.2 and 2.3, we learned that neurons are organized into brain structures and regions, analogous to the nervous systems of many vertebrate species. In this chapter, we will study the anatomical and functional organization of the human CNS and PNS in more detail. Before we do that, you should revisit the terms that you learnt in Sections 1.3 and 2.2 which were used to guide you around the nervous system of animal nervous systems. We will define the terms used to describe the relative positions of parts of the human nervous system here. These terms will become familiar through usage, but you may want to use this section for reference for a while yet. Figure 1.12 introduced the anatomical notation used to describe the human spinal cord and brain, but it separated the notation used above and below the neck. Figure 3.1 is a better representation of the anatomical directions in humans.

- ◆ Look at Figure 3.1 showing the human brain and spinal cord. What is the position of the brain in relation to the spinal cord?
- ◆ As in other vertebrates, the human brain is a rostral structure – towards the face – in relation to the spinal cord. (The human spinal cord is a caudal structure – towards the tail-end, which in humans is the lower end of the backbone.)

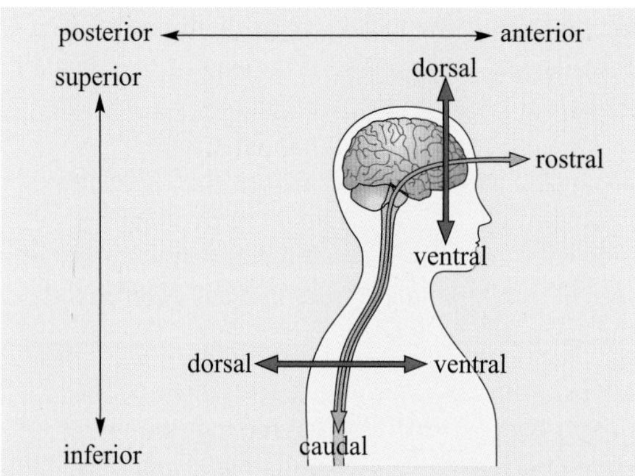

Figure 3.1 The anatomical directions above and below the neck in a human.

When looking at specific structures within the human brain and spinal cord, the terms rostral and caudal, and dorsal and ventral, need to be slightly reassessed because of the vertical posture of the human body; the spinal cord is vertical while in contrast, the brain remains horizontal. The terms rostral and caudal, although less often used for humans, have the same meaning as they have in other animals, but they run along different axes depending on the location to which they refer – along a horizontal axis at the level of the brain and along a vertical axis at the level of the spinal cord (Figure 3.1). Dorsal and ventral also represent different positions depending on whether we are talking about the human brain or the spinal cord. Below the neck, the expression 'ventral' means towards the front of the body, whereas 'dorsal' means towards the back of the body. Above the neck, the expression 'ventral' means towards the bottom of the brain, whereas 'dorsal' means towards the top of the brain. To simplify matters, other terms that have the same meaning for both the human brain and spinal cord in spite of their different axes are often used to describe positions: **anterior** means towards the front whereas **posterior** means toward the back, and **inferior** means towards the bottom whereas **superior** means towards the top (Figure 3.1).

Other terms can be used unambiguously for both animals that stand with the spinal cord horizontal and those which stand with the spinal cord vertical and walk upright. As in other bilateral animals, the human body can be divided into two halves along the midline, and there are terms that are used to describe the relationship between one side and the other (Figure 3.2). If a structure is closer to the vertical plane down the midline (called the medial plane) than is another structure, it is said to be medial, whereas if it is further away from the midline it is lateral. (For example, your nose would be said to be medial, whereas your ears are lateral.) If two structures are on the same side of the plane they are said to be **ipsilateral** to one another, and if on opposite sides, they are said to be **contralateral**. For example, your left hand and left foot are in an ipsilateral position, whereas your two hands are contralateral to each other. Other useful terms are **proximal** and **distal**. Proximal refers to a structure that is closer to any point of reference and distal to a structure that is further away from it. For example, a nerve running along the arm has a proximal part (that part closest to the spinal cord) and a distal end (that part furthest away from the spinal cord).

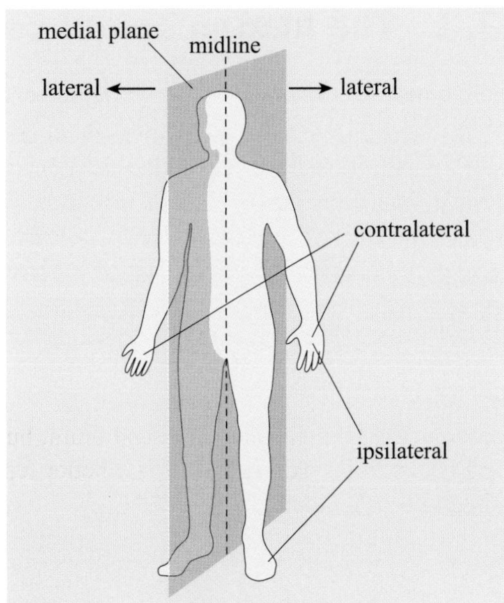

Figure 3.2 The lateral anatomical directions.

Finally, we should consider the cross-sections that you would obtain if you were to take slices through various parts of the body, in particular the brain (Figure 3.3). The planes of reference that result have special names. If you cut the brain horizontally at any level you obtain a section through the **horizontal plane**. If you cut the brain vertically along its midline separating its two cerebral hemispheres, you obtain a section through the **sagittal plane**. (Any plane parallel to that is called **parasagittal**.) The **coronal plane** is at right-angles to the sagittal plane. Another term you may encounter is the **transverse plane**, which runs along a dorsal–ventral axis, so in the brain it is the same as the coronal plane and in the spinal cord it is the same as the horizontal plane. These planes of reference have proved extremely useful for anatomists to locate different structures within the brain. They should help you visualize the three-dimensional structure of the brain and spinal cord from the two-dimensional illustrations in this course.

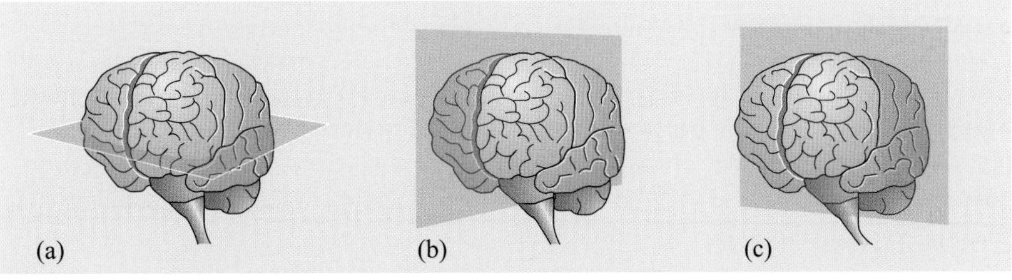

Figure 3.3 The three section planes: (a) horizontal; (b) sagittal; (c) coronal.

3.3 The human spinal cord

The human CNS, as with other vertebrates, consists of a brain and spinal cord (Figure 3.4a). We will start by looking at the structure of the spinal cord, which in many respects, is the simplest part of the CNS.

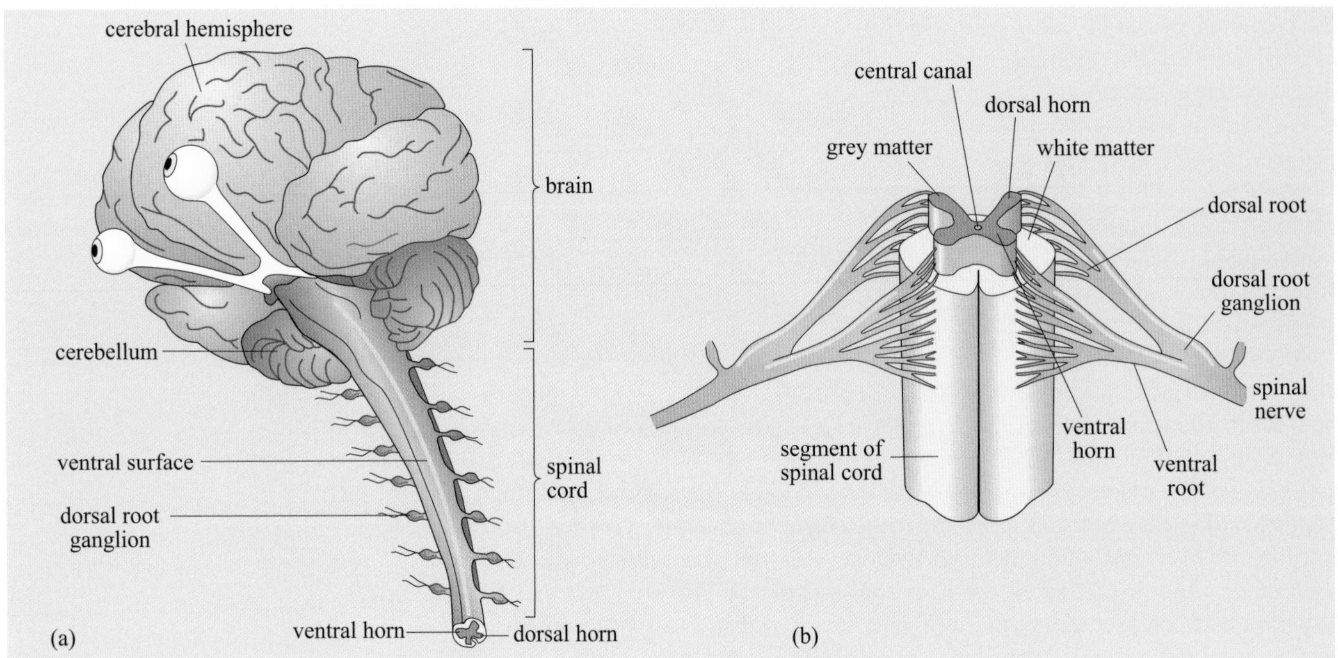

Figure 3.4 (a) The human brain and upper part of the spinal cord showing the characteristic white and grey matter on the exposed surface. Note the ventral and dorsal horns in the grey matter. (b) A length of the spinal cord. Note the bilaterally symmetrical arrangement of the pairs of dorsal root (sensory) and ventral root (motor) nerves. Together these constitute the spinal nerves which branch out further to form the peripheral nerves. Note also the dorsal root ganglion, where the cell bodies of sensory neurons are situated.

3.3.1 Anatomy of the human spinal cord

The spinal cord is a long, thin cylinder of nervous tissue encased within the spinal column – the backbone, formed by the vertebrae. The internal organization of the spinal cord is similar in all vertebrates, including humans. If you were to remove the spinal cord from the backbone and examine it, you would notice that it appears pinkish because it is well supplied by blood vessels. (The brain is no different in this respect and also appears pinkish.) If you were to use fixatives to preserve the tissue, and then cut the spinal cord across its length (a horizontal section or transverse section), you would observe two different regions (Figure 3.4b) – a pale, greyish butterfly-shaped region (the grey matter mainly consisting of cell bodies) surrounded by noticeably whiter areas, the myelinated white matter (Section 2.4.4). The dorsal half of the grey matter consists of the two **dorsal horns**, and the ventral half consists of the two **ventral horns**. The central canal is the hollow centre of the tube from which the brain and spinal cord are formed. The central canal is filled with a liquid, the cerebrospinal fluid (CSF) that circulates from the hollow cavities of the brain, the ventricles; these will be discussed in Section 3.5.2.

The dorsal and ventral horns in the grey matter are functionally distinct. The dorsal horns are predominantly sensory whereas the ventral horns contain mainly motor neurons. In each segment of the spinal cord (that is, in the section of spinal cord contained within a single vertebra) there are two bundles of axons on each side forming the spinal nerves (Figures 3.4 and 3.5). The bundles entering the dorsal side of the spinal cord are called the **dorsal roots** and consist of axons of sensory neurons that receive information from sensory receptors in the periphery (such as stretch receptors on muscles, temperature receptors on skin). The bundles exiting the ventral surface, the **ventral roots**, consist of axons of motor neurons, whose cell bodies are located within the grey matter. Just outside the spinal cord, the dorsal and ventral roots join to form spinal nerves. So, for each segment of the spinal cord there is one dorsal root, one ventral root and one spinal nerve on each side of the body. The spinal nerve may branch further away from the spinal cord to form the peripheral nerves.

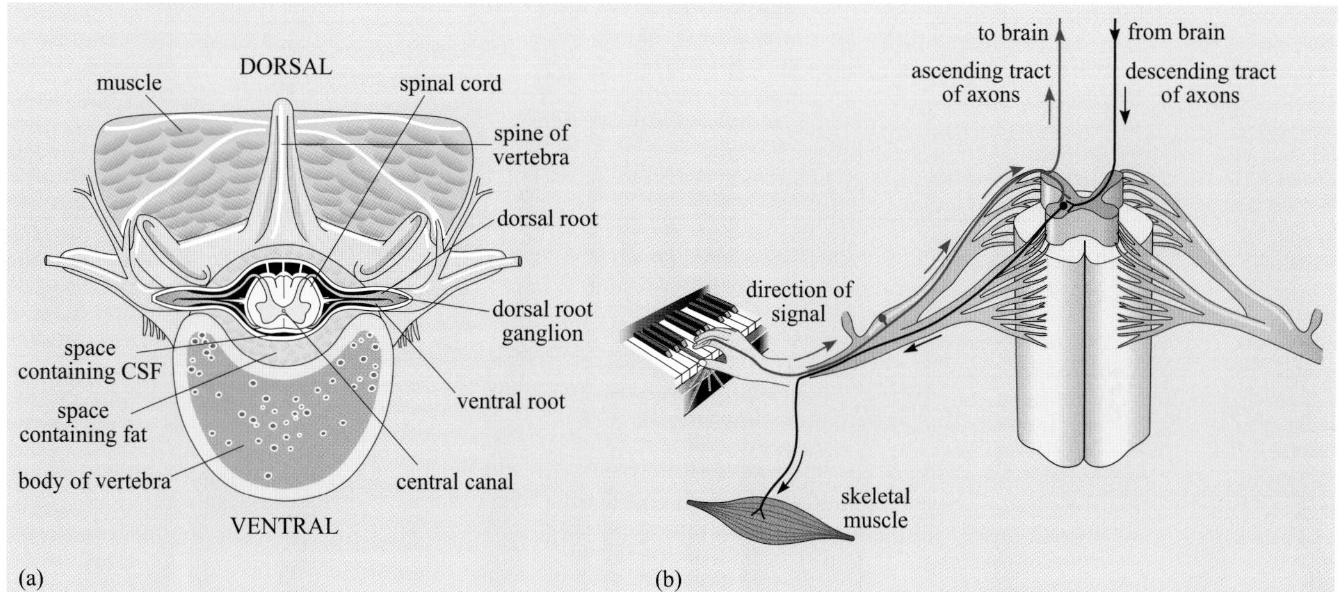

Figure 3.5 (a) Transverse section through the vertebral column showing the spinal cord. (b) Diagram showing the structure of the spinal cord and its spinal nerves, in a segment of the spinal cord. Note the direction of the signals from sensory neurons in the periphery to the dorsal horn and from motor neurons in the ventral horn to skeletal muscle. Note also the connections to (ascending) and from (descending) the brain.

The cell bodies of sensory neurons are encased within enlargements of the dorsal roots found outside the spinal cord. These swellings are called **dorsal root ganglia** (Figure 3.5a). The dorsal root ganglion cells convey sensory information to the spinal cord about skin touch and pressure, temperature, noxious stimuli, tissue damage, joint position and movement, as well as the tension within the muscle. Because of their function, these cells have an unusual structure: they have no dendrites and only one axon which branches very close to the cell body. One branch extends out to the periphery where it either contacts sensory receptors or has its own special sensitive ending. The other branch enters the spinal cord via the dorsal horn. Action potentials travel from the periphery all the way to the spinal cord without involving the cell body of the dorsal root ganglion cell.

◆ Dorsal root ganglion cells are neurons that contain a single process that divides into two branches. What class of neurons do these fall into?

◆ They are pseudounipolar neurons (Section 2.4.3 and Figure 2.26a).

When the axons of sensory neurons reach the grey matter in the dorsal horn of the spinal cord, they branch extensively and make synaptic contacts with many neurons in the same segment or in neighbouring segments of the spinal cord. Often there is also a main axon branch that ascends towards the brain (Figure 3.5b). Some of the connections those neurons make are with dendrites of motor neurons. Many of the motor neurons within the spinal cord have huge and complex dendritic trees extending over great areas of the grey matter and very large cell bodies in the ventral horn.

◆ What type of cells do motor neurons innervate?

◆ Motor neurons innervate effector cells such as skeletal muscle cells in the periphery.

Each motor neuron contacts a small number of muscle fibres within an individual muscle. The motor neuron and the fibres it contacts form what is collectively known as a **motor unit**. How motor neurons control the contraction of a muscle will be studied in Book 4, Chapter 2.

Some axon terminals of sensory neurons will make connections with spinal interneurons. Because their processes do not extend beyond the spinal cord they are called local interneurons (Section 2.4.3). Others may relay information to neighbouring segments of the spinal cord or even to different structures within the brain – these are called projection neurons (Section 2.4.3). The white matter surrounding the dorsal and ventral horns consists mainly of large numbers of myelinated axons of projection neurons that lead to or from the brain. These axons are arranged in large longitudinal bundles, or tracts, that are described as descending (from the brain) or ascending (to the brain), depending on the direction of information flow (Figure 3.5b).

As in the nerve cord of invertebrates and the spinal cord of other vertebrates, segmentation is a prominent feature of the human spinal cord. Each segment of the spinal cord, encased within its vertebra, receives sensory information and controls the activity of muscles and other effectors of a particular part of the body. The different segments are named after the vertebrae within which they are encased, dividing the spinal cord into four major regions (Figure 3.6a). In humans, there are eight **cervical** segments which include those in the neck and those supplying the arms and hands; twelve **thoracic** segments that innervate the chest or thorax and the upper abdomen and back; five **lumbar** segments that innervate the lower abdomen and back and the front of the legs; and five **sacral** segments that innervate the genitals, the region surrounding the anus and the back of the legs. There are 31 pairs of spinal nerves which are classified sequentially according to the segment of the spinal cord they stem from and so:

- the cervical nerves are called C1 through to C8;
- the thoracic nerves, T1 through to T12;
- the lumbar nerves, L1 through to L5;
- the sacral nerves, S1 through to S5;
- there is an additional spinal nerve called the coccygeal nerve (Co1) that exits from the tail end of the spinal cord at the level of the coccyx.

Each dorsal root ganglion receives sensory information from very specific areas of skin called **dermatomes** (Figure 3.6b). The existence of these is useful to clinicians for locating the level at which damage has occurred in patients with complete or partial transection of the spinal cord – a relatively common event in modern life (Box 3.1).

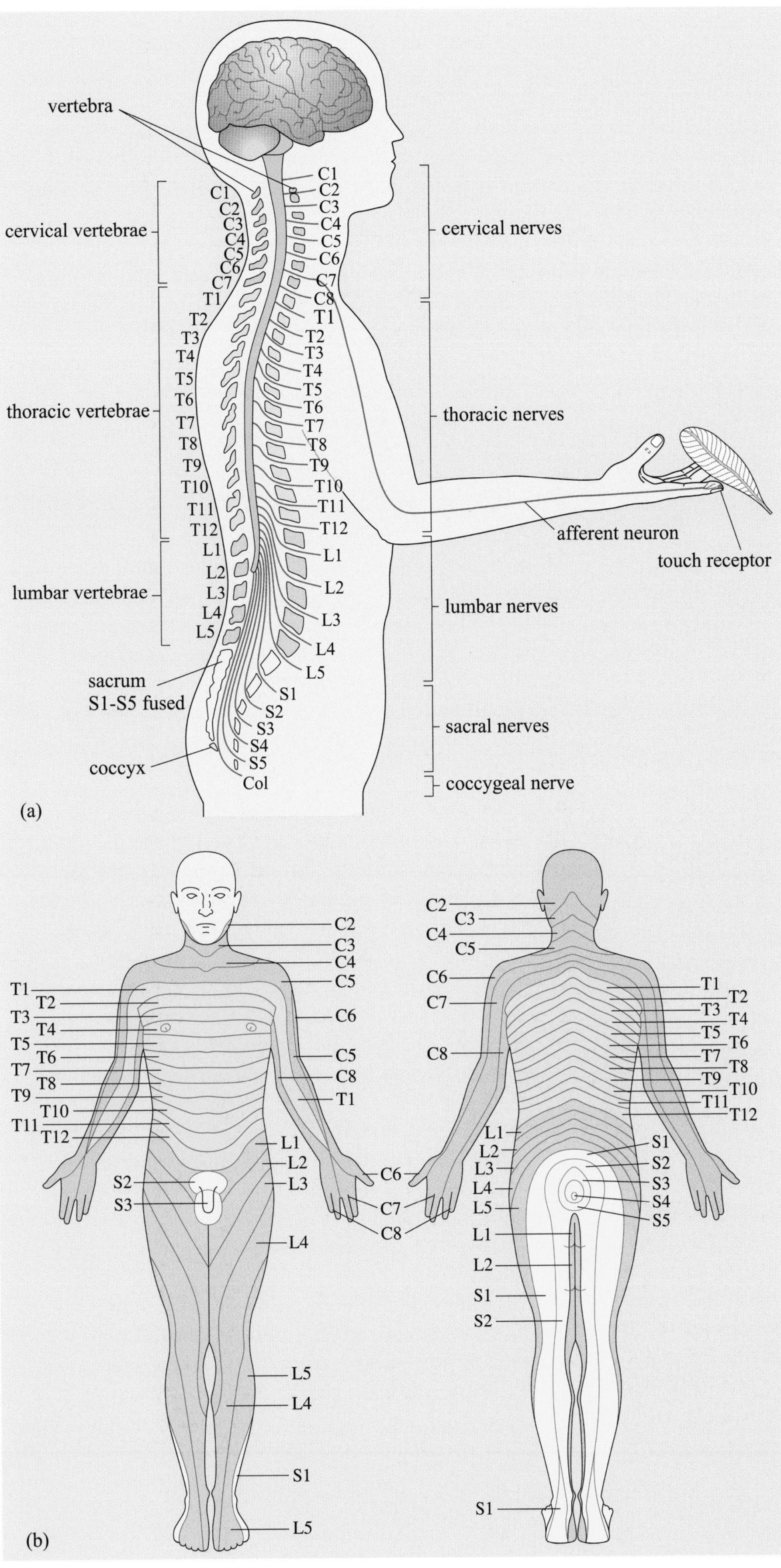

Figure 3.6 (a) Each segment of the spinal cord receives sensory information and sends motor output through a corresponding set of spinal nerves. These are named with the prefix letters C, T, L, S and Co which refer to the cervical (neck), thoracic (chest), lumbar (lower back), sacral (hip) and coccygeal (tail) regions of the vertebral column. Both vertebrae and spinal nerves are numbered sequentially corresponding to their position. Note that the first set of cervical nerves C1 is situated above the first vertebrae C1. This anatomical feature means that the numbering of spinal nerves and the vertebrae that encase the segments of the spinal cord they connect to do not correspond. For example, the spinal nerve C8 receiving information from the hand connects to the segment of the spinal cord encased within the cervical vertebrae C7. (b) The dermatomes are areas of skin that correspond to the segmented structure of the spinal cord. Each dorsal root ganglion receives sensory information from the area of the skin forming its corresponding dermatome. Note: the face is innervated by the trigeminal nerve, one of the cranial nerves (see Table 3.1, in Section 3.4.1).

The spinal cord is not a uniform structure and it varies in shape and size along its rostrocaudal axis. The spinal cord is thicker in the cervical and also in the lumbar regions. There are two main reasons for this. First, the projections from the brain to the spinal cord terminate mainly at the cervical level, with progressively fewer endings as you descend the spinal cord. Second, the dorsal and ventral horns in the cervical and lumbar regions are larger as many more sensory and motor neurons are required to control the fine movement of the arms and the legs than the muscles in the trunk. Another difference between different regions in the spinal cord concerns the effectors from which and to which they receive and send information. In the thoracic and the first two segments of the lumbar region, and in the sacral region, sensory information and motor output are not only concerned with regulating the movement of skeletal muscle, the nerves exiting from these regions also innervate internal organs and form the autonomic nervous system (see Section 3.5.1).

Box 3.1 Spinal cord injury

Events such as a car or bike accident, a fall, an accident during a sporting activity, an act of violence involving a knife or a gun, may result in a very frequent outcome – spinal cord injury (SCI). SCI may also be caused by stroke, infectious diseases or tumours. Some 800 people suffer from SCI every year in the UK, which means that around 40 000 individuals live with its effects at any one time. SCI may result from a complete transection of the spinal cord but more often than not it is the consequence of mechanical compression to spinal cord tissue, a result of either a broken vertebra or, for example, pressure exerted by a tumour (Figure 3.7a). This leads to the death of neurons and damage to axons. Over time, cysts filled with fluid are formed within and around the area of initial damage. As a result, axons that were originally spared may be crushed and their surrounding myelin may be lost. Astrocytes may also divide uncontrollably forming scar tissue which makes regeneration of axons through the damaged area difficult.

SCI often leads to loss of function below the level of injury, as not only the grey matter but also the white matter containing ascending and descending bundles of myelinated fibres is generally affected. Loss of motor function occurs when descending pathways are damaged whereas sensory disturbances are the result of injury to ascending tracts. The higher in the spinal cord the injury, the more extensive the loss of function the patient endures (Figure 3.7b). Lesions in between C1 and C8 result in loss of sensation and motor control in both legs and arms, a condition termed quadriplegia or tetraplegia. Lesions above C3 require the rapid use of ventilators as some vital functions such as breathing can also be affected. Injuries to the thoracic, lumbar and sacral regions affect primarily the trunk and legs (Figure 3.6b), and result in a sensory and motor disorder commonly known as paraplegia.

Apart from the level of the spinal cord at which it occurs, another important determinant of the patient's outcome is the type of lesion. SCI can be complete, where all sensation and motor control below the lesion is lost, or incomplete, where only a part of the spinal cord is affected. Incomplete SCI happens more frequently than complete transection of the spinal cord and it results in the loss of motor function in one side of the body. (The resulting syndrome is called hemiplegia.) It may also result in a complex collection of sensory symptoms where the left and right sides of the body are differentially affected. An example of this is a rare disorder called Brown–Sequard syndrome, after the French-American doctor who first described it, where an incomplete lesion in the thoracic region is characterized by ipsilateral loss of touch and contralateral loss of pain and temperature sensation. (This is due to the different position of ascending pathways conveying either touch or pain and temperature information from the periphery to the brain, as you will learn later in Section 3.4.6)

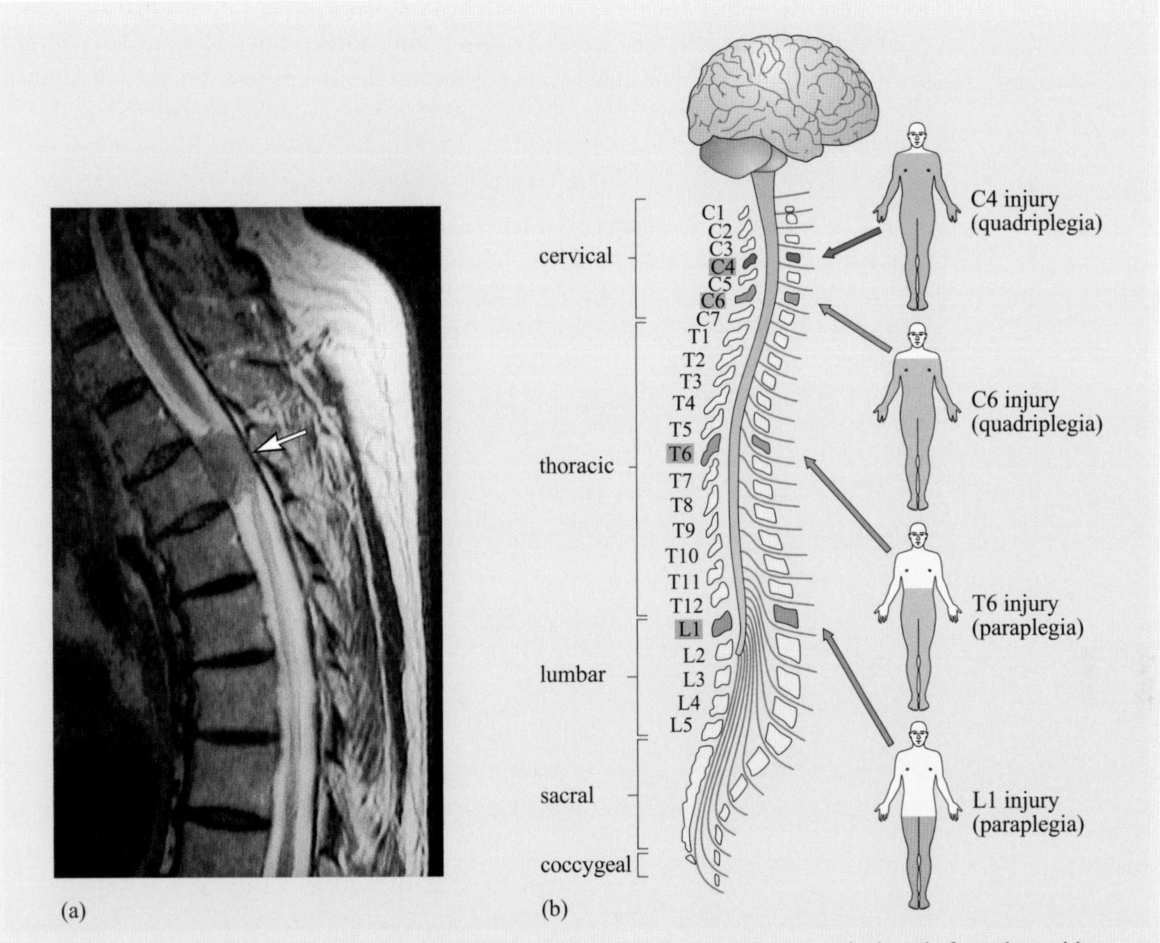

Figure 3.7 (a) A magnetic resonance image (MRI) showing the cervical and thoracic spinal cord of a patient with a spinal tumour. Note the dark brown mass (arrow) showing the tumour at the level of T1 and compressing the spinal cord which runs through the middle of the vertebrae. (b) Diagram showing the corresponding loss of sensory and motor function following injury at different levels of the spinal cord.

3.3.2 Relating structure to function: the stretch reflex

How does the organization of the spinal cord translate into coordinated action? We can illustrate how just a few neurons can interact to produce a simple behaviour by describing an example of a **spinal reflex**, a relatively stereotyped and automatic movement organized solely at the level of the spinal cord. Muscles such as the ones in the leg or arm are attached to the skeleton and are responsible for moving the body in the external world. This type of muscle is known as skeletal muscle (Section 1.3.2). All movements of our skeletal muscles are mediated and coordinated by motor neurons whose cell bodies are located in the grey matter of the spinal cord. Each motor neuron receives inputs from several sources which allow the coordination of refined movement. These sources are:

- spinal cord sensory neurons that receive input from the periphery,
- spinal cord interneurons,
- axons of neurons projecting from the brain.

However, the spinal cord contains sufficient neuronal circuitry to mediate reflexes, and even some complex patterns of locomotion, without intervention from neurons projecting from the brain. This section looks at a reflex, where the action taken can be understood simply in terms of the sensory properties and motor output at the periphery of the body. In the context of generation of automatic reflex responses, there is little or no complex processing by the brain.

Figure 3.8 illustrates a **muscle stretch reflex** that, in this example, serves to stabilize the muscles when the load held by a hand is increased. The physical stimulus of the extra weight results in an increase in the length of the muscle fibres in the arm, and the reflex response is to contract the homonymous muscle (the muscle that has been lengthened). The physical disturbance, the muscle stretch caused by the added weight, triggers electrical activity at the tip of sensory neurons that innervate the stretched muscle. This is represented as neuron 1.

- What form does this electrical activity take?
- Action potentials, spikes of electricity (Section 2.4.3).

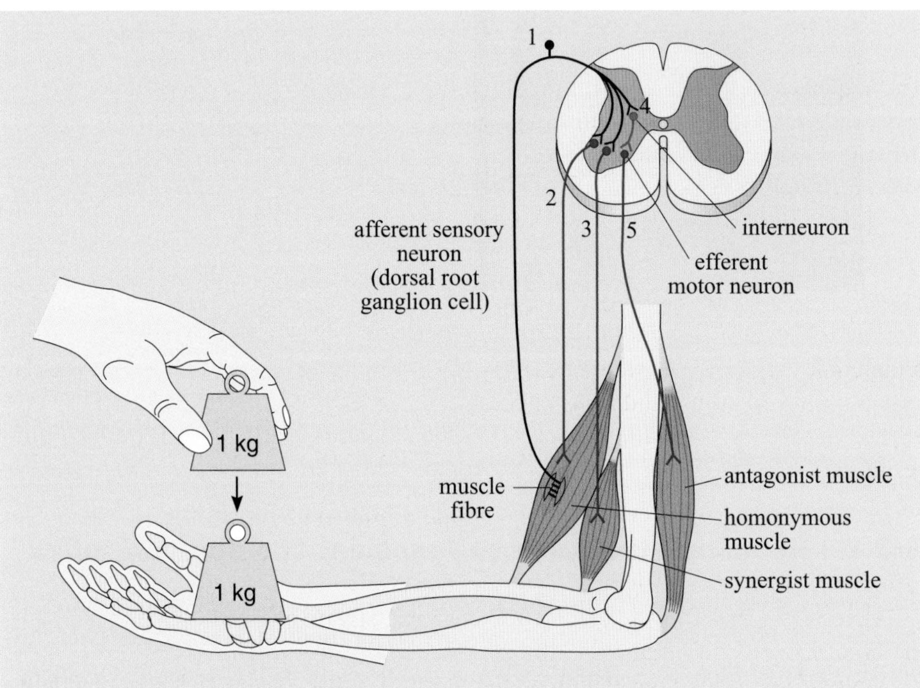

Figure 3.8 Diagram showing the neuronal pathways involved in a muscle stretch reflex. Note the different types of neurons involved, an afferent sensory neuron (neuron 1), motor neurons (neurons 2, 3 and 5) and an interneuron (neuron 4).

A number of sensory neurons operate in parallel and will be affected by the extra weight, though for convenience only one is shown in Figure 3.8. The tip of the sensory neuron is specialized to respond to increases in muscle length by increasing its firing rate. Action potentials arising at the tip, travel the length of neuron 1. When they reach its terminals they cause the release of a neurotransmitter, which rapidly migrates across the synapse and occupies receptors on the postsynaptic neurons. This event involves two different types of postsynaptic neurons in the spinal cord.

The first type is a motor neuron. The output of neuron 1 excites action potentials in neuron 2, a motor neuron that innervates the same muscle where the signal first originated (the homonymous muscle, which in this example is the flexor muscle of the arm) and causes its contraction. Neuron 1 also excites other motor neurons such as neuron 3 that innervate muscles that are synergistic (muscles that help the action of the muscle where the signal is originated) to the homonymous muscle. The coordination of both muscle contractions stabilizes the tension of the limb and counteracts the stretch.

Neuron 1 also connects and activates a second type of neuron known as a local spinal cord interneuron (neuron 4 in Figure 3.8). The activation of neuron 4 results in the release of a neurotransmitter and the activation of receptors on neuron 5. In contrast to neurons 2 and 3, neuron 5 responds by decreasing, rather than increasing the likelihood of generating an action potential. Neuron 4 is therefore an inhibitory interneuron. The result is a relaxation of the antagonist muscles (muscles that counteract the action of the muscle where the signal is originated) instead of a contraction. The excitation of one group of muscles and inhibition of their antagonists is called **reciprocal innervation**. It is the coordination of contraction of synergistic muscles and relaxation of antagonist muscles that gives skeletal muscle its spring-like properties.

The sequence of events constituting the muscle stretch reflex is very rapid and takes a relatively stereotyped form. Note that the reflex is organized at a local site in the spinal cord, which allows a high speed of reaction. The information on the muscle stretch does not need to travel to the brain in order for action to be instigated. The reflex starts to work before we are even consciously aware of a muscle increasing its length.

In everyday life, stretch reflexes are used to correct and compensate for small variations in load that may be carried by either arms or legs. One of the most widely known muscle stretch reflexes is the knee jerk, used by medical doctors. By tapping the tendon just under the kneecap with a medical hammer, the extensor muscle in the thigh is made to contract as the stretch reflex is brought into play, resulting in a sudden forward kick of the leg.

The muscle stretch reflex is not the only type of movement generated at the level of the spinal cord. Another example of a spinal reflex is the nociceptive withdrawal reflex, when you rapidly withdraw a limb after tissue damage has occurred. This reflex response is then followed by the sensation of pain as there is a slight delay in the processing of information by the brain compared to the spinal cord. For example, if you prick your thumb on the thorn of a rose as you pick it, you would probably immediately let go of the rose as a reflex action (an action mediated by the spinal cord), only after which would you start to feel the throbbing and stinging sensation in your thumb (which is mediated by different brain structures).

For many years, reflexes were viewed as automatic movements in response to the activation of sensory receptors, which occurred independently from any input by higher centres in the brain. However, now we also have to consider that reflexes are not just isolated responses and that they are usually incorporated into more complex **willed movements** (i.e. voluntary movements) initiated in the brain. For example, reciprocal innervation of muscles is useful for rhythmic willed actions such as scratching. In this case, particular areas in the brain modulate the activity of the same spinal cord neurons involved in the contraction and relaxation of muscles that occurs during the stretch reflex. Another example of brain control of spinal reflexes involves the withdrawal reflex, which may be dampened down and even suppressed when tissue damage is anticipated (e.g. when you watch a nurse about to insert a needle into your arm). In other words, the brain controls the function of the spinal cord by the large ascending and descending tracts connecting the two structures, as we shall see in Section 3.4.6.

Summary of Section 3.3

The spinal cord consists of both white and grey matter areas. Input from sensory receptors is conveyed by the peripheral nerves to the dorsal root ganglion cells and hence into the grey matter of the dorsal horn. Some of these neurons connect direct to the dendrites of motor neurons whose cell bodies are located in the ventral horn whereas others connect via interneurons. These direct or indirect contacts between dorsal root ganglion cells and motor neurons mediate simple reflex movements. Bundles of myelinated fibres (the white matter) project to and from diverse structures in the brain allowing a central regulation of motor coordination.

3.4 The human brain

Before we consider each of the brain regions in detail, it will be useful to look at several features that are common to the anatomical organization of different brain structures. These features also apply to the structure of the spinal cord, which you have already studied in the preceding section. First, the organization and overall anatomy of the brain varies very little from individual to individual. Second, because our bodies are bilateral and essentially symmetrical, almost identical structures are found on both sides of the brain. However, you will see later in the course that, although the cerebral hemispheres are similar in appearance, they are neither completely symmetrical nor equivalent in function.

The distinction between the forebrain, the midbrain and the hindbrain that was previously made for other vertebrate brains can still be applied to the human brain, although the divisions are less clear, especially in the adult brain. The human brain can be subdivided into six structures within the three major divisions (Figure 3.9): (i) the telencephalon or cerebral hemispheres and (ii) the diencephalon which, together with the telencephalon, makes up the forebrain; (iii) the midbrain (or mesencephalon); and the hindbrain, that consists of (iv) the pons, (v) the medulla and (vi) the cerebellum. To complicate matters a little, the term **brainstem** is often used collectively to describe the midbrain, the medulla and the pons (a terminology that applies also to other vertebrates, see Figure 2.9).

From Chapters 1 and 2, you have learnt that different regions within the brain are specialized for different functions. However, each structure does not function in isolation. Rather, structures are connected to each other by bundles of axons that are often myelinated. As fibre bundles are rich in myelin, they have a whitish appearance and are thus designated white matter areas. The white matter areas are particularly evident when the brain is sectioned through any plane of reference, for example a coronal section through the forebrain (Figure 3.10). When you look at the surface of the section, it does not appear uniform; there are white matter areas and also grey matter areas that consist of densely packed cell bodies. These clusters of neuronal cell bodies are called **nuclei** (singular: nucleus). Note that some collections of brain nuclei in vertebrates, including humans, are called ganglia; these

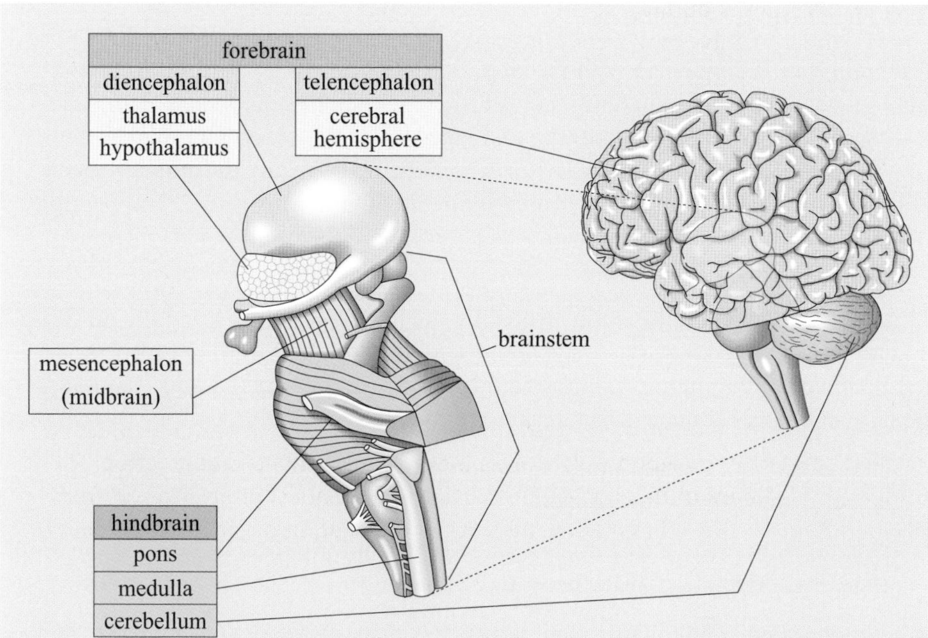

Figure 3.9 The human brain showing the different brain structures within its three major divisions, the forebrain, the midbrain and the hindbrain.

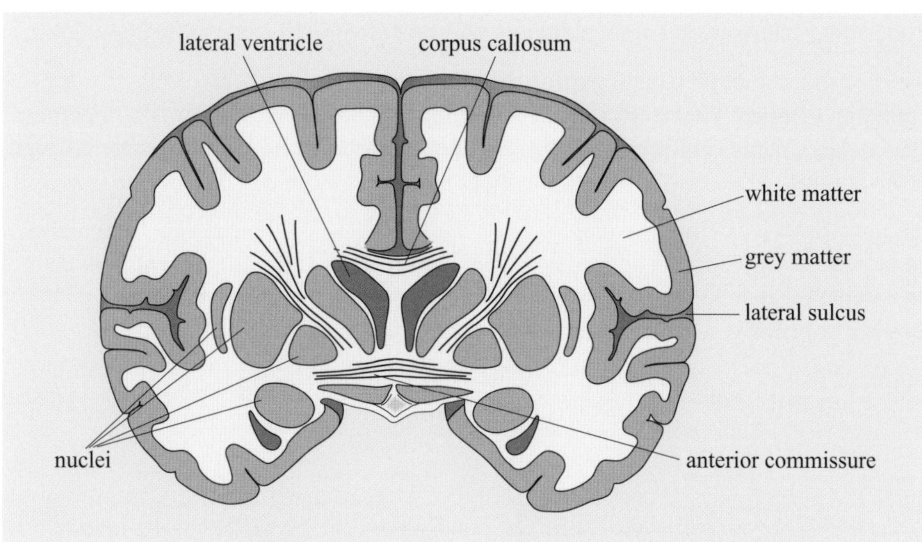

Figure 3.10 A coronal section of the human brain showing white and grey matter areas. Note that the grey matter is found as an outer layer and as a collection of nuclei deep within the cerebral hemispheres. Note also the bundles of myelinated axons connecting the left and right cerebral hemispheres (anterior commissure and corpus callosum).

are not to be confused with the ganglia of invertebrates. Note also that the term nucleus is also used to designate the region of the cell that contains genetic material (Section 2.4.1).

We have so far used the terms 'afferent' and 'efferent' in the context of peripheral nerves and the CNS, and described them as carrying information either to the CNS or away from the CNS, respectively. These terms can also be applied to structures within the CNS; axons from projection neurons carrying information to a particular area of the CNS are called afferent axons, whereas those carrying information away from that structure are called efferent axons.

We will now study each brain structure in turn, starting caudally with the brainstem (which is an extension of the spinal cord) and moving along the rostrocaudal axis towards the cerebral hemispheres. The functions of the structures described below will be discussed further in several other parts of the course.

3.4.1 The brainstem

The brainstem is concerned with the basic activities necessary for life. Although these responses are not inherently human, they may include extremely complex behaviours such as feeding, drinking and emergency responses. Complex as they may be, some aspects of these activities are made up of relatively simple sensory and motor processes that are controlled by neurons in the brainstem. For example, drinking may involve the coordination of several particular movements including sucking, licking and swallowing.

As noted earlier, the brainstem is formed by the medulla, the pons and the midbrain (Figure 3.9). Collectively, the brainstem resembles the spinal cord in organization and function, in that motor functions are located ventrally and sensory components dorsally in brainstem nuclei. As a result, the brainstem has:

- structures that integrate motor output and project to the cerebral cortex, the spinal cord and the cerebellum;
- structures that play a role in receiving sensory information (e.g. vision, hearing, taste, and orientation of the head and neck).

In addition, many white matter fibre tracts pass through the brainstem, either in a caudal to rostral direction (ascending pathways) or in a rostral to caudal direction (descending pathways). These pathways will be explained further in Section 3.4.6.

The medulla, the most caudal part of the brainstem, is concerned with the regulation of many vital roles such as breathing and blood circulation. The medulla also contains nuclei involved in functions such as taste, hearing and balance, as well as the control of the movement of the head and neck muscles.

The pons protrudes from the underside of the brain. On its ventral side, it contains nuclei whose projections connect and relay information about movement between the cerebral cortex and the cerebellum. On the dorsal side, other structures in the pons are concerned with the regulation of breathing, taste and sleep.

Figure 3.11 Cut-away section highlighting different structures within the human brain. You do not need to concern yourself with the names of the various structures that form the basal ganglia at this point as they are described either in the text below or later on in the course.

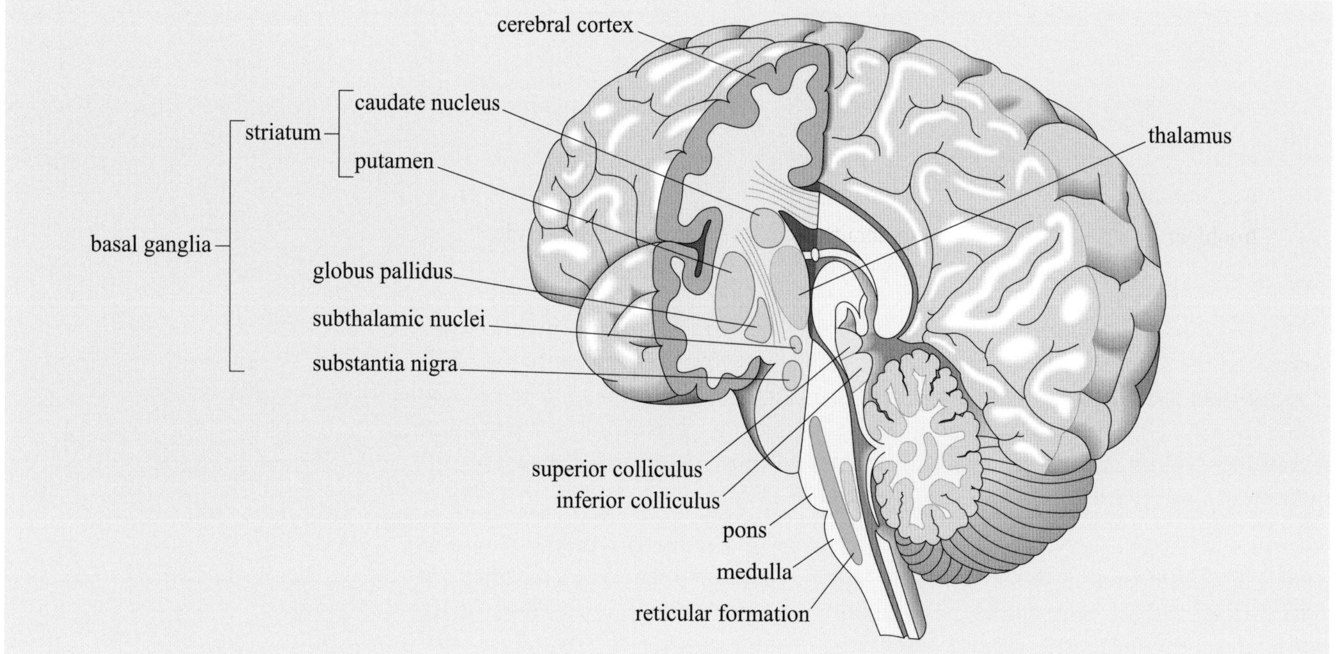

The midbrain is the anterior part of the brainstem and is divided into tectum and tegmentum (as you have seen in Section 2.3.2). The tegmentum contains several nuclei that establish connections between many areas in the brain concerned with motor control, in particular the cerebellum and structures within the cerebral hemispheres. The tectum, is the outer layer of the midbrain and, in mammals, is divided into the superior and inferior colliculi (singular: colliculus). It has a specialized role controlling sensory information, especially visual and auditory information. The superior colliculi receive mainly visual input but also nociceptive (tissue-damage receptors) and tactile input and are concerned with the control of eye movement and orientation to external stimuli (Figure 3.11). The inferior colliculi (Figure 3.11) are concerned with the analysis of auditory information. Both the inferior and superior colliculi relay information to the cerebral cortex via a structure in the diencephalon, the thalamus (see Section 3.4.3).

Just as the spinal cord is the site of entry into the CNS for the spinal nerves, the brainstem controls motor output and receives sensory information from the areas above the neck via the cranial nerves. In humans, there are twelve pairs of cranial nerves that innervate various regions of the head. Anatomists usually refer to each of these pairs of nerves by number (sometimes written in Roman numerals) or a name (see Table 3.1). The nerves are all visible from the ventral side of the brain (Figure 3.12). Cranial nerves are similar in function to spinal nerves in that they may have both sensory and motor components, although some of them may be purely motor or purely sensory (see Table 3.1). An important structure that coordinates reflexes and simple motor responses mediated by the cranial nerves is the **reticular formation** (Figure 3.11). This is a collection of neuronal cell bodies along the core of the brainstem. The reticular formation is equivalent to the grey matter in the spinal cord and is mainly formed by interneurons that modulate the activity of neurons in other brain regions and in the spinal cord. In this way, the reticular formation controls the information passing between the brain and the spinal cord. It also plays an important role in regulating the sleep–wake cycle. To demonstrate this point, it has been shown that electrical stimulation of the reticular formation promotes wakefulness in experimental animals whereas damage to the area induces a comatose state.

Table 3.1 List of human cranial nerves with their corresponding function. (You do not have to learn the contents of this table.)

No.	Name	Exit from brain	Function
1	olfactory	forebrain	sense of smell
2	optic	diencephalon	vision
3	oculomotor	midbrain	control of eye muscles and pupil muscles
4	trochlear	midbrain	control of eye muscles
5	trigeminal	hindbrain	sensory input from head; control of jaw muscles
6	abducens	hindbrain	control of eye muscles
7	facial	hindbrain	control of muscles of facial expression; sensory input from tongue
8	vestibulocochlear (vestibular + auditory nerves)	hindbrain	sense of balance (vestibular nerve) and hearing (auditory nerve)
9	glossopharyngeal	hindbrain	sensory input from tongue; control of throat muscles
10	vagus	hindbrain	sensory input from external ear, tongue and internal organs; control of muscles in throat and larynx; parasympathetic axons to heart and internal organs
11	accessory	hindbrain	control of muscles in the ear
12	hypoglossal	hindbrain	control of tongue muscles

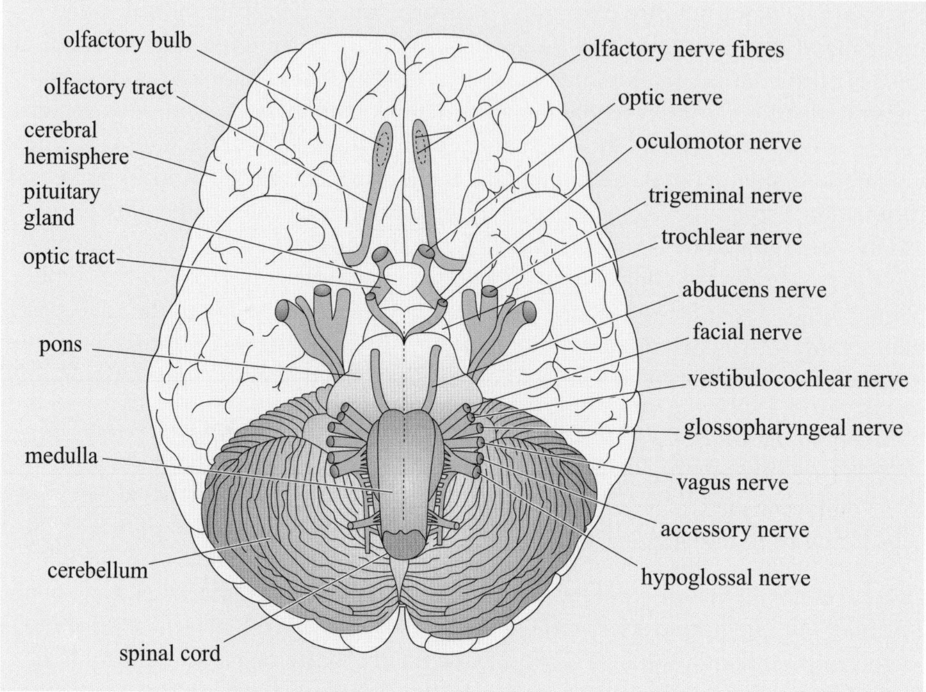

Figure 3.12 The ventral surface of the human brain showing the twelve pairs of cranial nerves. (Only one nerve in each pair has been labelled.)

3.4.2 The cerebellum

The cerebellum, together with the medulla and the pons, constitutes the hindbrain (Figure 3.9). The cerebellum is a cauliflower-shaped structure that lies over the brainstem. Although it is a paired symmetrical structure, similar to other structures in the brain, the two halves are so closely joined together that it is usually referred to in the singular. (The pons contains fibres that link the two halves of the cerebellum.) Like the cerebral cortex, it is a deeply folded structure and the cell bodies of neurons in the outer layer of the cerebellum form a cortex (called the cerebellar cortex) surrounding the white matter. It is also divided into several regions called lobes which are separated by distinct grooves.

The cerebellum is concerned with coordinating body movements rather than initiating them, and it ensures that intended movements can be executed. When movements are repeated, for example when playing the piano, the cerebellum generates corrective signals that ensure coordinated movement with a decreasing number of errors. Lesions in the cerebellum lead to mistakes when coordinating large numbers of skeletal muscles, rather than resulting in muscle paralysis or involuntary movements that are common when other motor areas are damaged. The cerebellum is also important in maintaining posture and in learning motor skills. From all these functions, it is evident why the cerebellum has been considered for a long time to be mainly a motor structure. However, more recent imaging studies have shown that it is also involved in language and other cognitive functions (see Book 5, Chapter 2).

The details of the local neuronal circuitry in the cerebellar cortex and its connections are well known. This is chiefly because its internal structure is organized into a highly ordered pattern. The cerebellar cortex is composed of three layers of cells, although only one layer (the most prominent one) is shown in detail here (Figure 3.13). This layer is formed by the large Purkinje cells (named after the anatomist Johannes Purkinje), which have elaborate, large, flat dendritic trees arranged in rows. In humans, there are about 15 million Purkinje cells, with a combined dendritic surface area equal to that of two front doors. (Note that the dendritic trees of different neurons overlap and therefore their combined area is comparatively greater than that of the surface of the cerebellar cortex.) The axons of the Purkinje cells form the only output from the cerebellar cortex and project to areas in the pons. Deep within the white matter in the cerebellum there are nuclei that send projections to motor neurons in the spinal cord and the medulla, and also relay information back to the cerebral cortex via the thalamus. Maintenance of posture and coordination of movements requires the integration of a large number of sensory inputs. Those related to posture and balance are routed directly to the cerebellum via the spinal cord and the medulla. Other inputs – such as touch, sight and hearing, arrive as projections from the appropriate regions of the cerebral cortex and the superior colliculus.

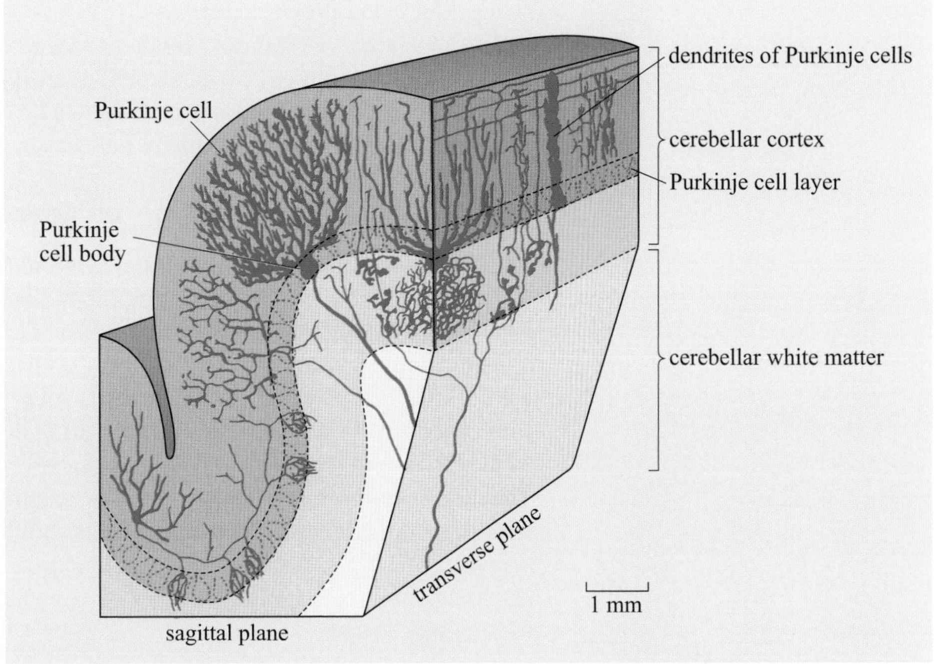

Figure 3.13 The structure of the human cerebellar cortex highlighting the organization of the Purkinje cell layer. For clarity, the cell bodies and dendritic trees of only three Purkinje cells are shown; the cell bodies of other Purkinje cells are indicated with dashed lines. The details of the other layers and cell types are not relevant here.

3.4.3 The diencephalon

The diencephalon is the caudal half of the forebrain: it contains the **thalamus** and the **hypothalamus** (Figure 3.9). The thalamus is an essential relay centre not only between the cerebral cortex and the rest of the brain, but also from the periphery to the cerebral cortex. Although the word 'relay' conveys an idea of sensory information just being passed on from the periphery to the cerebral cortex or from one brain area to another, the thalamus also plays an important role in processing incoming signals. In reality, it is the thalamus that determines whether sensory information will reach the cerebral cortex. The thalamus contains a number of nuclei that are each specific for a particular category of sensation (with the exception of olfaction). For example, the lateral geniculate nucleus processes visual information, and the medial geniculate nucleus processes auditory information. There are other nuclei involved in relaying less specific sensory information (the non-specific areas) and some thalamic nuclei have functions in motor control systems (Book 4, Chapter 2).

Below the thalamus, the hypothalamus ('hypo' means below) is concerned in maintaining the internal environment of the body (homeostasis). It does this by controlling the normal functioning of the autonomic nervous system (ANS) – as described in Section 3.5.1 – and various endocrine systems. Immediately below the hypothalamus (and intimately connected to it) is the **pituitary gland** (Figure 3.12) that secretes many hormones directly into the bloodstream, a process that is controlled by the activity of hypothalamic neurons. Some neurons in the hypothalamus are responsive to changes in the concentration of glucose in the blood (which is associated with the need to feed). Other hypothalamic neurons respond to changes in blood pressure, salt loss (which is associated with the need to drink) or body temperature. Responses which include alterations in the heart rate, gastrointestinal motility (the movement of food along the gut) and goose-pimples (the erection of hairs in the skin) are initiated by the hypothalamus and usually accompany the expression of many human emotions.

3.4.4 The telencephalon or cerebral hemispheres

The first remarkable feature about the cerebral hemispheres is their size. They constitute the most prominent part of the human brain. To the naked eye, it is evident that the left and the right hemispheres are separated by a longitudinal division along the midline. However, this division is not complete as there are connections between both hemispheres that are not immediately apparent. These connections allow the transfer of information between similar regions on each side of the brain, and are formed by bundles of myelinated axons called **commissures**. The largest commissure is the corpus callosum (Section 1.3.2), barely visible deep within the dorsal surface, which connects the two hemispheres across the midline (Figure 3.10). Ventral to the corpus callosum, there is another means of communication between the anterior parts of both hemispheres, termed the anterior commissure (Figure 3.10).

A striking characteristic of the human cerebral hemispheres is the highly folded appearance of their outer layer called the cerebral cortex (Sections 1.3.2 and 2.3.2). The ridges are called gyri and the valleys are called sulci or, if a sulcus is large, it can be called a fissure such as the longitudinal fissure between the two hemispheres (Figure 3.14). The human cerebral cortex varies little in thickness from about 4 mm in the precentral gyrus (in the middle) to 1.5 mm near the area around the calcarine sulcus (at the back). Although the thickness of this layer does not vary much compared to that in other mammals and indeed to that in other primate species, the high number of folds and ridges on the human cerebral cortex enables it to have a much larger surface area. Spread out, the human cortex would have a surface area of 0.22 m^2, or the area of one page of a broadsheet newspaper. It is estimated that this surface area allows at least 10–15 thousand million neurons and about ten times as many glial cells to be densely packed within this layer.

◆ Is the area labelled as grey matter in Figure 3.10 the same as the cerebral cortex?

◆ Yes. The outer layer of the cerebral hemispheres, labelled as grey matter in Figure 3.10, is the cerebral cortex.

Based on its outer appearance and on the names of the overlying bones in the skull, the human cerebral cortex can be divided anatomically into four major lobes: the frontal, temporal, parietal and occipital lobes (Figures 3.14 and 3.15a). The lateral sulcus (also known as the Sylvian fissure) provides the boundary between the frontal and temporal lobes. The central sulcus separates the frontal and parietal lobes and is surrounded by two important gyri: the precentral gyrus and the postcentral gyrus. Different cortices are then named according to the lobe within which they are located – the temporal cortex, the occipital cortex, and so on. Two additional regions of the cerebral cortex that are not immediately visible are the cingulate cortex (Figure 3.16), surrounding the dorsal area of the corpus callosum, and the insular cortex, the internal region of the cortex formed by the lateral sulcus.

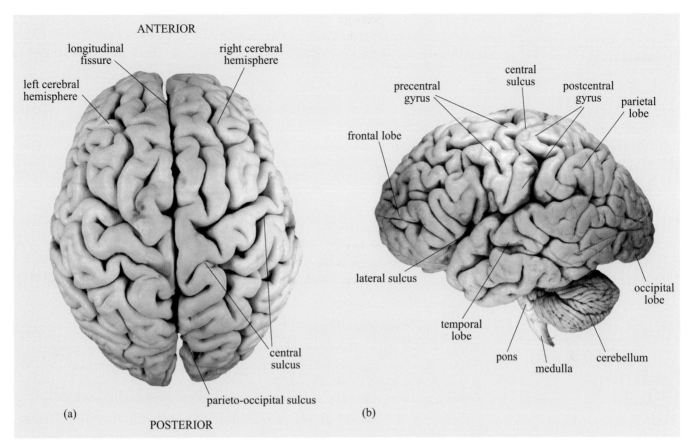

Figure 3.14 The human brain highlighting some sulci and gyri on the cerebral hemispheres. (a) Superior view, (b) lateral view.

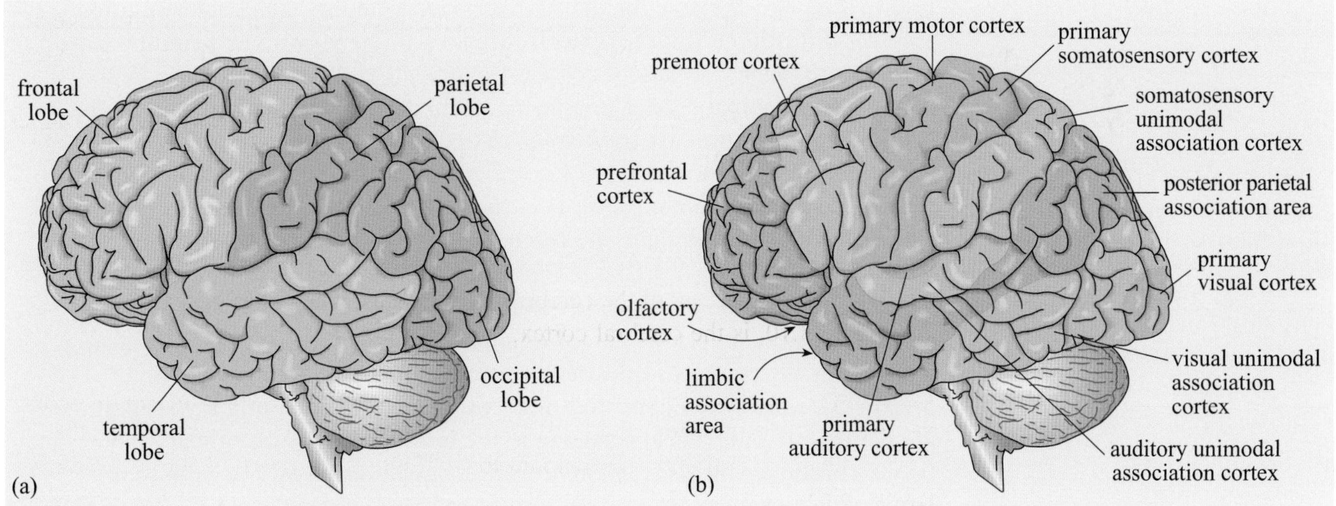

Figure 3.15 (a) The four lobes of each cerebral hemisphere. (b) The main primary sensory, primary motor and association areas of the human cortex. Examples of the various association areas are as follows, the limbic association areas include the cingulate cortex and parahippocampal cortex, the frontal association area is the prefontal cortex, and the posterior association area includes the posterior parietal cortex. The primary sensory and motor cortical areas are given in blue, the unimodal association areas are in green and the multimodal areas are in red. The unimodal and multimodal association areas will be explained in Section 3.4.6.

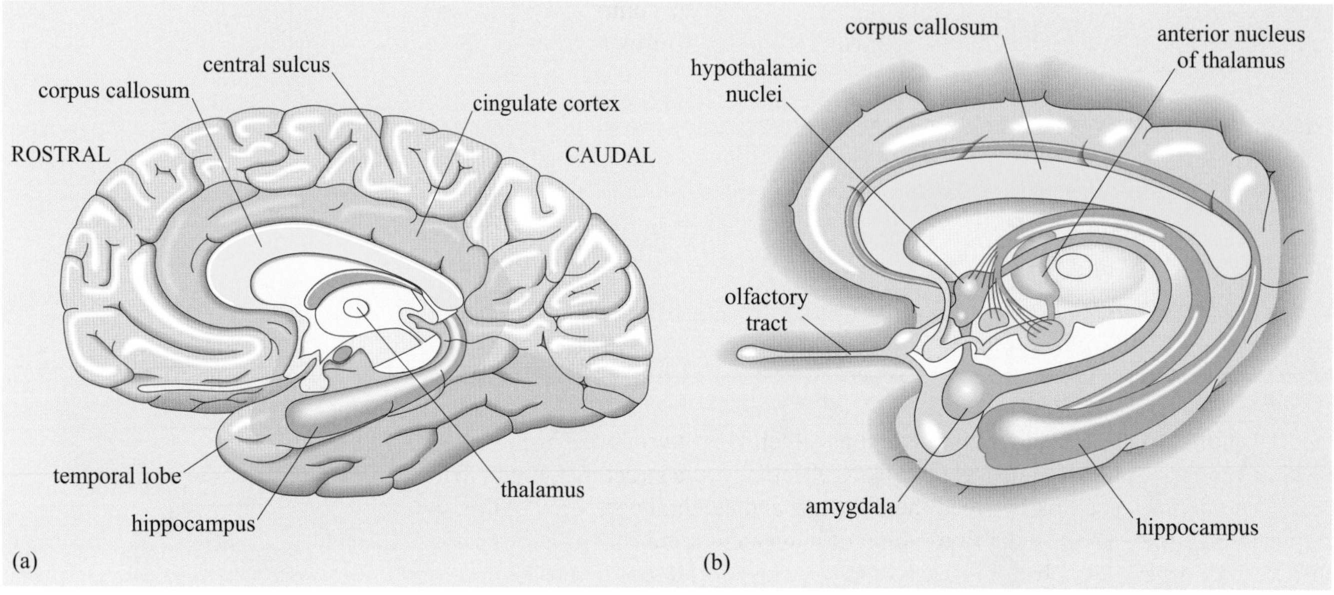

Figure 3.16 (a) Sagittal sections of the human brain highlighting some telencephalic structures. (b) Detail of centre of (a).

There are also major functional divisions in the human cortex as shown in Figure 3.15b. The cortex receives and processes information from each category of sensation or **sensory modality**: auditory (hearing), visual (vision), olfactory (smell), gustatory (taste), and **somatosensory** (which comprises touch, temperature, pain and posture). Each of these tasks is dealt with by different areas in the cortex, so we can talk of a motor cortex and of somatosensory, visual, auditory, gustatory and olfactory cortices. The latter are called **primary sensory cortical areas** (or **primary sensory cortex**) because they receive sensory information directly from the thalamus (though note that the olfactory cortex receives direct input from peripheral receptors in the nose). The **primary motor cortex** is so named because it contains neurons that project directly to motor neurons in the spinal cord. The primary visual cortex is located caudally in the occipital lobe, the primary auditory cortex is located in the temporal lobe and the primary somatosensory cortex is located in the parietal lobe, on the postcentral gyrus. The primary motor cortex is located on the frontal lobe, on the precentral gyrus, immediately rostral to the central sulcus. As we will see in Section 3.4.6, there are connections from the primary sensory and motor cortical areas to other adjacent areas in the cortex called **cortical association areas** (or **association cortex**). Sensory association areas refine and integrate the sensory information received by the cortex whereas motor association areas are involved in the preparation of motor actions. In a way, we can say that the primary sensory areas are the port of entry for information to the cortex whereas the primary motor cortex constitutes the exit. In between, the association areas integrate sensory inputs with motor actions and perform cognitive processes associated with them (such as the integration of sensory information with that stored in the memory).

The cerebral cortex is closely connected with most other brain structures. There are large tracts of fibres – remember that fibres is a term used for axons (and dendrites) – entering the cerebral cortex called the ascending tracts, and others leaving it, the descending tracts. The white matter that underlies the cortex consists of myelinated axons that run in three main directions: the association fibres connect gyri to other cortical areas within the ipsilateral cerebral hemisphere, the commissural fibres connect gyri with their equivalents in the contralateral cerebral hemisphere, and the projection fibres connect the cerebral cortex to other brain structures and the spinal cord.

The cerebral cortex is able not only to process sensory information and initiate an action, but also to store information as memories and link this information with different emotional states and feelings. All these actions are modulated by three structures located deep within the cerebral hemispheres: the **basal ganglia** (Figure 3.11), the **hippocampus** and the **amygdala** (Figure 3.16).

In the ventral part of the cerebral hemispheres, the basal ganglia are formed by a collection of interconnected subcortical nuclei and other nuclei located in the forebrain. At this point in the course you don't need to concern yourself with the detailed structure of the basal ganglia shown in Figure 3.11. You just need to know that the substantia nigra and striatum (regions which were introduced in Section 1.3.2) are part of the basal ganglia. Collectively, the structures within the basal ganglia provide a link between the thalamus and cerebral cortex and play an important integrative role in the fine-tuning of movement initiated by the cerebral cortex. They are also involved in the planning of motor actions and in learning motor skills. Neuronal dysfunction in the basal ganglia is relatively common and may involve either diminished movement as in Parkinson's disease patients or excessive uncontrollable movement as in Huntington's disease.

- How can patients with Huntington's disease and Parkinson's disease have such different symptoms if both diseases affect the basal ganglia?
- From Section 1.5.2, you might recall that each of these disorders has been associated with malfunction of different types of neurons in different structures within the basal ganglia. Parkinson's disease affects the production of dopamine by neurons in the substantia nigra whereas Huntington's disease is characterized by the death of neurons that employ GABA as a neurotransmitter in the striatum.

The hippocampus is a banana-shaped structure that connects the cerebral cortex with the rest of the forebrain (Figure 3.16). The hippocampus and its associated structures are important in the formation of long-term memories from our day-to-day experiences. Damage to this area impairs the ability to form new factual memories although memories of past events before damage occurred remain intact. It has important links with regions of the brain that are involved in motivation and emotional responses such as the amygdala (Book 6, Chapters 1 and 2, and Figure 3.16 in this chapter).

- From Chapter 1, can you recall an example of an individual where changes in behaviour may be compatible with damage to the hippocampus?
- Patient H.M. suffered profound disturbances to his memory following an operation to relieve his epilepsy.

The amygdala is concerned with attaching emotional significance to sensory information, and therefore has a role in memory. It also has close ties with the hypothalamus, which influences many endocrine and autonomic responses. It is possible that the links between structures such as the amygdala and hypothalamus might account for the changes in respiration and blood pressure brought about by strong emotional experiences.

The hippocampus, amygdala and hypothalamus are important components of the limbic system (see Box 3.2).

Box 3.2 The limbic system

One of the most frequently described systems in the CNS, the **limbic system** is also among the most controversial. The term limbic (from the Latin *limbus*, a border) was first used by the French anatomist Paul Broca (1824–1880) to describe *le grand lobe limbique*, a band of structures on the inner surface of the cerebral hemispheres, around the diencephalon. Included in this are the hippocampus, amygdala, parts of the cerebral cortex and the hypothalamus. Broca only noted anatomical connections (which do indeed exist) between these structures but did not ascribe any function to them. However, this tissue formed the core of the Papez circuit, described in 1937 by James Papez (1883–1958) and proposed as being critical for the expression of emotion. In the 1950s, Paul MacLean elaborated further on this, expanding the number of structures in it and using the term limbic system to describe it. Like Papez, he believed that this system was important for emotion.

However, many neuroscientists and psychologists now believe that the idea of emotion being contained in a single system like this is implausible, and that it is better understood as a very widely distributed process. Moreover, it is argued that the functions of the components of the limbic system can be understood in more specifically designated ways, rather than by use of the general terms *emotion* or *emotionality*. Some have argued that the term limbic system should be abandoned – for example, the neuroanatomist Per Brodal thought the term limbic system involved 'substituting magical naming for understanding'. Others disagree and believe it still has value. Ultimately this is an argument that will be decided on evidence – is it possible to describe a coherent function for this brain tissue? In the meantime, you will come across the term limbic system, referring to these parts of the brain, and you will also encounter the single word limbic, used as a synonym for 'emotion'.

Summary of Sections 3.4.1–3.4.4

At this point in the chapter, you should have a working knowledge of the basic plan of the human brain. Before you move on to the following section, we suggest you revise the terms learnt in Sections 3.4.1 to 3.4.4 – these are summarized in Figure 3.17. Note that the diagram in Figure 3.17 does not constitute an extensive list of the anatomical structures found in the human brain.

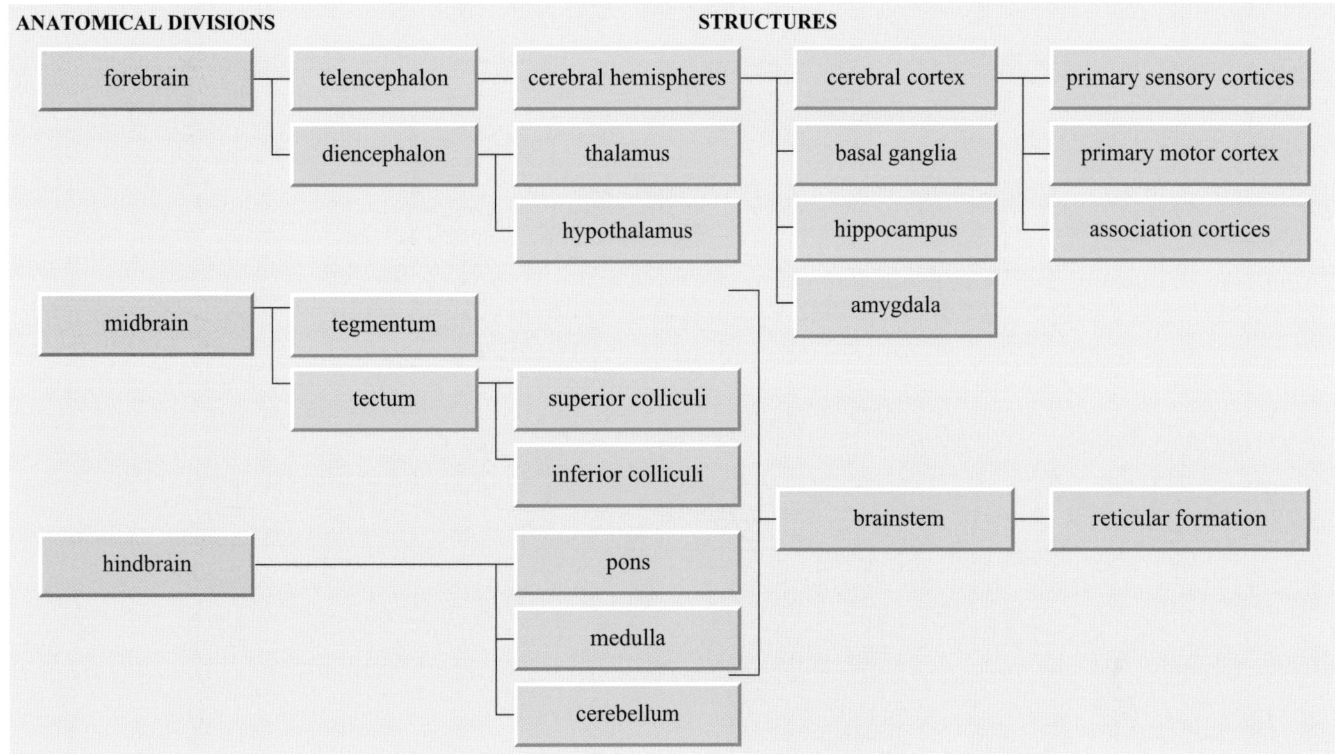

Figure 3.17 Basic summary of the human brain.

3.4.5 Anatomy of the cerebral cortex

Each structure described in the preceding sections has its own particular organization of neurons related to its function (for example, the cerebellar cortex described in Section 3.4.2). However, describing the cellular anatomy of each brain region is beyond the scope of this chapter. Rather we will provide here an illustrative example of a specific cellular plan, that of the cerebral cortex. At the cellular level, the cerebral cortex has a characteristic appearance and is not completely uniform. Although it may not be immediately obvious from looking at Figure 3.18a, there are six anatomically distinguishable layers which are arranged horizontally (Figure 3.18b). The horizontally layered pattern is due to variations in the densities of cell bodies. These six layers of cells are identified by the sizes and shapes of their constituent cell bodies. By using a combination of different types of cell staining techniques, the nature of the cells in the different layers can be deduced. Each layer is referred to by a Roman numeral, with the lowest number at the outer surface. (Some texts use Arabic numerals to describe the layers.)

Although not immediately apparent even with staining techniques, there is also a dominant vertical patterning, which is due to the functional grouping of neurons into *columns* running vertically down the cortex (Figure 3.18c). These columns are the basic functional units of the cortex and form complex local networks. Cortical processing occurs within these columns so that functionally each cortical region is a mosaic of columns rather than a sheet of nervous tissue. Synaptic connections occur between columns, and the activity in one column may influence the activity of neighbouring columns, but these lateral interactions act to change the intensity with which a column responds rather than changing the way it processes its incoming neuronal activity.

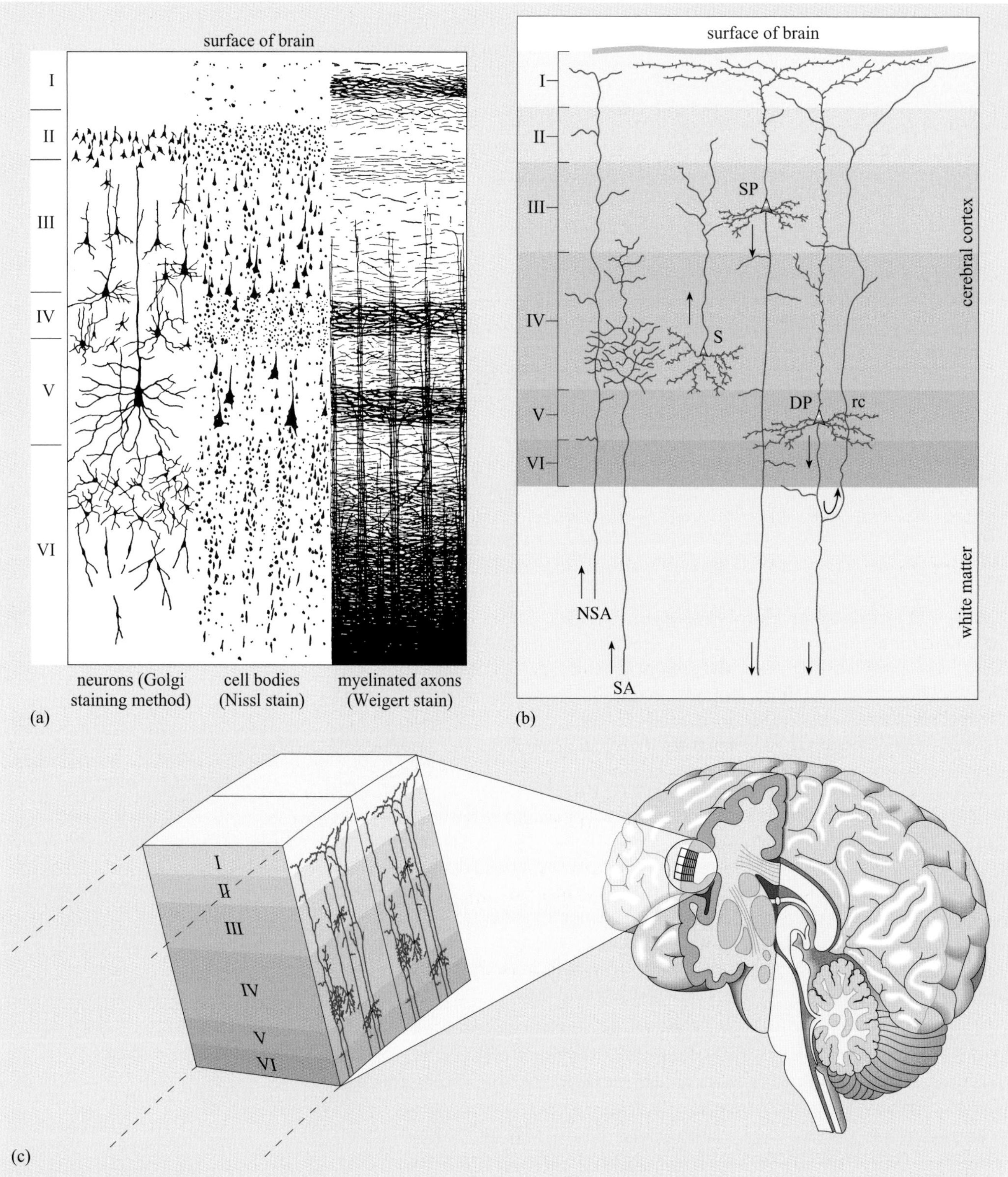

Figure 3.18 (a) A section through the human cortex variously stained to show the position of neurons, their cell bodies and their axons. (b) Diagram showing the shape of some of the cells and the branching pattern of the axons from the thalamus and the association axons. Arrows show the direction of action potential travel. SA = specific afferents from the thalamus, NSA = non-specific afferents from the thalamus, SP = superficial pyramidal cell, DP = deep pyramidal cell, S = stellate cell, rc = recurrent collateral axon. Dendrites are shown in red and axons in brown. (c) Columnar organization of the cerebral cortex. (Note that the relative thickness of the six layers varies between the different regions of the cortex.)

We will now have a closer look at how individual columns are organized into layers. In primary sensory cortical areas, specific sensory inputs from the thalamus terminate at layer IV of the cortex and have extensive, compact terminal branches (see SA in Figure 3.18b). Other non-specific thalamic inputs and those from association areas are much more diffuse spanning several layers. Layer IV, which is also called the granular layer, is made up of small spherical cell bodies of **stellate cells** (a type of local interneuron) and the dendritic trees of neurons in neighbouring layers. Its thickness depends on the specific sensory input from the thalamus. In fact, the thickness of all the layers varies with the cortical area. For example, layer IV is especially prominent in the human primary visual cortex, as humans rely mainly on vision to obtain information about our external environment.

◆ From the information given so far, would you expect layer IV in the human primary motor cortex to be thicker, thinner or the same depth as in the visual cortex? *Note*: remember that the thickness of layer IV is determined by the extent of the thalamic sensory input projecting onto the cortex.

◆ As we saw in the preceding section, the primary motor cortex is mostly an output area and thus receives little sensory information directly from the thalamus (although it receives information from other brain structures such as the basal ganglia via the thalamus). As a result, the primary motor cortex has a very thin, essentially non-existent layer IV. This is in contrast with the prominent layer IV of the primary human visual cortex, provided by a large and organized sensory input from the thalamus.

The output from the cortex is provided by a type of neuron whose cell body has a triangular shape, hence the name **pyramidal cells** (a type of projection neuron). There can be as many as 10 000 synaptic inputs to any given pyramidal cell from other cells in the cortex. The largest pyramidal cells are found in layers V and VI (Figure 3.18a). These cells have dendrites that span most of the six layers and extend laterally along the cortex into neighbouring columns. Their projection axons leave the cortex via the ventral white matter beneath to go to the non-cortical structures in both sides of the brain such as the basal ganglia, the thalamus and even the spinal cord. In layers II and III, there are smaller pyramidal cells. Their axons also descend to the white matter, but go to other areas of the cortex rather than to other regions of the brain. You will find these axons that link different areas of the cortex referred to as **association axons** (or cortico-cortical axons). Some of the longest association axons are to be found traversing the corpus callosum, the structure that links the two cerebral hemispheres together. The axons of pyramidal cells also branch whilst still in the cortex forming synapses with local neurons. These branches are known as **collaterals**, and some of these re-ascend through the cortex branching at many points on their pathway (Figure 3.18b).

In addition to pyramidal cells, which are projection neurons, there are also many other neurons of different sizes and shapes whose axons remain within individual cortical columns. These are called **intrinsic neurons**, and they are local interneurons in much the same way as those already described in the spinal cord (Section 3.3). Stellate cells, the interneurons in layer IV, are excitatory in nature and form synapses with nearby neurons, whereas other local interneurons with such florid names as chandelier cells and basket cells are inhibitory. It is the connections between local interneurons between the different layers that determine the width of the columns, as this relates mainly to the lateral extent of the dendrites of these cells.

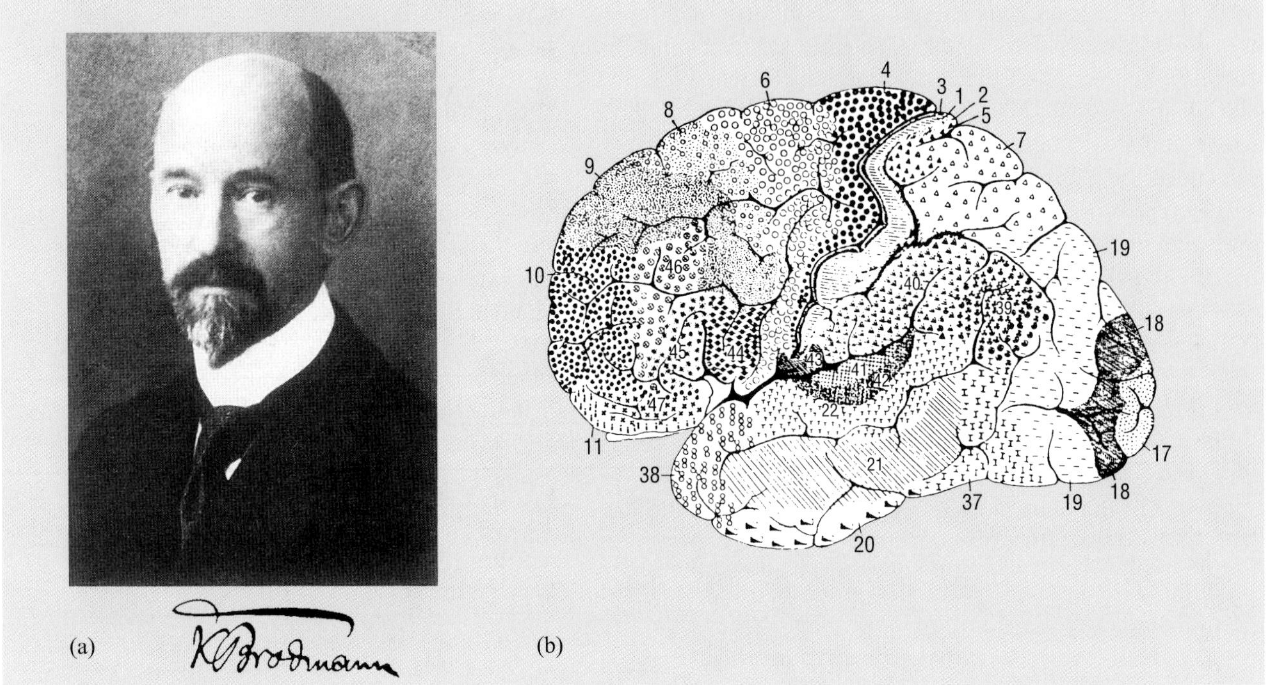

Figure 3.19 (a) Korbinian Brodmann. (b) Original drawing of some of the 47 zones or areas that form the cytoarchitectonic map identified by Brodmann.

As early as 1909, Korbinian Brodmann (Figure 3.19a) published a detailed description of the cellular architecture – cytoarchitecture – of the human cortex, dividing it into 47 areas, each with its own distinctive anatomy, on the basis of the arrangement of the layers and the neuronal structures (Figure 3.19b). These areas have often been found to have functional significance. For example, area 4 is the primary motor cortex, areas 1, 2 and 3, the primary somatosensory cortex, areas 41 and 42, the primary auditory cortex, and area 17, the primary visual cortex. Although this cytoarchitectural subdivision of the cortex has many failings, it is still widely used today, much modified by more recent neuroanatomical and electrophysiological techniques and neuroimaging methods (see Book 3, Chapter 2).

3.4.6 Relating structure to function: integration of sensory input and motor control

Up to this point, you have gained a working knowledge of the geography of the human nervous system. We have discussed the different brain structures mainly according to their anatomical location. However, we still have to consider how all the pieces of the puzzle fit together, how a particular behavioural response is produced.

From the preceding sections, you may have noticed that different brain areas appear to be involved in closely related functions. For example, structures that are involved in the execution of motor tasks include, amongst others, the primary motor cortex, the basal ganglia and the cerebellum. This is illustrated by Figure 3.20. Here a subject was asked to do a simple motor action, tapping a finger on a surface, while an activation map of the brain was produced using **functional magnetic resonance imaging** (fMRI). For the moment, you do not need to occupy yourself with the intricacies of this technique as they will be explained in Book 3, Section 2.4.1. You do need to know, however, that the activity in different areas in the brain (as measured by the rate of blood flow) is determined and compared between the control (resting) and the experimental (finger tapping) conditions in the same subject. Areas of the brain whose activity increases appear in a scale of red to yellow whereas those whose activity does not change are not coloured. The activation map obtained is superimposed on a scan that reveals the different brain structures on a grey scale. (The brain areas visible in grey are therefore those whose activity has not changed.) From the example shown in Figure 3.20, it is easy to conclude that even a simple task is not the result of activation of one single brain area but involves several brain structures that carry out different types of information processing. For the remainder of this section we will give you an example of how information is integrated by different structures in the brain to produce neural pathways of information flow. We will then discuss how information leaves the brain and is used for motor control to ultimately generate a behavioural response.

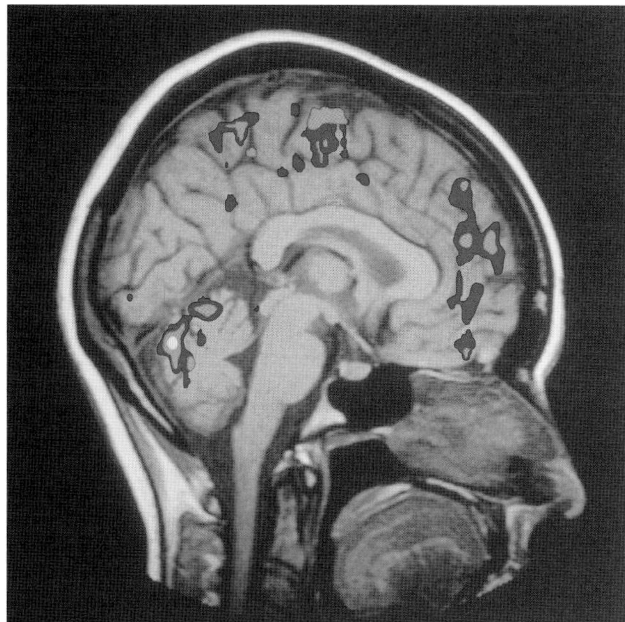

Figure 3.20 Functional magnetic resonance imaging (fMRI) of the human brain through the sagittal plane showing the activity of different brain structures during a finger tapping task. (The background grey areas indicate no change in activity, red indicates moderate increased activity and yellow indicates high increased activity.)

Ascending sensory pathways

Let us consider a more complex behaviour such as learning how to play the piano. When you first put your fingers on the surface of the keys, the first thing you may notice is how cold the keys are or the smoothness of their polished surface. There are a number of receptors in your skin that will respond to such physical stimuli. Those that respond to deformation of the skin providing information on texture are termed **mechanoreceptors** whereas those that get activated by changes in temperature are termed **thermoreceptors**. There are also receptors in the skin called **nociceptors** that respond to tissue damage giving a sensation of pain, and mechanoreceptors in joints and muscles that give information on the position and movement of body parts, i.e. your hands on the keyboard. The response to these stimuli is in the form of action potentials that then travel along the axons of the different sensory receptors into a segment of the spinal cord.

- ◈ Which region of the spinal cord will receive tactile information from your fingertips? You can find the answer in Figure 3.6.
- ◆ The sensory receptors from the dermatome area corresponding to the hands feed information into the C6–C8 cervical region of the spinal cord via the dorsal horns.

Axons of mechanoreceptors entering the dorsal horn may synapse directly with motor neurons on the ipsilateral side. These connections give rise to reflexes, as we saw in Section 3.3.2. However, sensory axons from the cells specialized for touch perception branch out as they enter the dorsal horn and the branches ascend the spinal cord towards the brainstem. Axons from mechanoreceptors ascend tightly packed together in discernible bundles that are called the **dorsal columns**, which can be clearly seen in a cross-section of the spinal cord (Figure 3.21). The ascending axons of the dorsal columns terminate in two nuclei of the medulla known as the **dorsal column nuclei** (Figure 3.22).

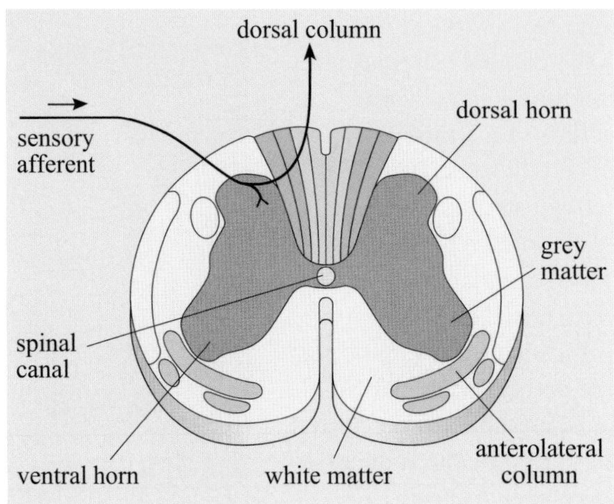

Figure 3.21 Cross-section of the spinal cord showing the branching of an axon from a mechanoreceptor in the grey matter of the dorsal horn. Some ascending pathways, dorsal and anterolateral columns, have been coloured for clarity.

An important feature of sensory neural pathways is that most of them cross over to the contralateral side – the same is true for motor neural pathways as you will see later. This is illustrated by fMRI studies that show that playing the piano with the right hand will activate the left somatosensory and motor cortices whereas using both hands activates cortical areas on both sides (Figure 3.23). The anatomical level at which the pathway crosses over the midline depends on the sensory modality. For fine touch, neurons in the dorsal column nuclei cross over to the contralateral side at the level of the medulla and project to the thalamus by way of a tract called the medial lemniscus (Figure 3.22). The thalamus is made up of several nuclei, and the one that receives tactile information is called the ventral posterior nucleus. The final destination of the neural pathways described here is the primary somatosensory cortex, so there are projections from the thalamus to this structure. The pathway that mediates sensations usually referred to as fine touch is called the dorsal column–medial lemniscal system (DCMLS).

There are obviously other pathways that mediate different modalities of sensation. An example of another somatic sensation is the pathway that mediates detection of changes in temperature on the skin and of tissue damage, called the anterolateral system (ALS) (Figure 3.22). In this pathway, the sensory neurons entering the spinal cord do not branch out but synapse with other neurons in the dorsal horn. These neurons project their axons across the midline to the contralateral side of the spinal cord and ascend in the anterolateral column towards the ventral posterior nucleus in the thalamus either directly or indirectly using the reticular formation in the medulla as a relay. Information about temperature (and noxious stimuli) is conveyed from the thalamus to three areas of the cortex: the primary somatosensory cortex and the insular and cingulate cortices. (Only the first two areas are shown in Figure 3.22.)

◆ How would the sensations of pain, temperature and touch of the legs be affected if a person had a lesion on the right side of the spinal cord at the level of T1 in the thoracic region?

◆ The person affected would have a collection of motor and sensory symptoms characteristic of hemiplegia affecting the trunk and lower extremities (see Box 3.1). At the level of the legs, sensory malfunction would be a complex phenomenon. The patient would experience changes in the sensation of pain and temperature on the contralateral side, the left leg, and in the sensation of touch on the ipsilateral side, the right leg. The dorsal column–medial lemniscal pathway (touch) crosses to the contralateral side at the level of the medulla above the lesion, whereas the anterolateral system (pain and temperature) crosses the midline at the spinal cord below the lesion.

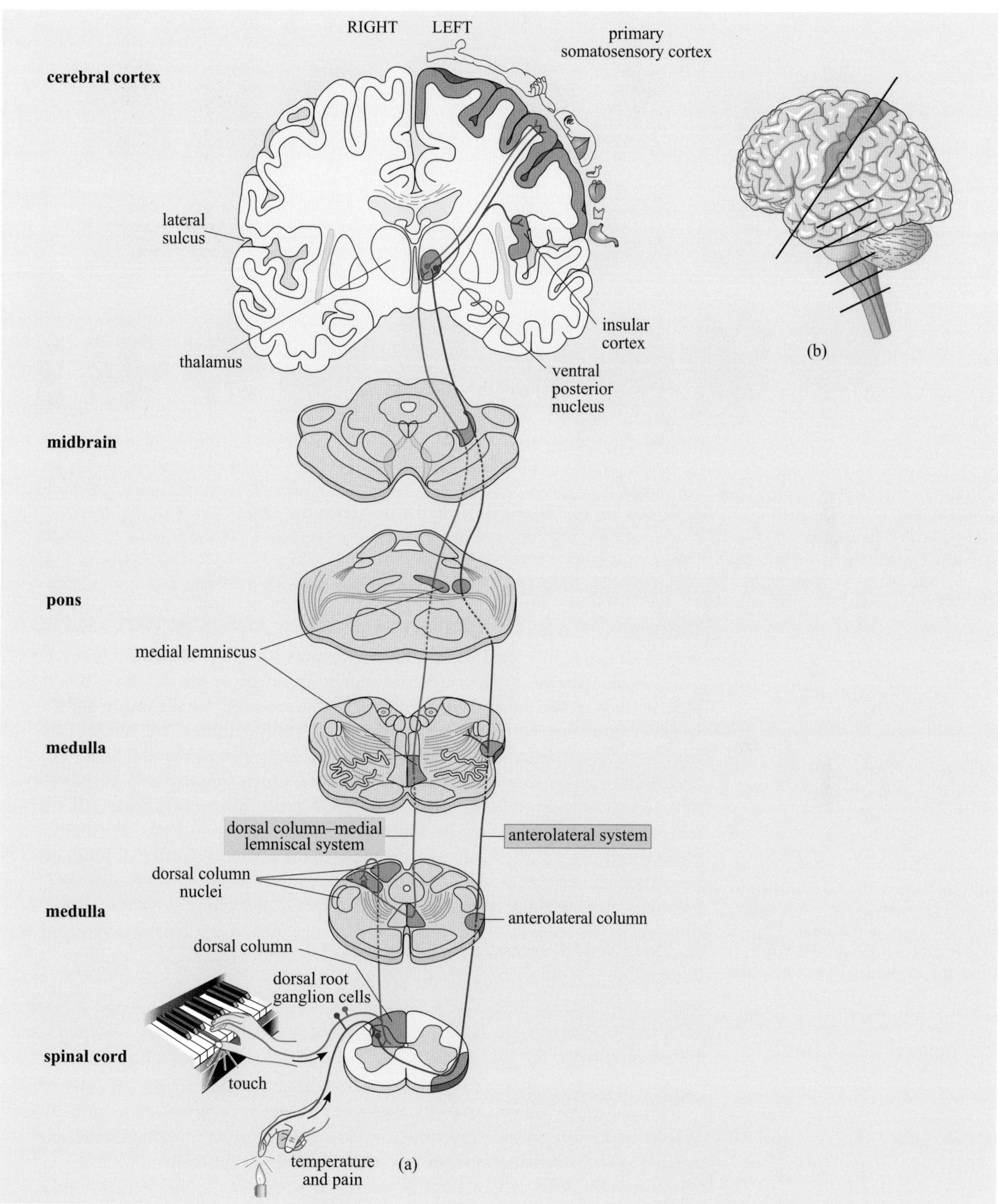

Figure 3.22 (a) Ascending sensory neural pathways from the periphery to the human cerebral cortex showing different sensory modalities. The pathway for touch, the dorsal column–medial lemniscal system (DCMLS), is indicated in red and that for temperature and noxious stimuli (that induce pain), the anterolateral system (ALS), is indicated in purple. Note that the pathways cross-over to the contralateral side at different anatomical levels, the spinal cord for the ALS and the medulla for the DCMLS. (b) The locations of the various cross-sections shown in (a) taken through the spinal cord and brain.

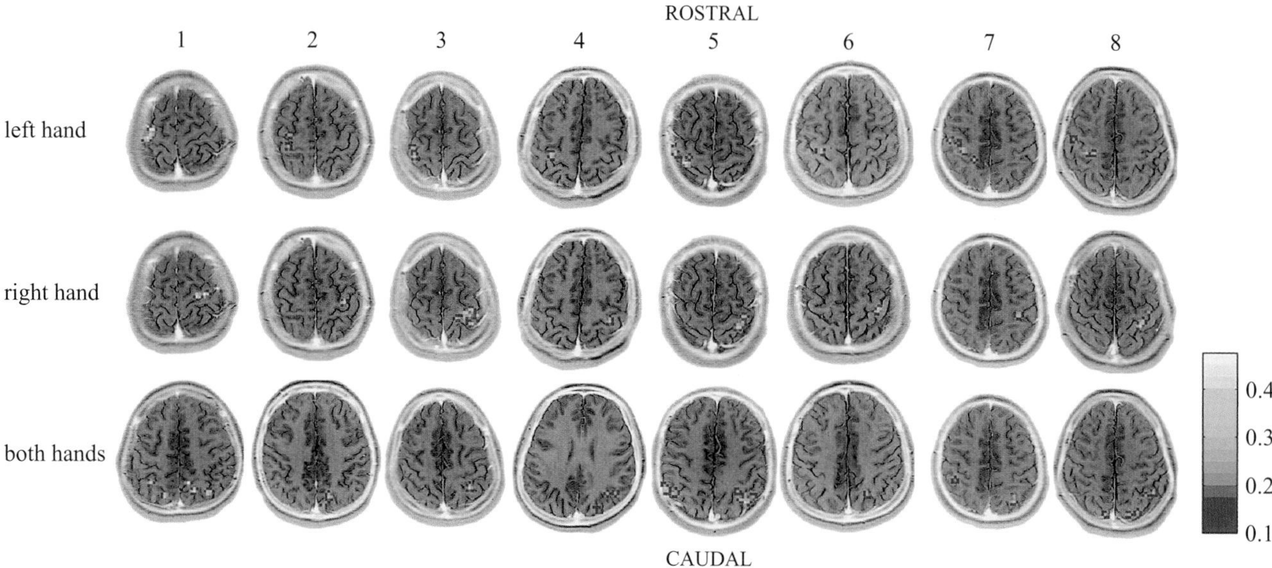

Figure 3.23 Functional magnetic resonance imaging (fMRI) sections of the human brain through the horizontal plane showing the activity of different brain structures during piano playing tasks for eight subjects labelled 1 through to 8 (grey indicates no changes in activity, red indicates moderate increased activity and yellow indicates high increased activity). In the top row, the images were obtained while the pianist used the left hand only; in the middle row, the right hand only; and, in the bottom row, both hands. For this experiment, subjects were asked not to look at the keyboard to engage only those brain structures activated by motor tasks and not those activated by visual stimuli. Note that for each section, the left hemisphere is represented on the right and the right hemisphere on the left.

The density of sensory receptors is higher on the finger pads than anywhere else on the skin resulting in a remarkable ability to distinguish different tactile stimuli. For example, humans can detect ridges on a smooth surface as low as 1 μm. When playing the piano or doing other complex hand movements, tactile information is usually complemented with visual information. This is useful when you first start learning as you usually look at the position of your fingers on the unfamiliar keys! Visual information also follows an orderly neural processing pathway as we saw with somatic sensation but it involves different brain structures (Figure 3.24a). The receptors on the retina (at the back of the eye) that respond to light are called **photoreceptors** and their activation modulates the activity of different types of neighbouring neurons. Some of these neurons project their axons towards the thalamus by way of the optic nerve but only half of the axons cross the midline at the level of the optic chiasma (Figure 3.24b). The area of the thalamus involved in processing visual information is called the lateral geniculate nucleus which projects to the primary visual cortex on the occipital lobe (the sensory pathways that convey visual information to the cortex will be further explained in Section 4.4 and in Book 4, Chapter 2). The thalamus is in fact an essential link between sensory receptors and the cerebral cortex for all sensory modalities (with the exception of olfaction).

You may sometimes see the alternative spelling of chiasm used for chiasma.

Cortical integration

Whatever the sensory modality, touch, vision or hearing, an important feature of sensory systems is that information is organized **topographically** at different levels of the sensory pathway (the same is true for motor systems). So, neighbouring mechanoreceptors on the skin, for example, project to neighbouring cells in the

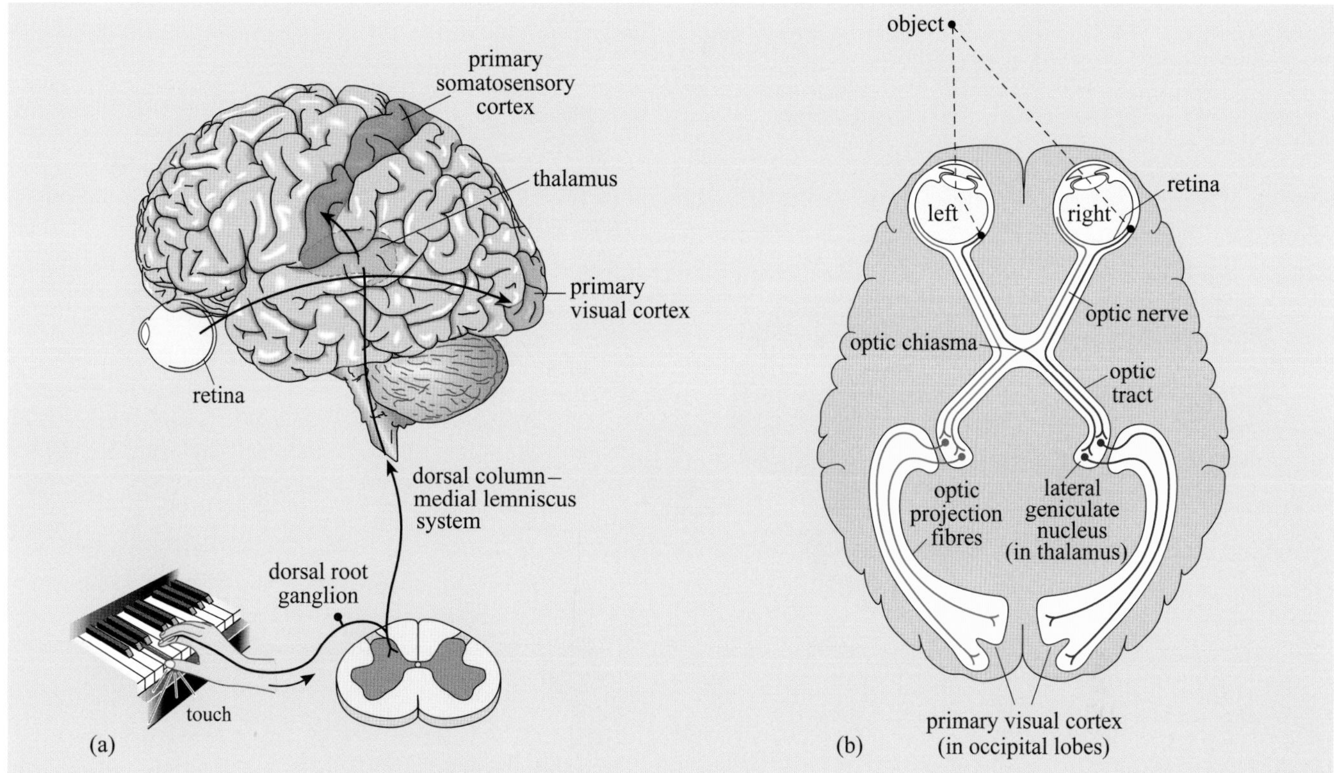

Figure 3.24 (a) Schematic diagram of the somatosensory and visual pathway. Information for all the sensory modalities (with the exception of olfaction) is processed by the thalamus before it reaches its respective cortical structure. Visual information from the photoreceptors in the eye is processed in the thalamus and then conveyed to the primary visual cortex in the occipital lobe. Somatosensory information from the periphery is relayed by the thalamus to the primary somatosensory cortex. (b) Visual pathway from the eye to the primary visual cortex.

dorsal column nuclei, which in turn project to neighbouring regions in the thalamus, and ultimately to neighbouring areas in the somatosensory cortex. An illustrative example of topographic representation is the sensory homunculus in the primary somatosensory cortex (Figure 3.25). The topographic representation of the human skin gives rise to what are called somatotopic maps on the cortex. The maps were obtained by noting which areas of the cortex were activated when a tactile stimulus was applied to different parts of the body. However, not every part of the body is represented equally. The amount of cortical tissue devoted to each region does not relate to the physical size of the region but to the density of receptors there, i.e. its sensitivity. Those areas of the body with the highest density of receptors, that is the largest number of receptors in the skin per unit area of surface, have the largest representation in the primary somatosensory cortex. The result is a topographical representation which at first sight appears bizarre with enormous fingers and lips, and small legs and trunk.

Thalamic input arrives in the primary somatosensory cortex where basic processing of tactile information is followed by integration of complex information. It is at this stage that the orientation of the edges of an object, such as a piano key, or the integrated posture of your hand on the keyboard can be recognized. Neurons in the primary somatosensory cortex project to other cortical areas called **unimodal** association cortical areas (Figures 3.15b and 3.26). They are unimodal because

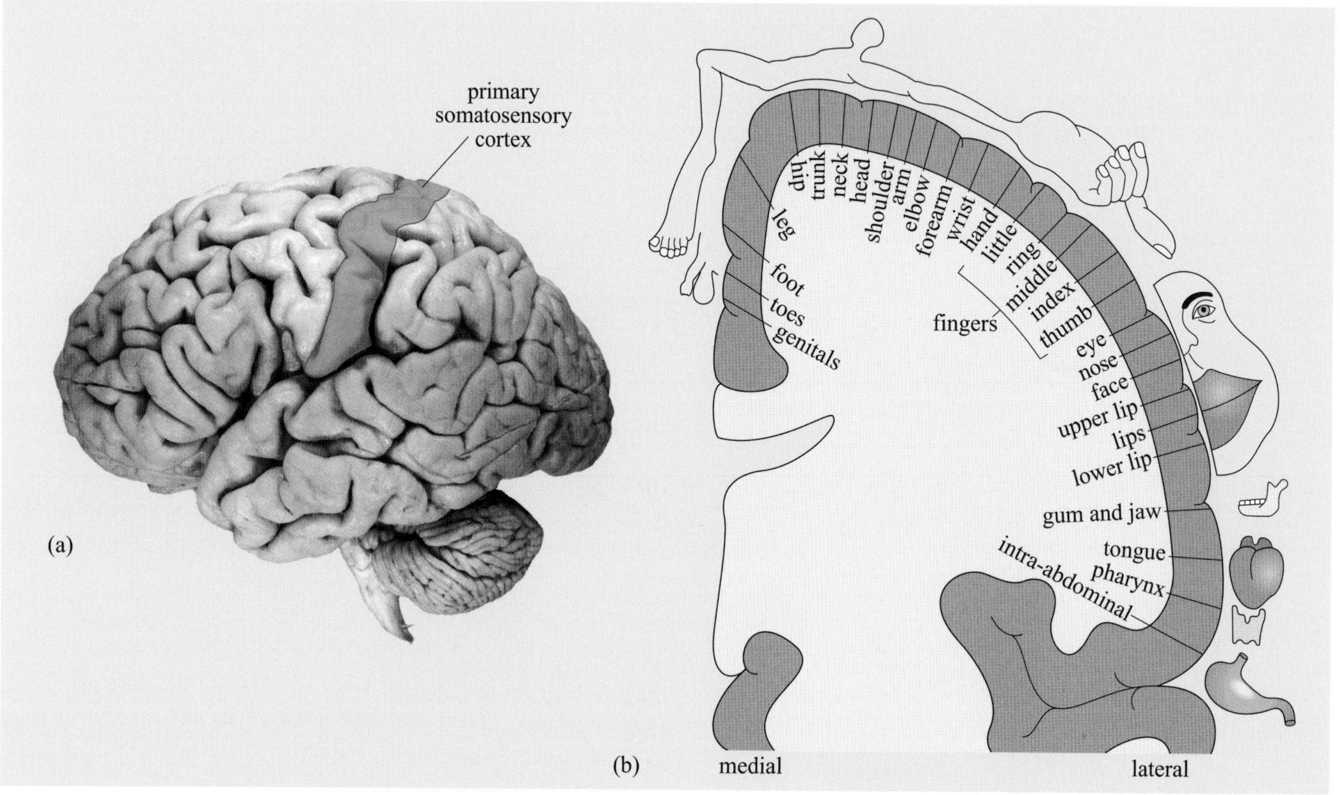

Figure 3.25 (a) The primary somatosensory cortex of the human brain. (b) The sensory homunculus. Body regions represented in the primary somatosensory cortex of humans. The size of each body part in the illustration roughly relates to the area of the cortical region dedicated to processing the information from that body part. The diagram shows a coronal section through the left cerebral hemisphere. (Note that the topographical representation of the somatosensory cortex on each cerebral hemisphere corresponds to the contralateral side of the body. The right cerebral hemisphere has not been drawn for clarity.)

they process and integrate information from only one sensory modality. So the somatosensory unimodal association area in the parietal cortex is responsible for associating information concerning touch and is involved in tactile object recognition, whereas the visual unimodal association area resides in the occipital and temporal lobes and receives information from the primary visual cortex. If information flow stopped at this stage, you would have the separate sensations of a relatively cold and smooth surface and a black and white blurred image, but you would be incapable of unifying them into a single percept (i.e. the piano keyboard, the perceived object). Neurons from the unimodal association areas project to **multimodal** association areas where information from different sensory modalities is combined (Figures 3.15b and 3.26). The posterior parietal cortex, a multimodal association area, integrates visual and spatial information to give a single percept, linking the feel of objects with their appearance and location in space. The single percept of a key on the piano would be formed in these areas from the combination of tactile and visual information. There are also other multimodal association areas that help you recognize the perceived object if it is already familiar to you. These include the temporal association cortex, the parahippocampal cortex and the cingulate cortex, all areas that are involved in linking sensory information to memory and emotion, and therefore mediate face and object recognition (see Section 4.4 in this book, Book 5, Chapter 1 and Book 6, Chapter 2). Frontal association areas such as the prefrontal cortex are more involved in planning motor actions (Figure 3.15b).

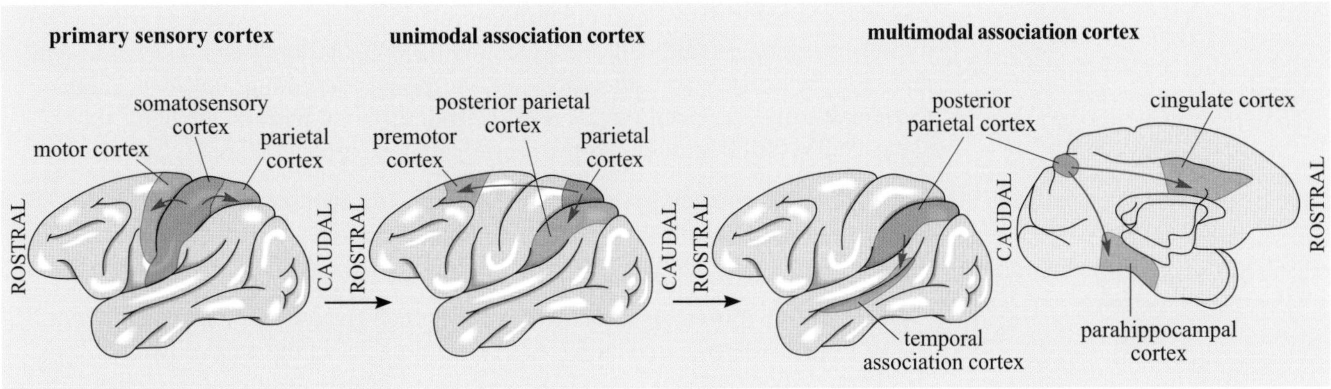

Figure 3.26 The flow of information through the different sensory, motor and association areas of a primate cortex. In each brain shown, the region where the projection originates is coloured green and the areas where the projection terminates are coloured grey. For the multimodal association cortex, two primate brains are shown – a whole brain (left) and a sagittal section (right) to help visualize the temporal association cortex on the outer surface, and the cingulate and parahippocampal cortices on the inner surface.

Descending motor pathways

We have explained how information is conveyed from the periphery to the brain and how it is integrated by the various cortical areas. We will now describe the output of the brain in terms of information pathways to effector organs.

One of the primary purposes of somatosensory information is to guide directed movement, in our example, playing the piano. Willed (voluntary) movement is mainly mediated by connections between the cerebral cortex and the spinal cord. The main output of the cerebral cortex is the primary motor cortex, which receives information from other cortical areas, such as the primary somatosensory cortex and sensory association areas (Figure 3.26). The premotor cortex, which is the association cortex in the frontal lobe, also receives information from sensory association areas (Figure 3.26) and projects to the primary motor cortex. This myriad of interconnections allows the planning of complex willed movements. In a

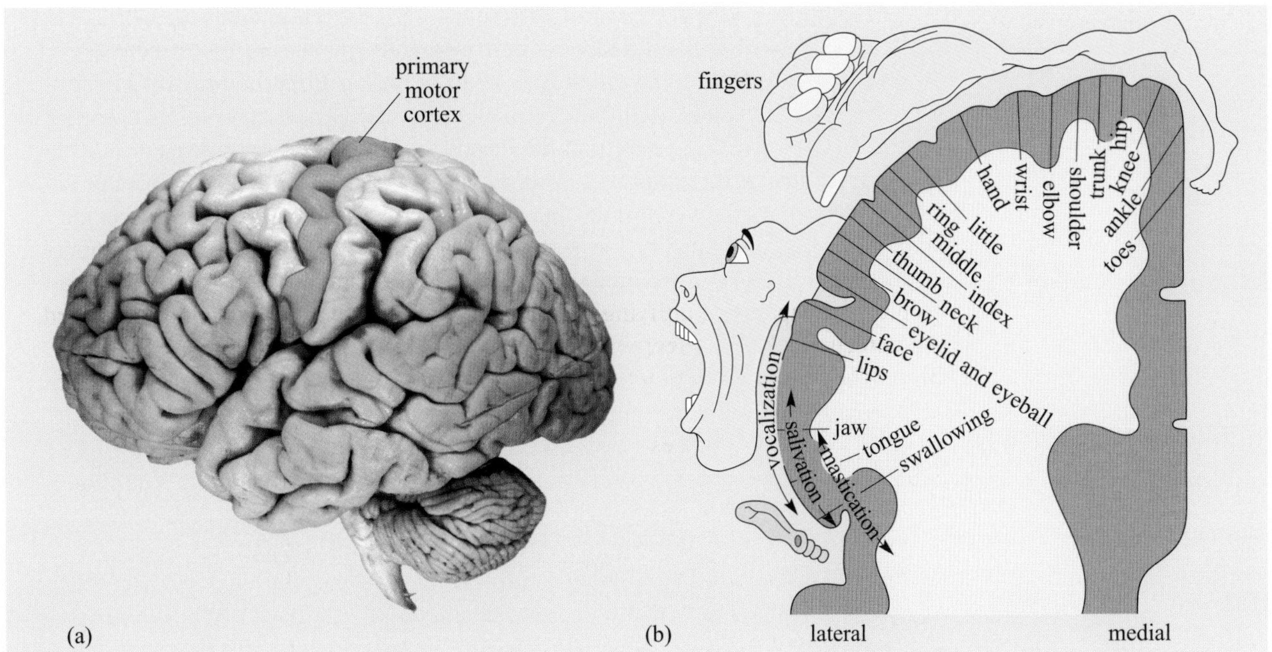

Figure 3.27 (a) The primary motor cortex of the human brain. (b) The motor homunculus. Body regions represented in the primary motor cortex of humans. The size of each body part in the illustration roughly relates to the area of the cortical region that controls skeletal muscle in that body part. The diagram shows a coronal section through the right cerebral hemisphere. As with Figure 3.25, just one side of the brain is shown for clarity.

way, the premotor cortex and the primary motor cortex are concerned respectively with the preparation and with the execution of motor tasks. It is important to note that, like the primary somatosensory cortex, the primary motor cortex is organized topographically – skeletal muscle groups from different parts of the body are controlled by different areas of the primary motor cortex (Figure 3.27).

The flow of information travelling from the primary motor cortex to the motor neurons in the spinal cord may be either direct or indirect.

(a) Direct pathways: some pyramidal neurons whose cell bodies are in layer V of the primary motor cortex (Figure 3.18) project their axons directly to motor neurons or interneurons in the ventral horn of the spinal cord (Figure 3.28). These axons descend together (in bundles) towards the spinal cord and form prominent pyramid-shaped swellings on the ventral surface of the medulla. They are collectively known as the **pyramidal tract** (also called the corticospinal tract; cortico- = from the cerebral cortex; -spinal = to the spinal cord). As with the ascending sensory systems, the primary motor cortex on each cerebral hemisphere controls the contralateral side of the body. The pyramidal tract crosses the midline at the level of the junction between the medulla and the spinal cord. The direct corticospinal connections from the cortex to spinal motor neurons are extremely important for smooth and coordinated skeletal muscle contractions and therefore for moving individual fingers as required for our favourite task, playing the piano.

(b) Indirect pathways: some neurons in the primary motor cortex project to other components of the motor system such as the cerebellum, the basal ganglia and several nuclei in the brainstem. Most of the inputs and outputs from the cerebellum and the basal ganglia terminate in brainstem nuclei, although some descend directly to the spinal cord. From the nuclei in the brainstem, descending pathways synapse with spinal cord local interneurons. Ultimately, the activity of indirect pathways converge into spinal cord motor neurons thereby modulating the direct flow of information from the primary motor cortex to the spinal cord. Indirect pathways mainly influence willed complex movements, making sure that they are accurate and properly sequenced. The importance of these indirect descending pathways in mediating movement is illustrated by the syndromes that result from their malfunctioning. A person with cerebellar dysfunction would find reaching the piano keyboard extremely difficult. The hand would move erratically and oscillate violently as the target was approached. This intention tremor would be in contrast to the rest tremor observed in Parkinson's disease individuals with dysfunctional basal ganglia, where the hand resting on the piano would shake continuously and the subject would have problems initiating movement.

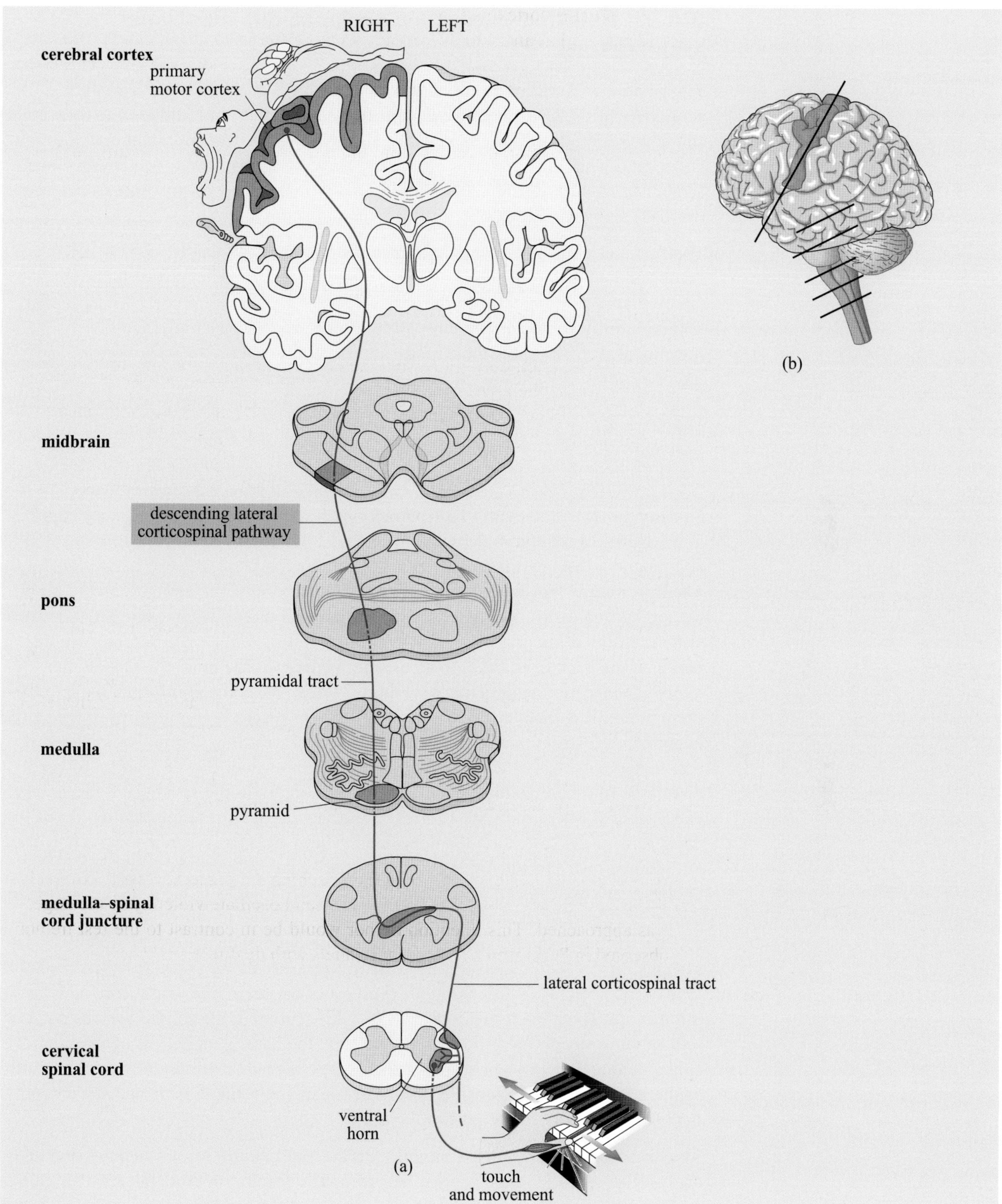

Figure 3.28 Descending motor pathways from the human cerebral cortex to skeletal muscle in the periphery.

3.4.7 Relating structure to function: functional architecture

This review of the principal divisions and structures provides a guide to the geography of the CNS, i.e. where identifiable structures are in relation to each other and how information flows in and out. However, while it is important that you understand what the structures are, where they are in relation to one another, and something about information flow, it is equally important that you understand how the CNS is organized, that is to say, its functional architecture.

The first and most obvious point to make is that the CNS can be seen as being organized into different neural systems, identifiable by special physical attributes (some shared anatomical features or neurochemistry for example), by a particular function, or by some combination of both physical and functional factors. Functional architecture is most easily appreciated when considering sensory and motor systems, as you saw in Section 3.4.6. Other functions such as memory or attention are perhaps a little less clear. With these we can identify structures that have a particular importance (the hippocampus and amygdala, for example) but it is nevertheless clear that several regions of the brain are involved: there is no one structure in the brain that we can say controls memory.

Sensory systems deal with visual, auditory, olfactory, tactile and gustatory (taste) information. In each case there are specialized detectors – the eye, ear, nose, skin and tongue – that send information into the brain (as we have seen in Section 3.4.6). The key point is that these systems are not found in any one structure in the brain, but are instead distributed across many of them. Consider, as an example, the visual system. Information on visual stimuli is conveyed from the photoreceptors in the retina, at the back of the eye, to an area in the base of the brain, just below the hypothalamus, via the optic nerve (Figure 3.24b). Once visual information is in the brain proper it is transferred to many sites. For example, it is registered in the hypothalamus (from where it regulates sleep–wake cycles), the midbrain (for fast preliminary analysis of visual information), the brainstem (for the control of gaze direction) and the thalamus, from where it has access to the specialized machinery of visual analysis in the visual cortex. From the visual cortex, information flows to other parts of the cortex via the dorsal and ventral streams (described in Section 4.4.2). So, although we can identify key parts of the visual system where specific functions operate, the visual system as a whole is best understood as being widely distributed over a large part of the brain: there is no one single site or structure where we can say that vision uniquely happens. The same principle applies to other sensory systems. Motor systems are similarly distributed, involving tissue from the frontal lobe of the cerebral cortex, through all levels of the brain, the spinal cord and out through spinal nerves to the muscles. As with sensory systems, the various parts of this motor system – the primary motor cortex, the basal ganglia, the cerebellum, the spinal cord and other sites besides these – have their own particular functions, but again, it is important to consider that there is no single site that we can say uniquely is the one-and-only motor part of the brain.

This dissociation between a straightforward geography of brain structures and an analysis based on function is not a new idea. The English neurologist John Hughlings Jackson (1884–1958) was the first to suggest that the brain is organized in a layered manner, with *all* levels having sensory input and being capable of generating motor output. Figure 3.29 illustrates how this layered architecture works across a sample of brain structures. It shows, in the context of the organization of defensive behaviour (from work based on laboratory rats, but equally applicable to other species, including humans), how different levels of processing in the CNS operate in regard to particular types of stimuli and responses. The general principle is essentially that low levels of the CNS operate reflexive responses to stimuli, intermediate levels are able to engage more complex processes involving learning and memory, while the highest levels are able to engage in the most sophisticated forms of sensory analysis and then to generate the most complex actions. The basal ganglia, the anatomy of which is remarkably unchanged across mammalian species, and indeed across most vertebrates, appear to function within this layered organization to select the appropriate response when more than one option is available. This layered organization makes sense in terms of defensive behaviours: stepping unawares on something sharp produces an immediate withdrawal response, which can be processed at low levels of the CNS. But knowing, for example, that a particular place is associated with danger is something that you need to learn, which requires a higher level of processing. The highest levels of processing, in the cerebral cortex, can undertake the most sophisticated level of analysis, and can engage in response suppression – that is, despite low level brain systems indicating one thing, the cerebral cortex can provide an override signal. For example, a particular place might be associated with danger but if you knew that on a certain day the danger could not be present, suppressing the normal avoidance response would be appropriate. Other sensory systems work in the same way: if one bites into a rotten apple, or takes a drink of wine that has gone bad, there is an immediate rejection reflex, the neural basis of which is represented in the medulla. On the other hand, if you are trying to discriminate between two different vintage wines, the full processing power of the cortical taste areas is required.

It is important to understand two apparently different types of organization: a straightforward geography of structures, and a more theoretically driven functional architecture. As you have just seen throughout Section 3.4, the CNS is divisible into

Figure 3.29 Conceptual model showing the hierarchical functional architecture of the CNS. Different levels of the CNS operate in a different way in regard to sensory information processing and motor output. (The basal ganglia have not been included as they interact with various parts of the structures shown, both influencing and being influenced by them at different levels.)

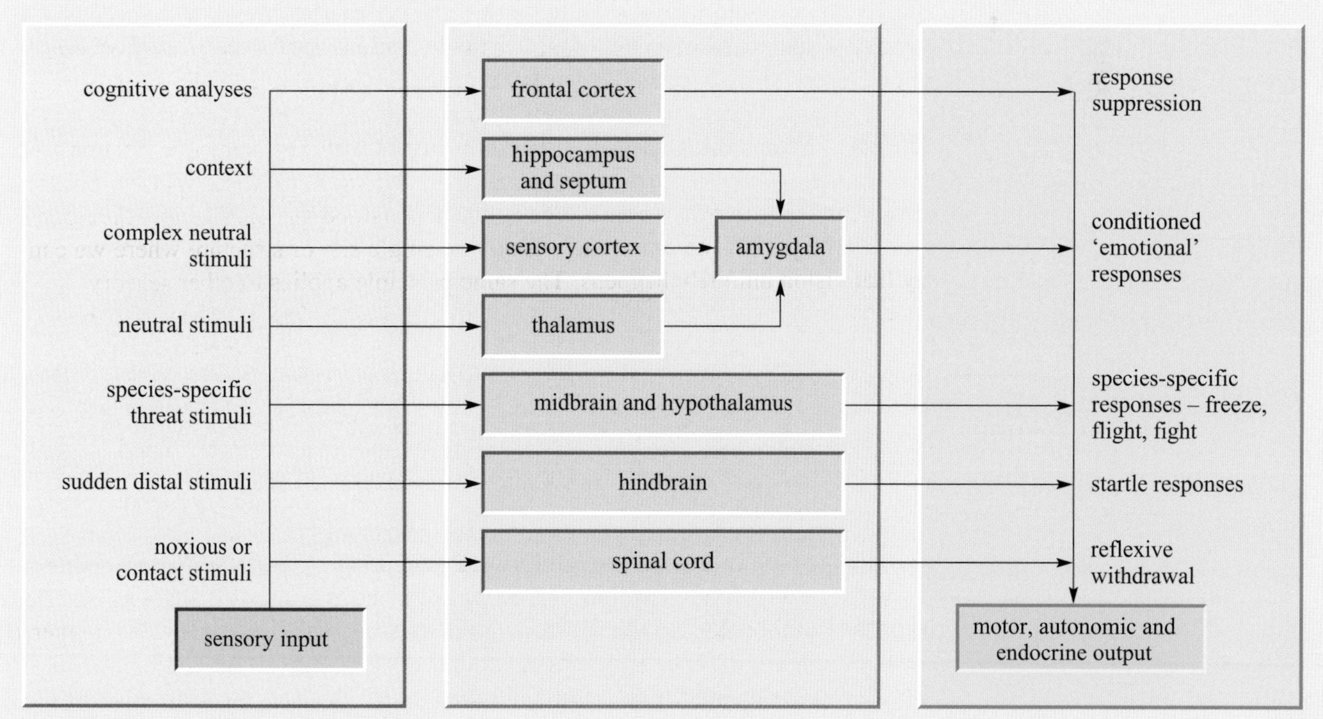

different parts, each with its own internal organization and connections, and identifiable with some functional property. But at the same time, it is important not to be drawn too far into the idea that the brain can be understood by identifying individual structures and simply ascribing a behavioural or psychological property to each one. The anatomy of systems – a functional architecture of the brain – is important in this regard.

Summary of Section 3.4

The human brain, like that of other vertebrates, can be divided into the forebrain, the midbrain and the hindbrain, and it contains different structures, each of them with diverse roles in the generation of behavioural responses. While having a working knowledge of how the brain is divided into different structures is essential to understanding how it works, it is important to emphasize that these brain structures are best described as having a layered functional architecture. Complex behaviour is mediated by elaborate neural pathways that involve the activation of several brain structures. The cerebral cortex forms the outer layer of the forebrain and constitutes the most advanced stage for sensory information input. The regions devoted to this task are the primary sensory areas, specific to individual sensory modalities, which project onto different association areas of the cerebral cortex where integration of information occurs. The output is mediated by the primary motor cortex which connects directly to the spinal cord and other structures, resulting in the generation of smooth movements.

3.5 Maintaining the internal environment

The last section dealt with describing the anatomy of the human nervous system and introduced how sensory input and motor output are integrated to form a behavioural response. This section deals with how the nervous system processes information to sustain the physiology of our body. At the end of this section, we will study how a stable environment is maintained within the human nervous system itself, an essential requirement for its extremely complex function.

3.5.1 The autonomic nervous system

The autonomic nervous system (ANS) regulates the internal organs that are responsible for maintaining the cells of the body under optimum conditions (homeostasis, introduced in Section 1.2.2). Signals come from receptors responding to internal stimuli such as the amount of oxygen in the blood, blood pressure, the movement of food along the gut, the heart rate, the amount of saliva in your mouth or body temperature. All these tasks and many others are under the control of the ANS by way of regulating the activity of muscles of internal organs and blood vessels. The muscle of internal organs and blood vessels is called smooth muscle, the exception being the muscle forming the heart, which is cardiac muscle. The ANS also controls secretion by certain cells such as those in the salivary glands. Many of these activities are usually considered as 'housekeeping' tasks and have to be performed at all times whether we are awake or asleep. The ANS is also important for behaviours that have proved extremely useful for our survival, such as the 'flight or fight' response, as we will see later in this section.

◆ From the principles you learnt in Chapter 1, can the activity of the ANS be considered a conscious process of our mind?

◆ No. We are usually unaware of how our internal organs are regulated. In a way, the ANS may be considered as unconscious processing.

The ANS is formed by ganglia and nerves. Sensory information flowing from internal organs (visceral sensation) arrives in the spinal cord via the dorsal root ganglia of the spinal nerves (Figure 3.30) or in the brainstem via the cranial nerves, in much the same way as somatic sensation. The motor output from the ANS initially leaves the spinal cord via the spinal nerves and the brainstem via the cranial nerves. However, in contrast to motor control of skeletal muscles, the ANS output makes a synapse within the autonomic ganglion before innervating effector cells, e.g. secretory cells, cardiac muscle or smooth muscle in, for example, the gut or blood vessels (Figure 3.30). As a result, ANS output is mediated by two groups of motor neurons: the **preganglionic neurons** (although strictly speaking they are interneurons) synapse in the autonomic ganglia with **postganglionic neurons** which directly innervate the effectors. Note that as in the case of the CNS, the connections within the spinal cord of the ANS (or within the nuclei in the brainstem) may involve additional local interneurons.

The ANS can be divided into the **sympathetic** and **parasympathetic** systems, based on the distribution of nerves and ganglia (Figure 3.30). The sympathetic division has pairs of ganglia on each side of the thoracic and some lumbar segments of the spinal cord (Figure 3.30b). The ganglia of the parasympathetic division are situated in the periphery within the effector organs themselves. The preganglionic axons of the parasympathetic division arise from the brainstem (exiting along some of the cranial nerves) and the sacral segments of the spinal cord. You can see from Figure 3.31 that no region of the brain or spinal cord innervates both sympathetic and parasympathetic divisions of the ANS whereas all internal organs have input from both divisions. You are not, of course, expected to remember all the details on this figure! The **enteric nervous system** is a separate part of the ANS and consists of networks of neurons not dissimilar to invertebrate nerve nets that control the motility and secretory activity of the gut.

Figure 3.30 (a) The afferent and efferent pathways of the ANS and the CNS. Sensory information to both arrives in the spinal cord via the dorsal root ganglia. The CNS motor neurons innervate the skeletal muscles directly whereas ANS neurons synapse to neurons within autonomic ganglia which then innervate muscles in, for example, the heart, gut or blood vessels. The connections within the spinal cord of both systems may involve additional interneurons. (b) The sympathetic trunk in relation to the spinal cord.

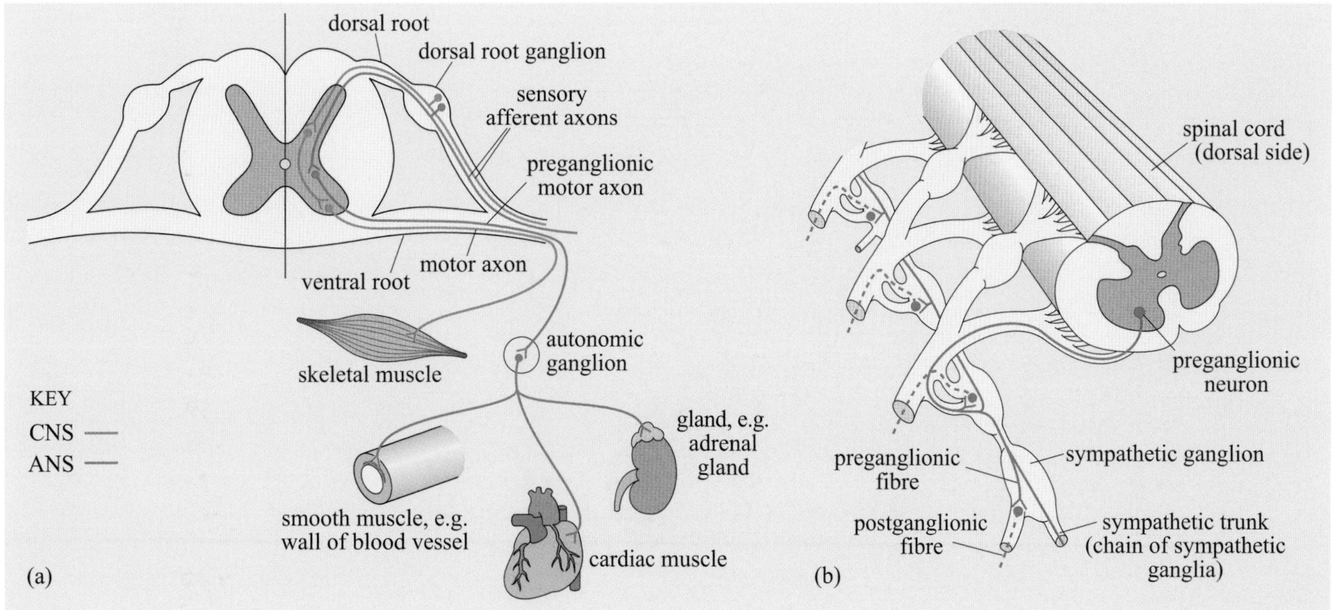

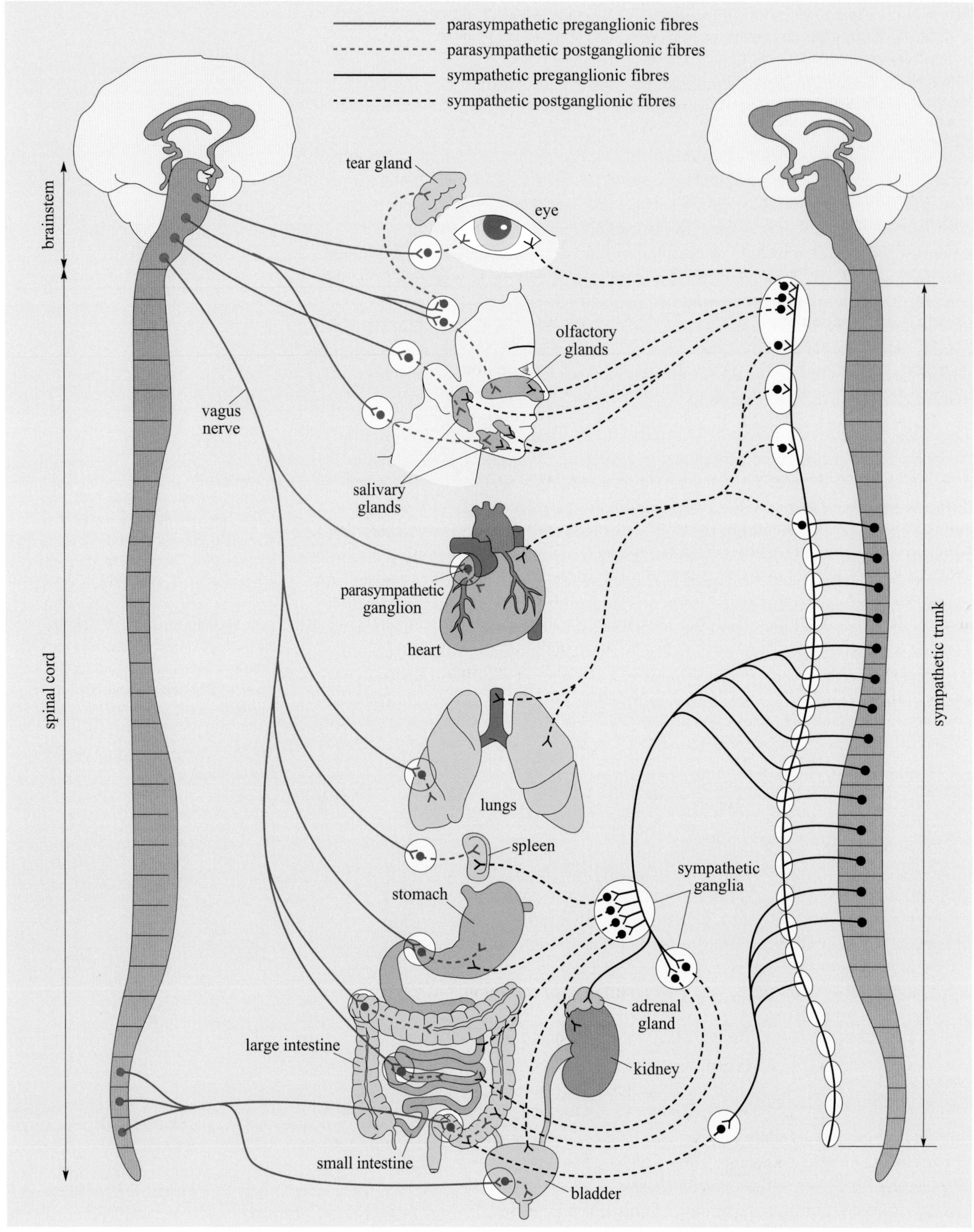
parasympathetic preganglionic fibres
parasympathetic postganglionic fibres
sympathetic preganglionic fibres
sympathetic postganglionic fibres
brainstem
tear gland
eye
olfactory glands
vagus nerve
salivary glands
parasympathetic ganglion
heart
lungs
spleen
stomach
sympathetic ganglia
adrenal gland
kidney
large intestine
small intestine
bladder
spinal cord
sympathetic trunk

Figure 3.31 The pathways and target organs of the parasympathetic and sympathetic divisions of the ANS. For clarity, the parasympathetic system is shown in purple on the left and the sympathetic system in black on the right although no left–right divisions are present in reality as both systems exist in both sides of the body. The preganglionic axons are shown with continuous lines and the postganglionic axons with dashed lines. Note that most of the sympathetic ganglia lie in a row on either side of the spinal cord whereas most parasympathetic ganglia are found within the target organs themselves.

The sympathetic and parasympathetic systems usually have opposing actions, which is illustrated by their effects upon the heart. Stimulation of the parasympathetic nervous system slows the heart down, whereas sympathetic action on the heart speeds it up. While the parasympathetic system is normally concerned with maintaining the resting state of internal organs, the sympathetic system helps us respond to sudden emergencies. The actions of both the sympathetic and the parasympathetic systems are mediated by the neurotransmitters they use. The neurotransmitter released by sympathetic postganglionic neurons is noradrenalin whereas that released by parasympathetic postganglionic neurons is acetylcholine. The preganglionic axon terminals of both systems release acetylcholine as a neurotransmitter.

The ANS also has a central component. The name 'autonomic' derives from the idea that such a system would operate independently of the CNS as it is autonomous of willed conscious control. It is now known that the ANS is closely controlled by the spinal cord and the brain, in particular the hypothalamus and the brainstem, but the old name has remained. For example, the hypothalamus controls, on the one hand, metabolism and food intake – and feeding behaviours in general – and, on the other hand, our 24-hour rhythms in metabolic and autonomic functions. The 'autonomy' is therefore relative, as sensation and control of our internal organs is an important part of the perception of our own self. In addition, there are links between the ANS and the endocrine and immune systems, and its activity influences not only the release of hormones into the blood but our ability to combat infections. An example of this is the effects of the ANS on the adrenal gland (see Box 3.3).

Box 3.3 Fight or flight

The rapid response of the ANS helps a potential vertebrate prey to escape from predators. (Remember from Chapter 2 that the ANS is not found in invertebrates.) In a way the existence of the ANS is paramount to our survival. As a result of its functioning, not only are we able to respond to threats in a manner that increases our chances of survival but we are also able to sit down and relax while reading this chapter. In fact, both types of situation, either stressful or relaxed, require one of the autonomic nervous systems to dominate over the other. Internal homeostasis is maintained by a fine balance between the activities of the sympathetic and parasympathetic systems of the ANS. This equilibrium may be tipped towards the activation of one of the systems under certain conditions. For instance, in situations of acute stress where an imminent danger is perceived, a car unexpectedly swerving in front of you while driving or a sudden noise behind your back, a pattern of behaviour known as the 'fight or flight' response is quickly generated to confront the perceived danger, and this supersedes conscious suppression or social conditioning. If this situation arises, the sympathetic system dominates over the parasympathetic system and allows a rapid reaction to threat. Activation of sympathetic axons innervating the adrenal glands causes the release of hormones such as adrenalin and noradrenalin from the adrenal medulla (an endocrine organ in the abdomen) into the blood. Adrenalin has widespread actions in the body, speeding up the heart beat, dilating the air passages in the lungs, decreasing movement of the stomach wall and mobilizing glucose in the liver. These activities prepare the body for 'fight or flight' by increasing the blood flow to skeletal muscles, making glucose readily available as an energy source, and increasing heart rate while shutting down unnecessary activities in the gut. In short, both nutrients and oxygen are made more readily available for the organs that matter most for this type of response – the brain, the skeletal muscles and the heart – thereby increasing the probabilities of survival of the individual.

The ANS does not function in isolation however, and a coordinated, somewhat slower, response by the neuroendocrine system ensues. This involves the secretion of multiple hormones by the hypothalamus–pituitary gland–adrenal axis. As long as the situation of danger persists, the hypothalamus contributes to the response by sending signals to the pituitary gland at the base of the brain, which releases a hormone into the blood called adrenocorticotropic hormone (ACTH). When ACTH reaches the adrenal glands, it induces the release of other hormones known as glucocorticoids – you may have heard of the glucocorticoid called cortisol in this context; all these chemicals together with adrenalin and noradrenalin continue the response described in the paragraph above.

When the situation of danger is perceived to have been resolved, the parasympathetic ANS takes over and counterbalances the effects of the sympathetic ANS, gradually returning the body to a more relaxed state. Problems, however, may arise if a threat is perceived as continuous or the response of fight or flight is no longer adequate as is the case in modern life. In this case, hormones such as cortisol which has amongst other effects, a long-term depressant action on the immune system, are maintained at high levels in the bloodstream. This is one of the consequences of chronic stress.

3.5.2 Brain circulation and cerebrospinal fluid

Brain circulation

While reading through this chapter, you may have asked yourself how this extremely complex structure, the human CNS, with millions of neurons firing at any one time, is maintained metabolically. Indeed, nervous systems have a high demand of oxygen and nutrients, and this is supplied by a mesh of blood vessels (Figure 3.32). The brain is a highly active organ, taking up to 20% of the oxygen used by the entire body (although it represents only 2% of the total body mass). Like in all other organs in the body, the blood provides glucose, oxygen and other nutrients whilst removing carbon dioxide, lactic acid and other metabolic waste products. Changes in the amount of blood flowing within specific regions of the brain influence the availability of nutrients such as glucose. As you saw in Section 1.3.2, glucose is an example of a molecule that can be used for imaging the brain as more active brain regions take up more glucose than less active ones. Imaging techniques such as fMRI (Section 3.4.6) determine local changes in blood flow which reflect changes in metabolic demand and in turn mirror neuronal activity. By measuring blood flow within a brain region, we can infer whether that region is more or less active.

The major blood vessels that carry oxygenated blood to any organ, such as the brain, are called arteries, whereas those leaving the organ are termed veins. In between, there is a mesh of very fine vessels termed capillaries where most of the exchange of nutrients and gases between the brain and blood occur. In each human brain, there are approximately 400 miles of blood capillaries. If you were to cut open all the blood capillaries of an average human brain and lay them out flat on the ground, they would cover a surface area of approximately 12 square metres.

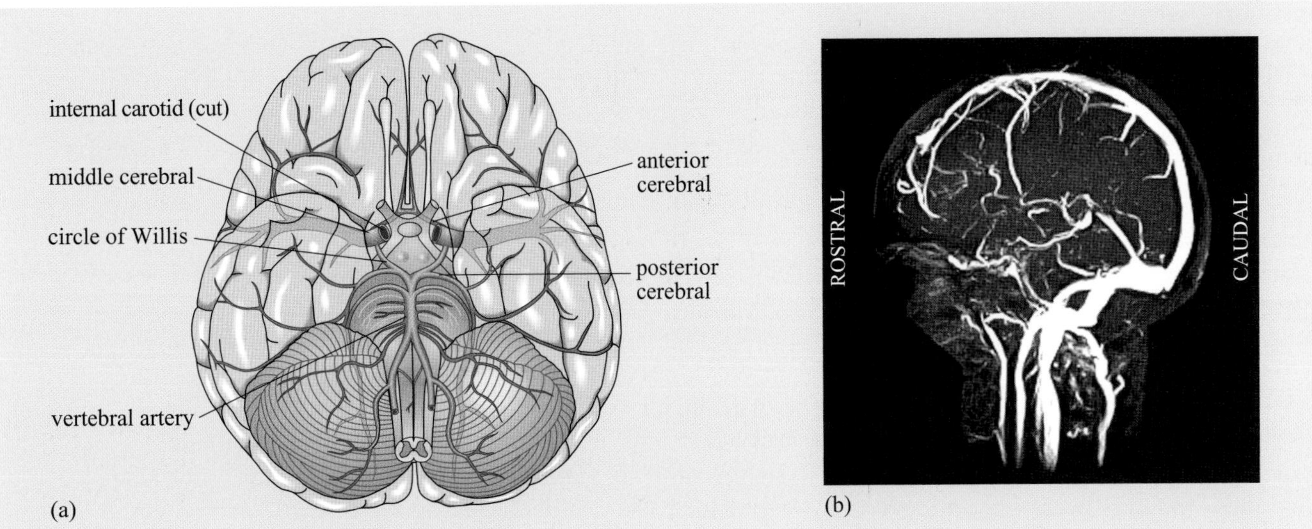

Figure 3.32 (a) Diagram depicting the major blood vessels of the human brain (ventral view). (b) Magnetic resonance angiography (MRA) of the brain of a patient showing the main cerebral vessels. MRA is a type of magnetic resonance imaging (MRI) that uses specific settings to visualize flowing blood within the heart and blood vessels in any part of the body.

There are two major sets of vessels that supply not only the brain but also the face and the scalp: the carotid and the vertebral arteries, both with a left and a right branch. Whereas the external carotid arteries supply the face and the scalp, the internal carotid arteries supply blood to the anterior part of the cerebral hemispheres, except for parts of the temporal and occipital lobes. The vertebral arteries supply the posterior area of the cerebral hemispheres, part of the cerebellum and the brainstem. The circle of Willis, at the base of the brain, is formed by the internal carotid and vertebral arteries, and serves to control blood pressure in the brain, allowing a continuous supply of oxygenated blood to the brain (Figure 3.32). In the event of one of the main arteries becoming obstructed, the circle of Willis enables the other main arteries to provide a continuous blood supply to most parts of the brain. From the circle of Willis, other secondary arteries, the anterior, middle and posterior cerebral arteries, arise and travel to all parts of the brain. It is at the level of these arteries that a decrease or even a transient interruption in the blood flow, a condition known as a stroke (as you will see in Box 3.4), can have serious consequences, such as blindness, numbness, weakness or paralysis on the contralateral side of the body.

Cerebral vessels are different to those in other organs in that they are highly restrictive to the passage of many molecules circulating in the blood – an anatomical feature known as the **blood–brain barrier** (Figure 3.33). The blood–brain barrier is present in all vertebrate brains and develops within the first three months of human fetal life. What is the advantage of the blood–brain barrier with respect to functioning of the CNS? The brain needs a barrier separating it from the blood to ensure the rigorous control of the brain microenvironment. As you shall see in Book 4, Section 1.3, the generation of action potentials in neurons is dependent on the concentration of ions in the extracellular space. In the absence of a barrier, small fluctuations in blood levels of, for example, sodium or potassium would cause neurons either to initiate action potentials independently of information flow or to be reticent in transmitting signals initiated in other parts of the brain. Therefore without a stable extracellular environment, the complex neural signalling that characterizes the CNS would fall apart. The blood–brain barrier also prevents many noxious agents, such as bacteria, viruses and environmental toxins that make it into the bloodstream from tainting the brain's pristine habitat. For many years, researchers were puzzled as to which cell type constituted the anatomical and physical barrier. We now know from electron microscopy studies that the barrier is

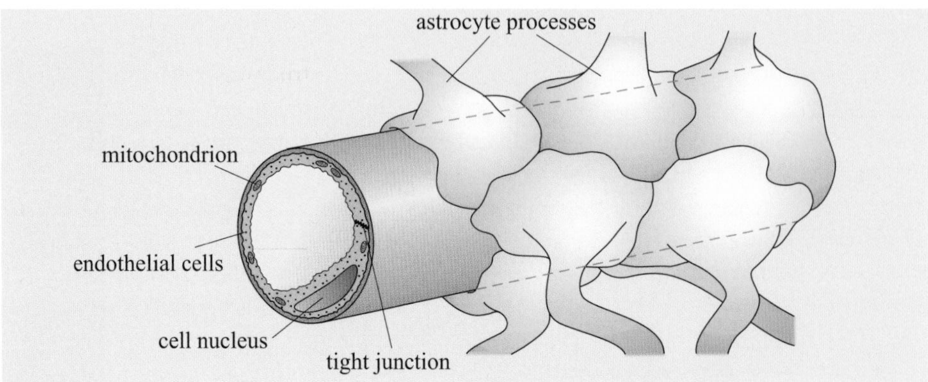

Figure 3.33 Schematic drawing of a cerebral blood vessel. Brain capillaries are formed by a continuous layer of endothelial cells with tight junctions between them that are much more effective in excluding small water-soluble substances and ions than those in non-brain capillaries. Astrocyte processes surround cerebral vessels and are thought to induce barrier properties in endothelial cells.

formed by brain endothelial cells which, unlike those of other organs, are cemented together by specialized intercellular structures called **tight junctions** (Figures 3.33 and 3.34). Tight junctions are zipper-like structures linking adjacent endothelial cells. They restrict the passage of molecules to a greater or lesser extent. Although tight junctions are extremely impermeable, effectively preventing most water-soluble substances and ions from entering the brain, they do allow the passage of small molecules such as oxygen. Cerebral endothelial cells also regulate the passage of nutrients such as glucose into the brain. They can be considered as the 'gatekeepers' of the brain. However, there are areas within the brain where this barrier is much more relaxed in that the junctions between endothelial cells are not as tight, to allow the passage of blood-borne molecules into the brain space. These brain regions, called the **circumventricular organs**, are located close to the cerebral ventricles (see below) and contain neurons that respond to fluctuations in chemical substances in the blood thereby monitoring important blood parameters such as glucose, pH and salinity.

- ◇ From the definitions of the functional roles of the different brain regions given in Section 3.4, can you think of an example of a brain structure with extensive connections to the circumventricular organs?
- ◆ The hypothalamus. The neurons contained within different areas in the hypothalamus are able to respond to fluctuations in the blood levels of specific chemicals such as salts and hormones, and to do that they project extensively onto adjacent circumventricular organs with a 'leakier' blood–brain barrier.

Figure 3.34 (a) Electron micrograph of the point of contact between two endothelial cells. Their plasma membrane is easily recognizable as a double line which at times forms tight connections (arrows), an anatomical feature known as a tight junction. (b) Immunofluorescence micrograph showing the distribution of a protein that forms part of the tight junctions in cultured human brain endothelial cells. Note the strong staining in the areas of contact between the cells (green) in contrast to the absence of staining in the cytoplasm (black). Note also that individual endothelial cells can be distinguished by the faint staining of their nuclei.

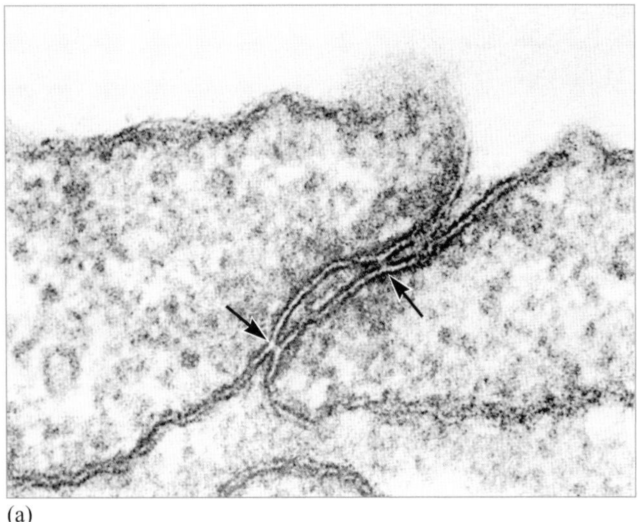

(a)

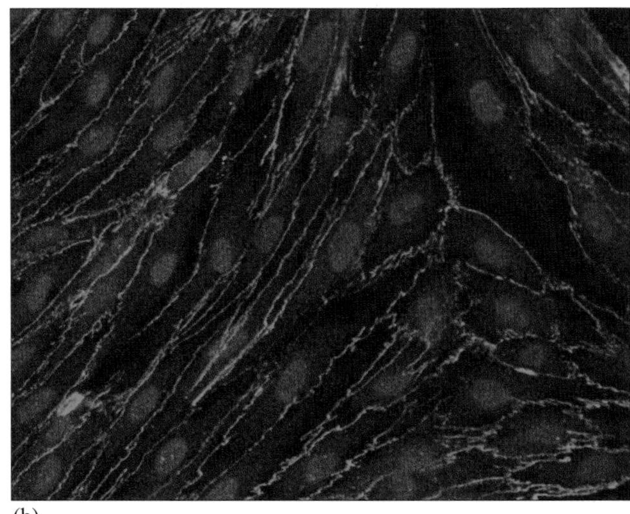

(b)

Cerebrospinal fluid

The brain and spinal cord are not completely compact structures, rather they contain cavities that communicate with each other. In the brain, there are four such large spaces, called **ventricles**, the hollow in the middle of the spinal cord is called the **central canal** (Figure 3.35). The cerebral ventricles and the central canal contain a fluid known as cerebrospinal fluid (CSF). The CSF is also found in the **subarachnoid space**, which lies in between the surface of the brain and the spinal cord and the protective sheets surrounding these structures, collectively known as **meninges**. A line of ependymal cells (Figure 2.16) makes up the interface between the cerebral ventricles and the nervous tissue. These cells are therefore a site of interchange between the CSF and the extracellular space surrounding neurons and other glial cells in the CNS. The fluid circulates in a specific one-way pathway from the cerebral ventricles, where it is produced, to the central canal, from here to the subarachnoid space, and hence into the major veins exiting the brain. The flow of the CSF is aided by the ependymal cells, and by arterial pulsations created by heart contractions. The CSF is secreted by a specialized type of ependymal cell which resides in a network of capillaries lying on the ventricles – the **choroid plexus epithelium**. The liquid secreted by these cells is generally similar in composition to the blood in terms of ions and nutrients, but there are very few cells in it and little protein.

The CSF performs several functions. As it circulates through the human CNS, it constitutes a major route by which potentially harmful substances can be removed into the blood (but it can also be used to deliver hormones and other substances to remote sites in the nervous system). By this and other actions, it maintains a stable extracellular environment in which neurons can function normally. The most important function of the CSF, however, is to provide mechanical support to the brain and spinal cord. It gives the brain buoyancy, allowing it to float like a body in salty water. It also acts as a protective cushion when the skull or the vertebral column suffers potentially damaging blows (see Box 3.1). The importance of the CSF is illustrated by a disease termed hydrocephalus, which literally means 'watery brain' (Box 3.4).

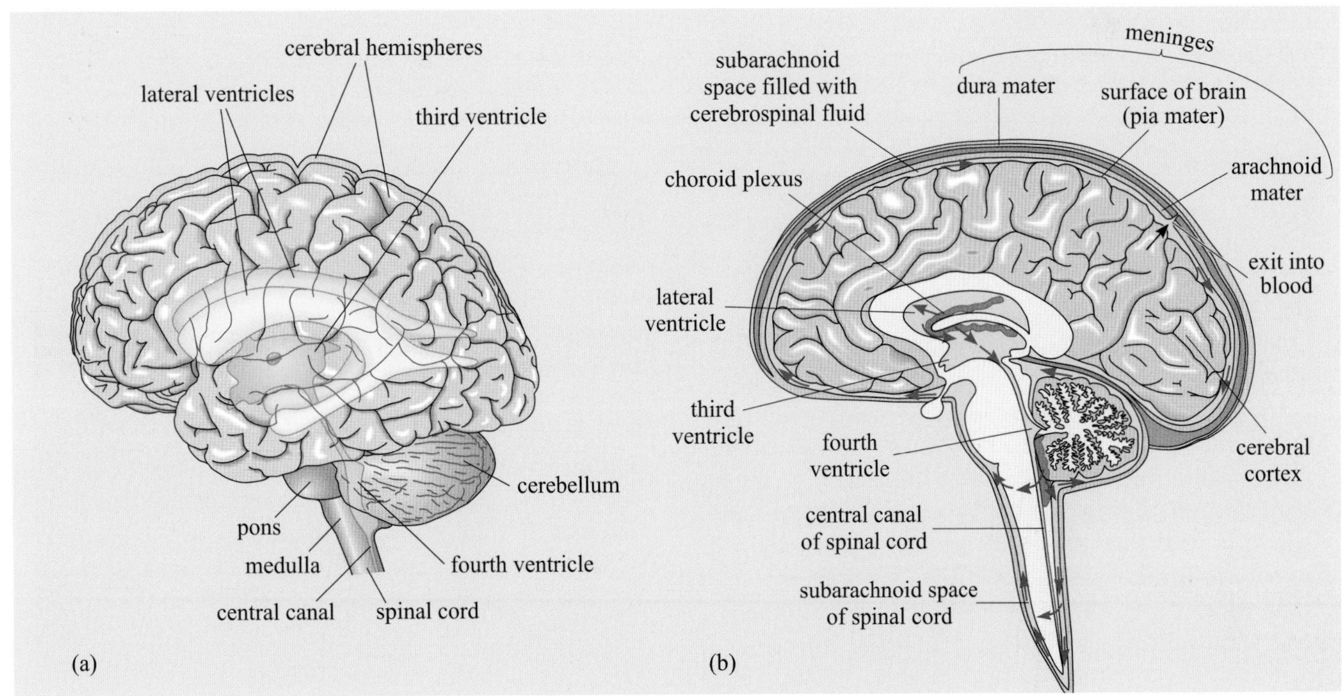

Figure 3.35 (a) View of the human brain showing the ventricles inside the cerebral hemispheres.
(b) A diagram showing a sagittal view of the human brain with cerebrospinal fluid (CSF) filled spaces (the central canal in the spinal cord and ventricles in the brain; subarachnoid space in both the brain and the spinal cord) and meninges (pia mater, dura mater and arachnoid mater).

Box 3.4 Diseases associated with cerebral circulation and cerebrospinal fluid – some examples

Stroke

Bleeding from or a blockage of blood vessels results in cerebrovascular damage, commonly known as a stroke (Figure 3.36). A stroke causes a reduction in the supply of blood to specific regions of the brain, a phenomenon called ischaemia. If the brain is starved of oxygen for more than 5 to 10 minutes, then nerve cells will start to die, probably because the lack of blood flow causes a build up of toxins. A more serious stroke can then result in an infarct, a region of dead or dying cells. Strokes are not equally likely to occur in all parts of the brain. To start with, most strokes are due to damage to arteries and it is uncommon for veins to be involved. There are also some areas of the arterial system that are more likely to be damaged than others, such as the major branch points. The symptoms that result from a stroke depend on the area of the brain affected, which depends on the blood vessel damaged. For example, occlusion (i.e. a blockage) of the posterior cerebral artery which supplies the occipital lobe and parts of the temporal lobe results in visual defects, loss of memory and disturbances of reading. In the UK, two people out of 1000 suffer a stroke each year. Some 35% of them die within three weeks, and about half of the survivors suffer some disability.

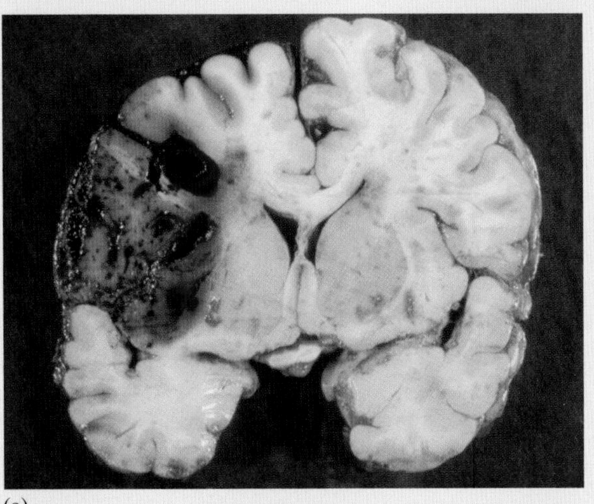

(a)

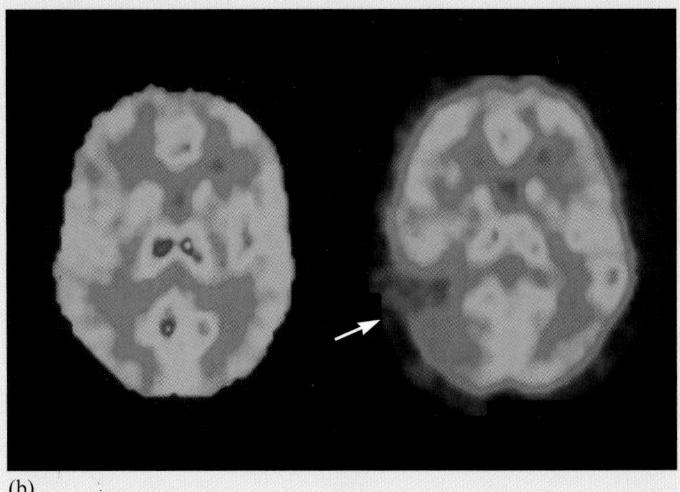

(b)

Figure 3.36 (a) Coronal section of the human brain showing an intracerebral haemorrhage. (b) Positron emission tomography (PET) scan of a healthy brain (left) and a brain of a patient with decreased blood flow in blue around an area of stroke (right). PET is a technique that measures the amount of blood and oxygen that reaches different areas within the brain. (See Book 3, Section 2.4.1.)

Hydrocephalus

Hydrocephalus is a condition that is caused by excessive accumulation of CSF within the brain. It affects around three births in every 1000. As a result, the ventricles fill up with CSF, pressure within the brain builds up and the skull of neonates born with this disorder appear enlarged (Figure 3.37a). Most prenatal cases result from developmental abnormalities although some *in utero* infections and rare familial disorders can also result in hydrocephalus in the neonate. If untreated, children born with this condition deteriorate slowly. Initially they frequently show irritability and minor impairment of motor skills. As the disease progresses, these symptoms become more prominent and, ultimately, respiratory centres may be affected.

Hydrocephalus can also occur in infants and adults, although the skull bone has already become rigid. Its consequences are not as clearly evident as they are in neonates. The most common causes of paediatric and adult hydrocephalus are brain tumours which cause obstruction of the ventricles, and haemorrhage within the subarachnoid space which stops the natural flow of the CSF (Figure 3.35b). Fortunately, most patients with hydrocephalus benefit from a surgical procedure that involves the insertion of a shunt into one of the ventricles (Figure 3.37b). A shunt is a device which diverts CSF into a drainage space such as the heart, the peritoneum or the gallbladder. It also has a valve to regulate pressure to prevent CSF backflow.

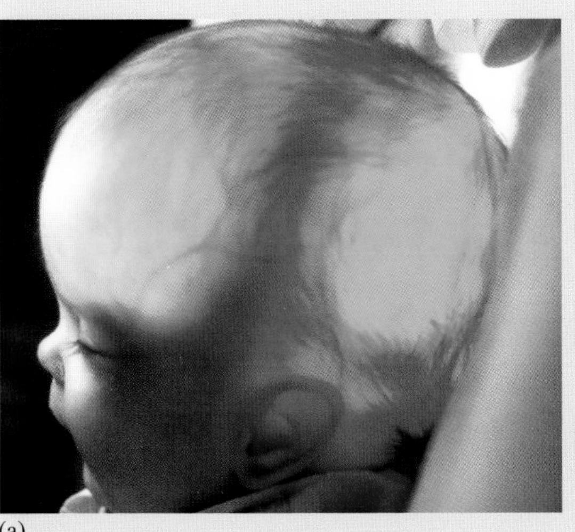
(a)

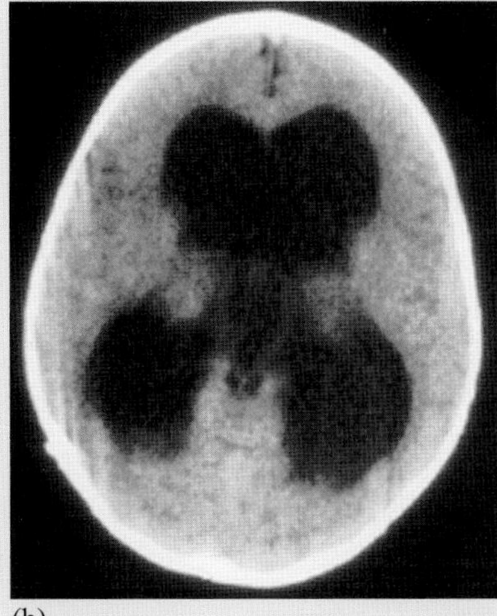
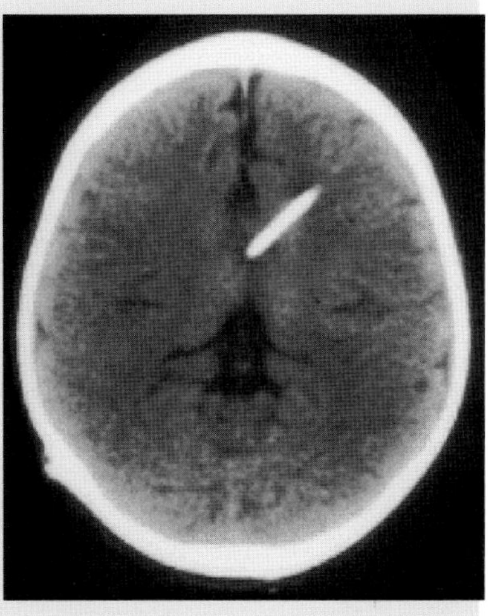
(b)

Figure 3.37 (a) Illumination, with a red light source, of the head of a baby with hydrocephalus. The illuminated yellow areas show fluid accumulation inside the skull which has caused enlargement of the baby's head. (b) A computerized tomography (CT) image of a brain of a patient with hydrocephalus before (left) and after (right) treatment. (CT scans are explained in Book 3, Section 2.4.1.) Note that before the operation the CSF accumulates within the ventricles which fill up and therefore appear enlarged (large black areas in the middle). The 'shunt' (bright white) is a tube with a valve that is implanted in the brain to allow the drainage of the CSF from the ventricles. After the operation, the ventricles promptly resume their natural size.

Summary of Section 3.5

The internal environment of the body is maintained by the ANS which innervates all the organs in the body. This control is effected by secretory glands, and by smooth and cardiac muscle. The divisions of the ANS are the sympathetic and parasympathetic systems. In addition, the enteric nervous system controls the function of the gut. The high metabolic demand of the CNS is met by a network of blood vessels supplying the brain and spinal cord. These are formed by endothelial cells which, unlike those of other organs, form a barrier that excludes unwanted substances from the brain – the blood–brain barrier. The cerebrospinal fluid fills up the cavities within the brain and spinal cord and plays an important protective role both mechanically and by maintaining a stable extracellular environment for neurons.

3.6 The human brain: is quantity better than quality?

The mass of an average human brain is 1.3 kg. This is not much compared to the size of a brain in a whale (5–8 kg) or an elephant (5 kg). One may assume that such large animals have more information to process and so need a larger brain. As a general rule, you may expect that the larger the body mass, the larger the brain. Indeed this relationship holds true for many vertebrates (even elephants and whales) (Figure 3.38). However, primates in general and humans in particular have brains that are larger than would be expected for their body size compared with other vertebrates. For example, the human brain represents around 2% of the total body mass, whereas the elephant brain represents only 0.2%. The significance of this is still unclear: does relative brain size distinguish humans with respect to their cognitive and intellectual abilities? Not necessarily. Relative brain size may set humans apart from many animals, like mice or elephants, but not from other primates. In fact, brain size is a very crude

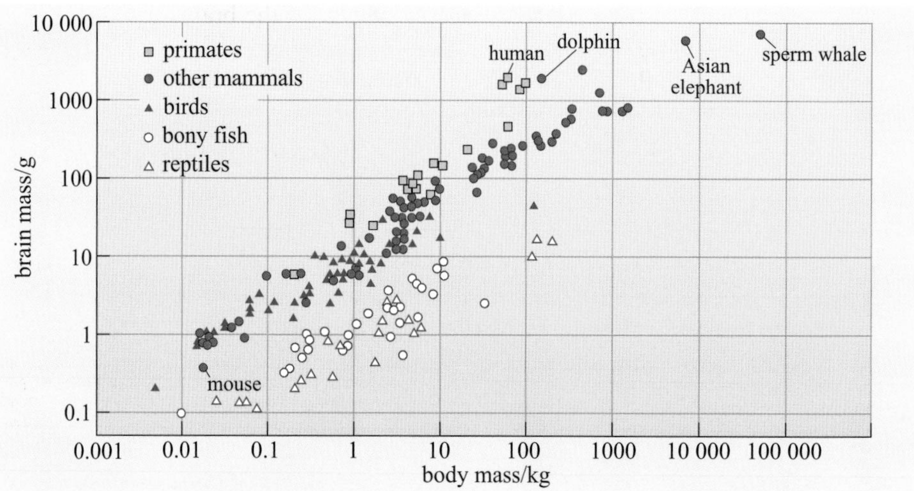

Figure 3.38 Correlation between brain mass and body mass. Brain mass plotted against body mass for more than 200 living vertebrate species. Note that, as a general rule, the higher the body mass, the larger the brain. Note also that the data appear to fall into two distinct groups: higher vertebrates (mammals and birds) and lower vertebrates (fish and reptiles).

measurement and does not take into account differences in size between different brain regions. We stated earlier that different structures within the brain deal with particular functions. As described in Section 2.3.2, the size of different brain structures will therefore depend on the amount of information processing by that structure and this will reflect differences in lifestyle or behaviour. The question one may ask is whether there are particular brain regions that are relatively larger in humans than in other primates and whether these would then be implicated in mediating our inherently human cognitive abilities.

Historically, much effort has been devoted to attempting to account for our human intellectual pre-eminence. The classic work of Brodmann in 1909 and other studies in the 1960s have mostly favoured the hypothesis that it is due to the large size of our frontal lobes. In particular, a multimodal association area of the cortex, the **prefrontal cortex**, has been proposed to be the factor responsible for the uniqueness of human cognitive specialization. The prefrontal cortex is the area of the cortex from the anterior portion of the central sulcus to the anterior part of the frontal lobe excluding the motor areas (Figure 3.15b). From studies on humans with damaged prefrontal cortex, this area appears to have a major role in planning motor actions ahead of their execution and in giving emotional value to sensory stimuli.

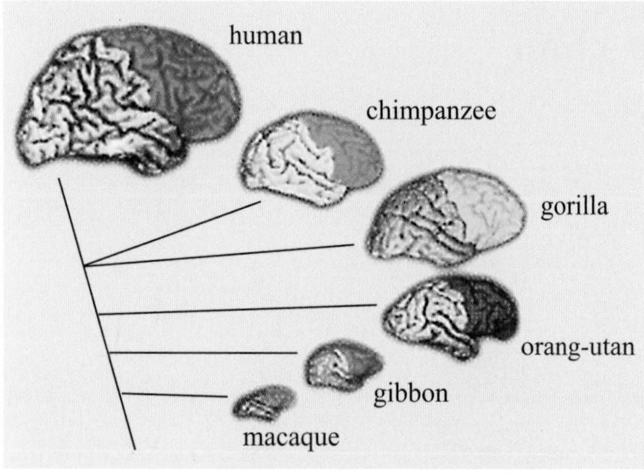

Figure 3.39 A comparison of the frontal lobes (coloured) in human and several non-human primate species. The evolutionary relationships among the species are indicated by the connecting lines.

◆ Can you think of an example of damage to the frontal areas of the human brain resulting in alterations in emotional responses?

◆ Phineas Gage, described in Section 1.1.4.

The size of the prefrontal cortex relative to the size of the cortex is 50% greater in humans than it is in lesser apes (gibbons) and monkeys (Figure 3.39). However, recent studies using imaging techniques cast doubt on the idea that it is greater than that in great apes, such as chimpanzees, gorillas and orang-utans. Nonetheless, although brain size, and in particular the relative size of the prefrontal cortex, may not be what sets humans apart from the great apes (our closest relatives), that does not diminish the role of the prefrontal cortex in human cognitive specialization. Whether our inherently human intellectual abilities rely on the organization and neuronal circuitry of the prefrontal cortex rather than on its size is still a subject of much debate. As we stated earlier in Section 3.4.7, it is important to consider the whole functional architecture of the brain and that there is no single brain structure that we can say is uniquely responsible for the particular cognitive abilities of humans.

- ◆ Is the human prefrontal cortex thicker than that in other primates, and if so, does this account for its larger surface area?
- ◆ In Section 3.4.4, you learnt that the thickness of the cerebral cortex is roughly the same in different areas and in different species, at around 1.5–4 mm, and cannot account for the enlarged surface area in humans. However, as the human cerebral cortex is highly folded, it accommodates many more columns (see Section 3.4.5) which are the basic functional information processing units.

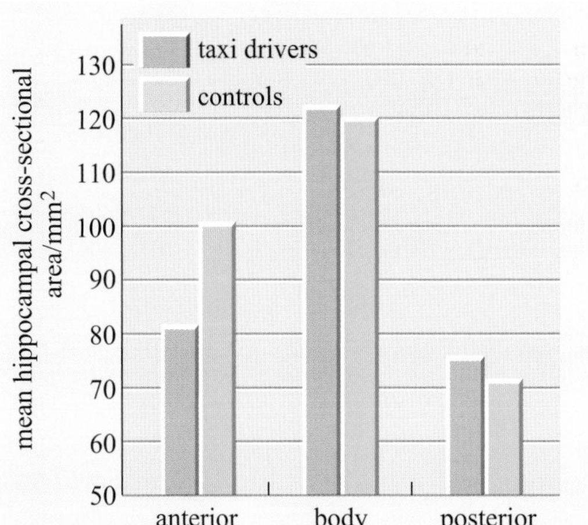

Figure 3.40 Hippocampus volume expressed in terms of cross-sectional area in three regions of the hippocampus (anterior, body and posterior) in the left hemisphere of London taxi drivers and human control subjects. Note that the volume of the hippocampus body shows no significant differences between the two groups, whereas the volume of the anterior hippocampus is significantly smaller and that of the posterior hippocampus is larger in taxi drivers compared to the controls. Similar results were also obtained in the right hippocampus. (Statistical significance will be discussed in Book 2, Section 1.5.)

One interesting last point, however, is that even within humans, we can find variability in the size of brain structures and this may be related to lifestyle. A research group from the Institute of Neurology in London compared the size of the hippocampus in licensed London taxi drivers and in control individuals that do not drive taxis (Figure 3.40). They found that the volume of the anterior part of the hippocampus was smaller in the taxi driver group whereas the volume of the posterior part was greater and these differences were more pronounced the longer the time spent as a taxi driver. The posterior part of the hippocampus is involved in spatial memory and an increased relative size may reflect better navigational skills for the individuals concerned – a major advantage if you have to drive around the multitude of jam-packed streets in London!

- ◆ From the definition of causation in Section 1.4.4, can we conclude whether there is a causal link between an enlarged hippocampus and driving a taxi in London?
- ◆ No, the type of study presented above does not prove causation but merely shows correlation. At present, we do not know whether the hippocampus increases in size after years of taxi driving. Another possibility may be that people with larger hippocampi, and hence better spatial memory, for example, may choose this profession over others, or that the larger the hippocampi, the longer these people are likely to remain being taxi drivers.

3.7 Concluding remarks

The CNS contains millions of neurons, each one integrating information received from a multitude of other neurons. In this chapter, you have seen how the human central nervous system can be divided into regions, each containing its own particular arrangement of neurons. We saw an example of the latter by describing the cellular anatomy of the cerebral cortex. Each region receives input, and its output depends upon the nature of that input. We have also learnt that brain structures are organized into functional divisions. No single function may be ascribed to a single brain structure but rather many brain regions are implicated in a particular behaviour. At a higher level, the whole CNS receives information and produces appropriate behavioural responses and responses related to the internal environment.

Figure 3.41 illustrates the flow of information from the sensory inputs to the motor outputs in the human CNS taking into account what we have learnt so far in this book. Figure 2.1, at the beginning of Chapter 2, is a very simplified version of this figure. A sensory stimulus, whether internal or external, might produce a simple motor response localized to the spinal cord or a more complex series of activities, mediated by elaborate neural pathways involving a number of brain structures. One of the questions that researchers are attempting to answer nowadays is how the brain constructs an internal representation from the external physical stimuli. As you hold this book, you do not see it as a separate black and white mass and a rectangular block, nor do you feel its smooth texture and its stationary position as independent features, rather you recognize the object you are looking at as an open book being held in your hands. These perceptual attributes, although unrelated and analysed through different neural pathways, are all coordinated in a single perception. How sensory information is unified to give a representation of a single object – or even a single identity, that of ourselves – is called the *binding problem*. Similarly, how conscious experience of ourselves as distinct individuals and of the world surrounding us emerges from sensory information is another significant question that is currently hotly debated by psychologists, neuroscientists and philosophers. These important questions emphasize the complexity of our nervous system and some of them will be addressed in the next chapter.

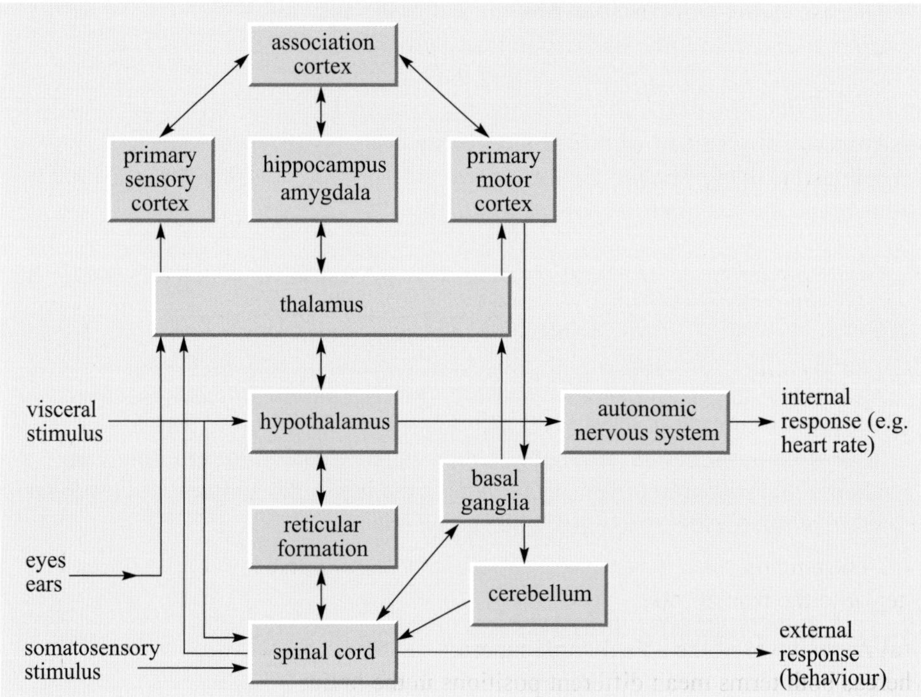

Figure 3.41 The flow of information through the various parts of the human CNS.

Learning outcomes for Chapter 3

After studying this chapter, you should be able to:

3.1 Recognize definitions and applications of each of the terms printed in **bold** in the text.

3.2 Use the correct anatomical terms to describe relative directions and positions within the human nervous system.

3.3 Describe the anatomy of the human spinal cord and the spinal nerves, with particular reference to their function.

3.4 Explain, in terms that involve the expressions motor neuron, sensory neuron and interneuron, the neuronal pathways involved in reflex responses mediated by the spinal cord.

3.5 Describe the basic plan of the human brain and recognize how it is divided geographically into different structures that are also organized into functional divisions.

3.6 Explain what is meant by integration of sensory and motor pathways and how input and output are reflected in the cellular organization of the human cortex.

3.7 Discuss the role and organization of the ANS in humans.

3.8 Describe the roles of brain circulation and cerebrospinal fluid in maintaining homeostasis in the human CNS.

3.9 Discuss how the size of different brain structures may be related to species and to lifestyle of the individual.

Questions for Chapter 3

Question 3.1 *(Learning outcomes 3.1 and 3.2)*

Each of the following sentences relating to human anatomy is composed of two statements, (a) and (b). Either one or both of the statements are false. For each sentence, select the false statement(s) and explain why.

1 (a) The left ear is caudal to the nose; (b) both anatomical features are contralateral in relation to each other.

2 (a) The temporal lobe is ventral to the parietal lobe whereas (b) the occipital lobe is anterior to the frontal lobe.

3 (a) At the level of the spinal cord, superior has the same meaning as dorsal (b) whereas both terms mean different positions in the brain.

4 (a) A vertical cut through the coronal plane along the midline separates the cerebral hemispheres into two roughly symmetrical left and right halves whereas (b) a sagittal cut results in a superior and an inferior half.

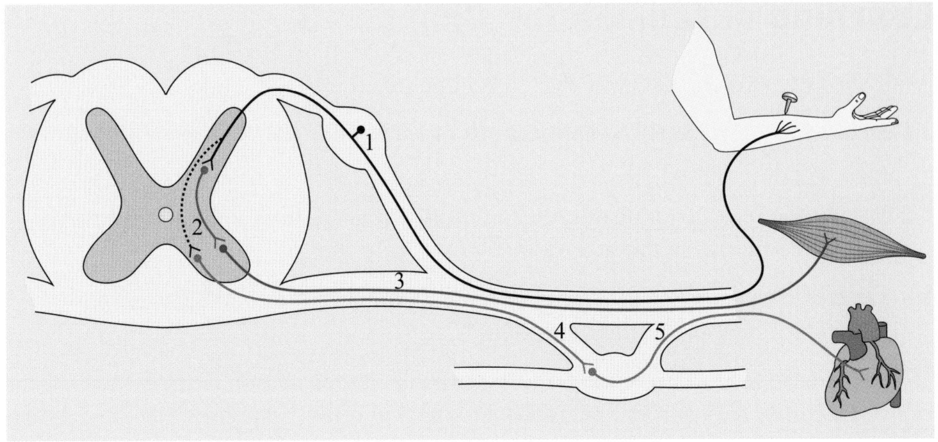

Figure 3.42 Diagram showing a transverse section of the human spinal cord. Note the dashed line between neuron 1 and neuron 4 which indicates indirect connections between them either via additional interneurons within the same or different segments, or via ascending and descending pathways to and from the brain. (For use with Questions 3.2 and 3.3.)

Question 3.2 *(Learning outcomes 3.1, 3.3 and 3.4)*

On Figure 3.42, label the dorsal root, dorsal horn, ventral root, ventral horn, white matter, dorsal root ganglion, autonomic ganglion, skeletal muscle and cardiac muscle. Can you classify neurons 1, 2, 3, 4 and 5 in Figure 3.42 according to their function?

Question 3.3 *(Learning outcomes 3.3, 3.4 and 3.7)*

Look again at Figure 3.42. Imagine a situation in which you get pricked by a needle in an area of the skin on the underside of your arm that is innervated by neuron 1. Answer the following questions:

(a) What kind of motor response would you expect to occur?

(b) If the noxious stimulus is sufficient to induce action potentials in neuron 1, what kind of sensory receptor could neuron 1 be?

(c) What region of the spinal cord will receive the incoming flow of sensory information? (You may need to look at Figure 3.6b to answer this question.)

(d) Would the autonomic ganglion depicted in Figure 3.42 be sympathetic or parasympathetic?

Question 3.4 *(Learning outcome 3.5)*

Label the following structures in the human nervous system depicted in Figure 3.43: medulla, pons, cerebellum, cerebral hemispheres, cerebral cortex, reticular formation, basal ganglia, thalamus, superior colliculus and inferior colliculus.

Question 3.5 *(Learning outcome 3.6)*

Explain what is meant by the following sentence: 'The cerebral cortex shows a high degree of vertical and horizontal patterns of organization'.

Question 3.6 *(Learning outcome 3.6)*

What areas in the cortex are responsible for integrating sensory information from different modalities?

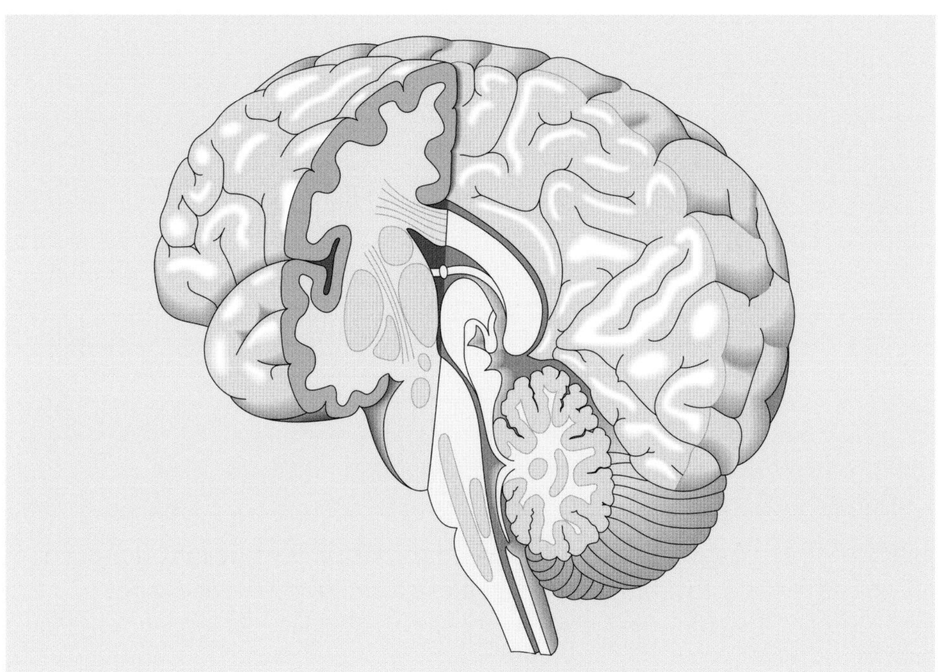

Figure 3.43 Cut-away section of the human brain. (For use with Question 3.4.)

Question 3.7 *(Learning outcome 3.7)*

'As she crept up the badly lit stairs, her heart was pounding. When she reached the landing, she thought she heard a noise behind her. The hairs in the back of her neck stiffened and she broke out in a cold sweat as she turned round...'

Which part of the nervous system is responsible for these symptoms? Explain what is happening.

Question 3.8 *(Learning outcomes 3.1 and 3.8)*

Explain what is meant by the term 'blood–brain barrier'.

Question 3.9 *(Learning outcome 3.9)*

In what ways would you expect the somatosensory 'homunculus' of the human brain to differ from the equivalent somatosensory map of the rat brain (which could be described as the 'ratunculus')?

CHAPTER 4

UNDERSTANDING THE MIND

4.1 Introduction

The explanation of consciousness is one of the major unsolved problems of science. The fact that consciousness is a subjective phenomenon raises questions in the minds of many scientists and philosophers about whether it can ever be a legitimate area of inquiry for science. Nevertheless, over the past 20 years or so there has been a tremendous growth of scientific interest in consciousness, and a determination to bring an empirical approach to its study.

In previous chapters, you obtained a broad overview of the structure, organization and functioning of nervous systems, including the human nervous system (Chapter 3). In this chapter, we turn to a more detailed consideration of the mind, which includes unconscious as well as conscious processes, and has been described as 'what the brain does' (Chapter 1, Section 1.2.3).

What is our subjective experience of consciousness like? For most of us, it is a very rich experience indeed. We are aware of ourselves as distinct and separate entities embedded in and interacting with a world teeming with a wonderful variety of phenomena. It is a world replete with colour, sound, taste, texture and motion, and there is a seamlessness and immediacy to our sensory experience. We are able to experience in the here-and-now, but also to reflect on the past and imagine the future. Sometimes, it seems as if we are playing a 'movie-in-the brain' (Damasio, 1999). The 19th century American psychologist William James similarly characterized conscious experience as a 'stream of thought, of consciousness, or of subjective life' (James, 1890).

We normally have a strong sense of our own self, and can observe ourselves thinking, feeling, and going about our lives. There seems to be an unshakeable sense of continuity to this self: although every night we sleep and become by and large unconscious of the outside world, we wake up in the morning knowing we are still ourselves. Part of our conscious experience is of having choices and making active decisions, in other words of having free will.

Indeed, consciousness seems to pervade our lives as humans, and it is impossible to imagine how human perception, language and culture could exist without it. Yet there is plenty of evidence, as we shall see, that we may overestimate its role in our lives.

The study of consciousness is a complex and rapidly expanding field of enquiry. It involves researchers as diverse as computer scientists interested in artificial intelligence, neuroscientists studying the 'nuts and bolts' of the brain, neurologists working with brain-damaged patients, psychologists and philosophers. It would be impossible to cover all of these aspects in detail in this chapter; therefore, we will focus instead on delineating some of the most important issues, and outlining some of the current thinking that is emerging about the links between the brain, body and mind.

4.2 Getting a handle on consciousness

4.2.1 Describing consciousness

You are probably not conscious of your eyes blinking from time to time as you read this chapter. However, if asked to notice your eye-blinks, you might direct your attention to them and become all too conscious of them! The difference between conscious and non-conscious states seems to be, for want of a better description, a kind of 'feeling of what happens' (Damasio, 1999). This is as close as we can get to describing the essence of subjective experience.

At one level, consciousness could be characterized as the raw feel of our sensations, of 'what it feels like' to be cold, smell a lily, taste chocolate and so on. This is the here-and-now of sensory experience, which does not require language or analysis – such as naming the feeling, or thinking to oneself: 'I feel really cold today' – to exist. This level of conscious experience is thought to be fundamental and widespread – for instance, it would be rather surprising if babies or dogs did not experience raw sensations. Philosophers use the term **qualia** (Latin for 'qualities'; singular: quale) to describe the here-and-now raw feelings of 'what it is like' to experience something. Qualia can be defined as the **phenomenal representations** of physical properties. For example, the quale of certain wavelengths of electromagnetic radiation reaching us from the Sun is the colour red. (Note that *phenomenal* here does not have the everyday meaning of amazing or extraordinary, but the philosophical meaning of 'known or perceived by the senses rather than the mind'.) Another term commonly used for the 'feeling experience' component of consciousness is **phenomenal consciousness** or awareness. (*Consciousness* and *awareness* are often used interchangeably in the literature and we adopt this practice.) The important point to remember is that phenomenal consciousness or awareness is considered not to need language, reasoning or conventional memory to exist (any memory required is very short term or ephemeral). This is easy to state, but it is impossible to describe what this kind of raw experience might actually feel like because it is impossible to convey in words a subjective phenomenal experience, such as coldness, to another person.

As adults, we undoubtedly find it difficult to be in a state of 'just feeling' because language, reasoning, cultural values and self-awareness are so readily brought to bear on any sensation we feel. Phenomenal consciousness is nevertheless a useful concept as it allows for the possibility of consciousness without language or the complex introspection with which we are familiar.

At the other end of the spectrum from phenomenal awareness is our experience of a 'self' observing and commenting on our actions and thoughts, a kind of awareness that seems to double up on itself, as in: 'I am looking at the pencil on my desk' or even 'I know I am looking at the pencil on my desk'. Such introspective awareness is described as **self-reflexive awareness**, or **self-consciousness**. Introspective knowledge of one's own states of mind is considered a very high-level faculty, and one that might be present only in the great apes (chimpanzees, orang-utans, gorillas) and humans. In humans, self-consciousness includes awareness of the self not only in the present but in the past, and by imaginative extension, into the future – this *autobiographical self* is enhanced by language. We will return to our capacity for self-awareness, and the extent to which it is unique to humans, in Book 6, Chapter 4.

While many of those (often philosophers) who have devised schema to classify consciousness more or less agree on these extremes, the ground between is defined much more erratically. There is considerable debate about the kinds of consciousness which might lie between phenomenal consciousness and full-blown human self-awareness, and about how they might be characterized. We will not concern ourselves with these classifications, except to note that our biological origins and evolutionary history are a central pillar in some, notably that of the neurologist Antonio Damasio (1999). The possibility of different levels of consciousness and a sense of self amongst animals other than the great apes and humans is now generally accepted, and we will also return to this topic at the end of this course.

4.2.2 The puzzles of consciousness

Consciousness poses many problems of explanation. Four of those most commonly recognized are considered below.

The hard problem

Sound, light and other sensory stimuli arriving at our sense organs give rise to physiological activity in our sensory organs and nerve cells, and arouse sensations with which we are familiar, such as warmth, the colour blue, a touch on the skin. All these have a subjective quality or 'feel' to them (phenomenal consciousness). Beyond simple sensations, we also of course have complex feelings and thoughts as part of our subjective experience. It is now generally accepted (at least as a working hypothesis) by neurobiologists, psychologists and philosophers that the 'mind is what the brain does', and that our sensations, emotions and thoughts must be linked to physiological events. However, it is not at all clear how subjective experience could arise from the operations of the brain and senses as we know them. The philosopher David Chalmers has called this the **hard problem** of consciousness (Chalmers, 1995).

There is something, Chalmers suggests, that 'it is like' to see the colour red. The problem is that at present we have absolutely no explanation for how physical mechanisms could give rise to this or any of the other subjective sensations, the qualia, of our inner life. There is, in other words, an *explanatory gap.* Chalmers himself decides that perhaps consciousness is an irreducible feature of the Universe, like space, mass or time, and that we may be mistaken in thinking that it could ever be understood in terms of anything else. However, his critics believe it is too early in the enterprise to give up hope of an explanation, and point out that the failure to imagine a mechanism does not mean that a mechanism does not exist. For instance, at the beginning of the 20th century 'vitalists' believed that life could not conceivably arise from gross matter and postulated 'life-force', a magical ingredient that was needed to invest matter with life. However, the discovery of DNA in 1953, which led to an understanding of the molecular machinery underlying life, made such speculation redundant. Our conception of consciousness as 'something' may turn out to seem as mistaken as the conception of 'life-force' appears today.

The general consensus is that it is not clear at present how the hard problem of consciousness could be studied, let alone solved, using current methods. However, the **easy problems** of consciousness (Chalmers, 1995) are perhaps more accessible. They include questions about the neural underpinnings of the processes that make it possible for us to discriminate environmental stimuli, to integrate information in the brain, to produce verbal reports and so on. These phenomena appear directly susceptible to investigation using the standard methods of science, as they could be explained in terms of computational or neural mechanisms.

Does consciousness have a function?

A second problem concerns the function of subjective conscious experience – what *use* is it to have such an experience, particularly as many processes seem to occur perfectly well without it (e.g. see Chapter 1, Section 1.2.3)? Like other living things, we are the products of millions of years of evolution. Many of our characteristics exist today because they were useful or even essential in enabling our ancestors to survive and reproduce more successfully than their competitors. In other words, such characteristics were *adaptive.* Is consciousness adaptive, and if so, what benefit(s) does it bring? Not every characteristic is adaptive – it could be a relic (like your appendix) or an unavoidable side-effect of something useful. For instance, I light a candle during a power cut because I need light. I also get heat, smoke and carbon dioxide from the combustion of the wax – none of them directly useful to me. Is consciousness like this – a functionless side-effect of the actual neural events that control our behaviour? In other words, is it an **epiphenomenon**? The issue of whether consciousness has any function is a difficult one to address. Nevertheless, you should bear it in mind as it is one of the underlying questions that we will keep returning to in this chapter.

The binding problem

The **binding problem** refers to the fact that while each of our senses provides us with different information, we perceive a unified world (Section 3.7). We know that the different features – for instance, the colour, sound and smell of a complex stimulus such as a red car spewing diesel fumes – are processed separately in different populations of neurons in various parts of the nervous system, albeit at the same time. In fact, this modular processing in parallel also occurs for the different kinds of information we get using a particular sense. Thus, when we see the red car, its colour, shape, movement and location are all processed separately. How does the brain bring all this separately processed information together, in other words bind it so that the different kinds of information are clearly associated with one object and not with another? Most of the time, we perceive several different objects at the same time. How does the brain know that the red colour belongs with the car and the diesel fumes and not with the tree nearby? It is tempting to assume that there is a particular place in the brain where all this information comes together and conscious perception is generated. However, so far, there is no evidence of such a site in the brain. Although the brain clearly has little difficulty in solving this problem, there is at present no generally accepted idea about how it accomplishes this feat. We will return briefly to this issue in Sections 4.4.3 and 4.5.3.

The concept of self

We operate from a very strong conscious sense of ourselves: we see everything from the first-person perspective. This is so strong that it is impossible for us to imagine what it would be like not to operate from this perspective. We also have the feeling of being able to observe our own actions and thoughts almost as if we were able to stand apart from ourselves. Finally, we feel that we actively make decisions and choices – that we have free will. Sometimes this has been characterized as the feeling of having a homunculus (meaning 'little man') inside, observing and making decisions! We will consider some aspects of the concept of self in Section 4.5, and will return to it in the final chapter of the course.

4.2.3 Studying consciousness scientifically

Given that subjective experience is by definition private, what is it actually possible to study about such experience using the methods of science? Private experience is 'in here', whereas science depends on information that is 'out there', and hence available to third parties. To clarify the options open to us, it is useful to classify the phenomena that interest students of the mind into three domains (Staddon, 2001). As you read the descriptions below, keep in mind that the domains do not refer to three separate, unrelated things. Rather, they represent three different angles on the same experience.

Domain 1: The *phenomenological* domain. The domain of felt experience or qualia. Phenomenological is a philosophical term meaning 'all the items that inhabit our conscious experience'. In the philosopher Daniel Dennett's inimitable phrase, it includes 'thoughts, smells, itches, pains, imagined purple cows, hunches and all the rest' (Dennett, 1991). As a private, first-person, subjective, experience, it can (by definition) never be available in this form to anyone but the individual experiencing it.

Domain 2: The *neurophysiological* or *physiological* domain. Using a variety of methods such as brain imaging techniques, or recording the electrical activity of individual neurons, it is possible to record events or changes in the brain that accompany experience. Changes may also occur in other parts of the body and include dilation of the pupil of the eye and **skin conductance responses (SCRs)**. The latter measure the ease with which the skin conducts an electrical current – sweaty skin is a better conductor.

Domain 3: The *behavioural data* domain. This includes reports from individuals about their experiences. If the reports can in principle be checked against those made by other individuals, they are *intersubjectively verifiable.*

- Look at Figure 4.1. Close your right eye and focus on the small black disc on the right with your left eye. Then bring the page towards you at roughly arm's length. What happens to the orange square in the purple field?

- Your report of this private experience can be checked against the reports of others. If you are like most people, the orange square will disappear without trace (without leaving a hole – apparently replaced by the same purple as the rest of the large disc) when the page is about 30 cm away. The effect is due to the blindspot in our visual field, an area of the retina where the optic nerve leaves the eye and there are no light receptors (Figure 4.2).

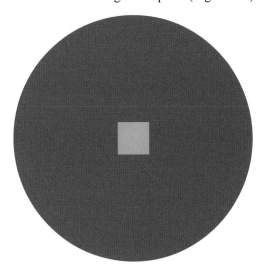

Figure 4.1 Purple field with inset orange square and small black disc to right, for use in the blindspot exercise.

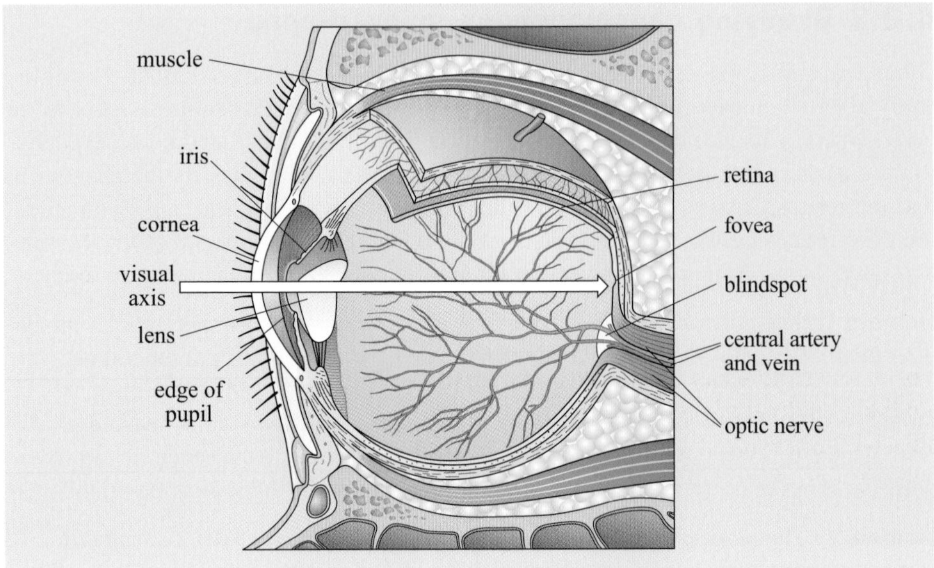

Figure 4.2 Diagram showing a cross-section of the human eye.

- ◆ In which domain is (a) your experience of the disappearance of the orange square?; (b) your report of the experience?
- ◆ (a) Domain 1 – the phenomenological domain; (b) domain 3 – the behavioural data domain.

The behavioural data domain also includes judgements, such as same or different. So, for instance, even though I may not know what a particular wine tastes like to you, I can find out if (to you) it tastes the same as or different from another. Reports and judgements need not be verbal so this gives us potential access to information about the perception and awareness of animals, as we shall see (Section 4.4.2).

Part of the skill of doing science successfully lies in focusing experimentation or exploration in the right areas. In much of the rest of this chapter, many of the examples we use involve the primate visual system. This reflects the fact that vision, which is the most highly developed and sophisticated sense in primates such as ourselves and monkeys, has also been the best-studied. In addition, there is a great deal of information on the effects of brain damage on vision and visual awareness. Finally, compared with the rest of the brain, there is a good understanding of the neurobiology and neuroanatomy of the visual system, and of its connections with other brain regions. A great deal of scientific research on conscious and unconscious processes is therefore focused on the primate visual system.

The scientific study of consciousness phenomena is still in its infancy, and the disparate findings can seem like the scattered pieces of a jigsaw yet to come together into a coherent whole. This reflects the current state of play in the field of consciousness studies. The aspects of consciousness currently being tackled using scientific methodology tend to be carefully limited and precise rather than broad and general. For instance, you will notice that much of this chapter is about trying to trace the neural correlates of phenomenal experiences – not trying to unravel more philosophical approaches to consciousness or exploring the consciousness involved in thinking about an issue or a problem.

4.3 Conscious and unconscious processes

4.3.1 The bottom line

Consciousness can refer to states of arousal such as being awake, asleep, attentive and so on. A certain degree of arousal is of course essential for any kind of conscious experience to occur. Arousal is mediated by the reticular formation in the brainstem (Section 3.4.1), and shock or damage to this system can cause a momentary loss of consciousness (unconsciousness) and, in more severe cases, coma. In this course, the term unconscious is not used in this sense, unless specifically stated.

Nor is it used to mean the unconscious in the sense of Freud (see Box 1.1). It is applied to individuals (or to cognitive processes in individuals) who are awake and alert but unaware of a particular stimulus. For instance, D.B. (Section 1.1.6) is unconscious of visual stimuli in his **blindfield**, i.e. that area of the visual field in which a patient with damage to the primary visual cortex, V1, is not conscious of seeing anything. The blindfield is on the contralesional side – so if the left V1 is damaged, the person is blind in the right visual field. This is an example of brain damage affecting awareness. However, there are also many instances of processes of which we are always and normally unconscious. Thus, we have no awareness of the innumerable and highly precise moment-to-moment adjustments in our muscles that enable us to carry out a myriad of activities, from maintaining our postural balance while walking, to picking up a pen, to breathing and speaking at the same time. Nor are we aware of the processes that occur in our brains before a thought, memory or idea occurs to us. Similarly, we are unaware of the physiological and biochemical processes constantly at work in our bodies, for instance, those maintaining homeostasis (Section 1.2.2), resulting in growth and development or underpinning memory formation.

Clearly, a vast number of processes continue in parallel in our bodies and brains without our conscious awareness. Conscious awareness is a relatively circumscribed state or occurrence. As we shall see, at present the only way in which we can know whether someone is conscious of a particular stimulus or not is to ask them to monitor their own awareness and to report back in some way.

4.3.2 Multiple pathways, multiple brains

Over the years, neurologists have reported many cases of patients in whom awareness is in some sense disconnected from seeing, learning or some other capacity. In Chapter 1 you came across some examples suggesting that sensory input of which people were not conscious must nevertheless have been processed by the brain.

◆ Can you recall what these examples were?

◆ (1) The blindsight patient, D.B., was able to point to, or orient eye movements towards, visual stimuli that he was not conscious of seeing (Section 1.1.6).

(2) Images of angry or happy faces affected the responses of participants towards a drink they were offered immediately afterwards, even though they did not consciously see the faces (Section 1.1.6).

(3) H.M. was able to learn new hand–eye coordination skills such as reverse mirror drawing without any memory of the task despite repeated practice (Section 1.1.5).

As we saw in Section 4.3.1, there are many processes of which we are always unconscious. However, what is striking about the above examples is that the people involved were unaware in situations where we might normally expect them to be aware. There are numerous other examples. For instance, in **prosopagnosia**, a disorder associated with damage to the inferior, posterior temporal lobe of the brain, particularly the right hemisphere, patients know perfectly well when they are seeing a face, but have no conscious awareness of whether the face is familiar (Book 4, Chapter 2). The deficit is confined to visual recognition, leading to the bizarre situation that a patient may not recognize his wife when she walks into the room, but recognizes her immediately when on the telephone! The neurologists Daniel Tranel and Antonio Damasio (Tranel and Damasio, 1985) showed prosopagnosics a series of slides of faces. *Target* faces were those with which the patients should have been familiar, such as their own face and faces of close family members. *Non-target* faces were unfamiliar faces. Asked to rate each face on a six-point scale of familiarity (1 being certain familiarity and 6 certain unfamiliarity), prosopagnosics did not rate *target* faces as more familiar than *non-target* faces. However, when wired up to a machine which measured the skin conductance response (SCR) – a way of measuring emotional arousal, similar to a lie-detector, which depends on how sweaty the skin is – they showed a much higher response to *target* than to *non-target* faces. Unconsciously, therefore, their autonomic nervous system recognized the difference between familiar and unfamiliar faces.

Example 2 above, involving the presentation of subliminal images, is particularly interesting because the participants were normal people who did not have any brain damage. In this case, you may remember, it was the speed with which visual images were presented to the participants that led to an inability to register them consciously. However, the images were indeed seen and processed unconsciously, as suggested by the emotional responses of participants to a drink presented immediately afterwards (Section 1.1.6 and Figure 1.2). There is now convincing evidence that a considerable amount of unconscious processing can occur in normal people, and we consider this further below.

Unconscious perception

The idea that perception can occur without us being aware of perceiving does not sit well with our common sense impression that we are always aware of stimuli that affect our feelings, thoughts or actions. Using some clever experiments, however, it is possible to show that perception can be unconscious as well as conscious, and that unconscious perception can have consequences for our subsequent behaviour. When this happens, we are not, of course, aware of what is affecting our responses! Unconscious perception could well underlie many instances of what we call intuition – the feeling we sometimes have of knowing or having insight, but without being able to back up our hunches with any clear reasons.

One method of studying unconscious perception depends on manipulating the presentation of visual images in the laboratory. Even a very brief visual stimulus, for instance one lasting only for 40 milliseconds (abbreviated to ms, these are thousandths of a second), can be perceived consciously when presented on its own. However, the same brief stimulus (let us call it the *target stimulus*) may not be perceived consciously if it is followed immediately by another stimulus, which therefore acts as a mask or *masking stimulus*. For instance, if people are shown a very quick flash (typically around 30 to 50 ms) of a visual image such as a face and then immediately afterwards given a longer flash of a different face, they are only aware of seeing the second face. This phenomenon is known as **backward masking** – the second image seems to prevent conscious perception of the first.

It is possible to determine objectively when the backward masking effect kicks in. The psychologist Anthony Marcel (Marcel, 1983) carried out an experiment in which each participant was told that on 50% of trials a word would come before the masking stimulus (an image of jumbled broken letter shapes) and on the other 50% of trials a blank card would come before the masking stimulus. The two types of trial were presented at random, and after each trial the participant had to say whether a word had been present or absent. The masking stimulus was always shown for the same duration (500 ms), but Marcel varied the duration of the target stimulus (a word or blank card) and found the target stimulus duration (D) at which each participant just began to make mistakes. (You may be interested to know that this varied hugely between participants, ranging from around 30 ms to around 120 ms!)

He progressively reduced the target stimulus duration by 5 ms steps (e.g. $D - 5$ ms, $D - 10$ ms and so on) and continued testing participants at each lower duration. On some trials, participants needed to decide if a word had been present or absent before the mask (presence–absence trials). On other trials (semantic-similarity trials), the participant knew a word would be presented, and was asked immediately afterwards to select, from a pair of different words, the word that was most similar in meaning to the target word (i.e. was semantically similar).

- ◆ If the target word is *friend*, which of two choice words, *buddy* or *bicycle*, is semantically similar to the target word?
- ◆ *Buddy* – it is closest in meaning to *friend.*

- ◆ If on a given trial (presence–absence or semantic-similarity) you were simply guessing the answer, what would be your chances of getting it right?
- ◆ You would have 1 chance in 2 (50 : 50 chance) of getting it right, as in each case there are only two possible answers. It is a bit like being asked to guess whether a tossed coin would show heads or tails. If you guessed tails, you would have a 1 in 2, or 50%, chance of being correct. The same would apply if you guessed heads.

Thus, you would expect participants in Marcel's experiment to get the answers right approximately 50% of the time simply by chance.

- ◆ What if the mask did not work, so that you could always consciously see what preceded it?
- ◆ At best, you would get all the answers correct, i.e. you would be 100% accurate.

As the experiment continued and the duration of the target stimulus continued to be reduced, most of the participants began to insist they could see nothing before the mask. Indeed, some of them found it quite disquieting to make semantic judgements about a word that, as far as they could see, did not exist! Nevertheless many continued, and chose whichever of the pair of choice words 'felt' right.

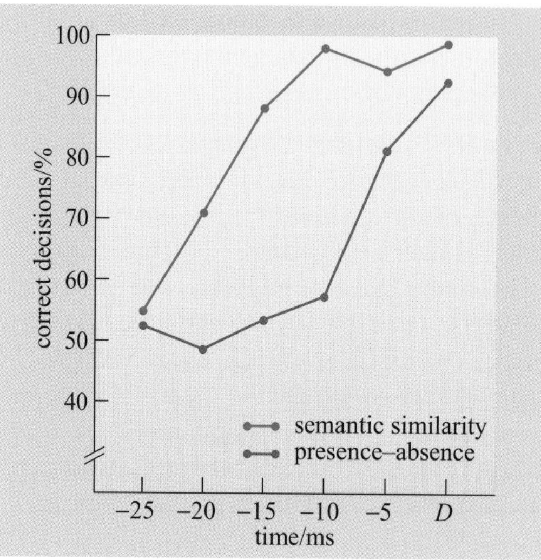

Figure 4.3 Percentage of correct decisions made about 'presence–absence' and 'semantic similarity', plotted against the time duration for which the target stimulus was displayed. Values shown are the means for 17 participants. '*D*' is the time duration at which errors in detecting 'presence–absence' were first seen. The duration for which the target stimulus was displayed was then progressively reduced (e.g. *D* – 5 ms, *D* – 10 ms and so on). 'Presence–absence': deciding whether a target word was or was not present before the masking stimulus; 'semantic similarity': deciding which of a pair of test words matched the target word in meaning.

At a target stimulus duration of *D* – 10 ms, participants tended to say they were not conscious of what preceded the mask, and indeed their accuracy at detecting whether a word was present or absent dropped sharply, to about 55%, almost chance level as Figure 4.3 shows.

- At this target stimulus duration, i.e. *D* – 10 ms, how often did they judge semantic similarity correctly for a word they said they could not see?
- Amazingly, they judged semantic similarity correctly over 90% of the time! This is well above the 50% level expected by chance (i.e. if they were guessing).

This experiment suggests that although participants did not perceive the target word consciously, unconscious perception was occurring. Also, the unconsciously perceived word must have been processed for meaning, otherwise a correct semantic judgement could not have been made.

There is now ample evidence that unconscious perception and processing occurs for many attributes of a stimulus. A common procedure is to present a backwardly masked target stimulus, and then to test if the response of the participants to a subsequent stimulus has been affected by the target. For instance, the masked target word 'flint' is presented, and participants are then asked to complete the word FL _ _ _ . Participants are far more likely to come up with the word flint than people who were not participants. (There are of course many other possibilities – fluid, flood, flame, flirt, etc.) This suggests that the participants have been *primed* with the word flint without their conscious knowledge. For obvious reasons, the phenomenon is called **masked priming**.

Paul Whalen and his colleagues (Whalen *et al.*, 1998) found that images of human facial expressions which participants were not able to see consciously affected brain activity and hence must have been perceived unconsciously. In their experiment, participants were shown a target image of a human face, with a happy or fearful expression, for 33 ms. This was followed immediately by a 167 ms masking image of a human face with a neutral expression. Afterwards, most participants said they had seen only the neutral face. However, brain scans taken as they looked at the happy or fearful target stimulus showed clear activation of the amygdala, a structure associated with emotional responses (see Section 3.4.4 and also Book 6, Chapter 2). Unconsciously, the participants also recognized the difference between happy and fearful expressions, as the amygdala was more strongly activated by the target faces signalling fear.

Procedures such as masked priming are carried out in laboratories where the conditions needed (such as very rapid flashes and succession of images) can be finely manipulated. You may wonder whether such effects occur in everyday life. It is conceivable that they sometimes occur if conditions are right. However, there are other, probably more common, situations in which we are not consciously aware of stimuli or events that we would generally expect to be aware of. Many of these involve the way in which we deploy our attention, as we shall see in Section 4.6.

The fear response

Rapid, unconscious registration of information, linked to an appropriate response, is likely to have played an important part during our evolutionary history, for instance in predator–prey interactions. Fear reactions (explored further in Box 3.3 and Book 6) play an important part in avoiding dangerous or unpleasant stimuli. Information reaching the amygdala can trigger the fight or flight response that we all experience when we feel in danger. It has been suggested that there are two distinct pathways in the fear system. One goes from a sense organ such as the eye → thalamus → amygdala. This is the 'direct' pathway. It is a **subcortical pathway**, which essentially means 'beneath the cortex'.

The other pathway runs from the eye → thalamus → visual cortex → amygdala. This is the 'indirect' pathway and is a **cortical pathway** because it passes through the cortex. What is the point of having two pathways in the fear system? The subcortical pathway is shorter, and hence carries information to the amygdala quicker. It carries less information about the stimulus and hence can trigger a fear response inappropriately (so you could jump at a harmless shadow). However, its value lies in the fact that it allows for a very rapid response that could save your life in an emergency. It has been characterized as a 'better safe than sorry' or 'quick and dirty' pathway. The cortical pathway is slower as it is longer. However, learning about the environment, about context, about the many different things the triggering stimulus could be an element of, could be brought to bear so fuller recognition and evaluation of the stimulus can take place. (The cortical pathway is estimated to add a delay of anything from 100–500 ms. This may not seem like much, but in some life or death situations a split second could make all the difference between success or failure.) The subcortical fear response is unconscious. By the time the slower, conscious cortical response has kicked in, you may have avoided some real harm – or you may be feeling a bit sheepish at having over-reacted to a harmless stimulus.

- ◆ What is the point of having a conscious response after the event?
- ◆ In many cases it could help in tailoring subsequent behaviour more appropriately to the situation. For instance, if it really was a bear that scared you it might help you to consider the available options. It you know about the behaviour of bears, you might decide that remaining passive is a better option than running away, for example.

Many emotional responses appear to occur at an unconscious level in humans (Book 6, Chapter 2).

4.3.3 Attention and consciousness

In our daily lives, we perform many actions in a habitual way that does not require attention. A skilled car driver can depress the clutch pedal and change gear 'automatically' and smoothly at the appropriate moment while paying close attention to what is happening on the road ahead. Learner drivers, on the other hand, find this extremely difficult. Learning to drive, to play a cello or acquire any other skill that involves the coordinated operation of the senses and the motor system is a demanding process that requires considerable practice or repetition, in a state of focused attention. However, once learned, sensory–motor coordination tends to occur beneath conscious awareness. It becomes automatic and relatively effortless, allowing us to direct focused attention elsewhere. This is clearly a very valuable capacity. As William James noted, 'if practice did not make perfect, nor habit economize the expense of nervous and muscular energy, man would be in a sorry plight' (James, 1890).

When people talk about **attention**, they usually mean conscious focused (or selective) attention. The term reflects our common experience that the same object or stimulus is perceived with much greater subjective clarity at some times than at others. Focused attention limits the range of information we are aware of; however it allows finer discrimination of that information. We can direct it voluntarily. For instance, at a wine-tasting, we can choose to focus attention on the taste of the wine rather than on the décor of the room or shape of the wine glasses, or on the taste of the wine rather than on its colour. Visual attention is often associated with willed eye movements directing the gaze to the centre of interest. This makes sense as it allows visual information to reach the **fovea** (Figure 4.2), a depression at the centre of the retina where the light receptors are very close together, allowing very sharp vision in that region. However, although visual attention is closely associated with gaze, it is not totally tied to gaze. It is possible to keep your gaze directed straight ahead and yet to direct your attention to a point, say, in the left of your visual field. Experiments have shown that participants are more likely to be aware of any changes in the area of the visual field to which *attention* has been directed, even if this is not at the centre of the field of vision. Attention is not just directed to sensory stimuli in the external environment, of course: it can be directed inwards at one's own thoughts.

Attention can also be captured by events – it is not always under voluntary control. If you have looked after a young baby, and had to wake up in the middle of the night to see to its needs, you will have had the experience of waking instantly at what seemed like a faint cry, even if you went to bed exhausted and slept right through the noisy party next door. Similarly, if someone mentions your name in a crowded and noisy room, you are instantly 'all ears'. These responses suggest that unconscious processing of sensory information is occurring before attention is captured by significant sensory input. Eye gaze can be directed voluntarily, as we saw above. However, gaze can also be directed as a reflex response, and extremely rapidly – as when a sudden movement seen out of the corner of your eye immediately captures your attention.

Some authors have gone so far as to equate selective attention with consciousness, but this is still a matter of controversy. Intuitively, most people feel that focused attention is intimately associated with conscious awareness. As we shall see, this intuition appears to be supported by several findings, including those described below. A number of studies have looked for differences in brain activity when people are engaged in learning a new task and when they have become familiar with it, in an attempt to identify how the neural bases of conscious attentive activity differ from those of automatic (thus unconscious and inattentive) activity *of the same kind.*

In one experiment, carried out by the American neurologist Marcus Raichle and his colleagues (Raichle *et al.*, 1994), participants had to respond with an appropriate verb (e.g. 'hit') when shown a noun such as 'hammer'. There were 40 nouns on the list altogether, presented at the rate of one every 1.5 seconds. The first time participants performed the exercise (the *naive* phase) they were relatively slow at generating verbs. However, they repeated the task with the same list of nouns, and by the tenth go (the *practised* phase) were considerably faster (Figure 4.4).

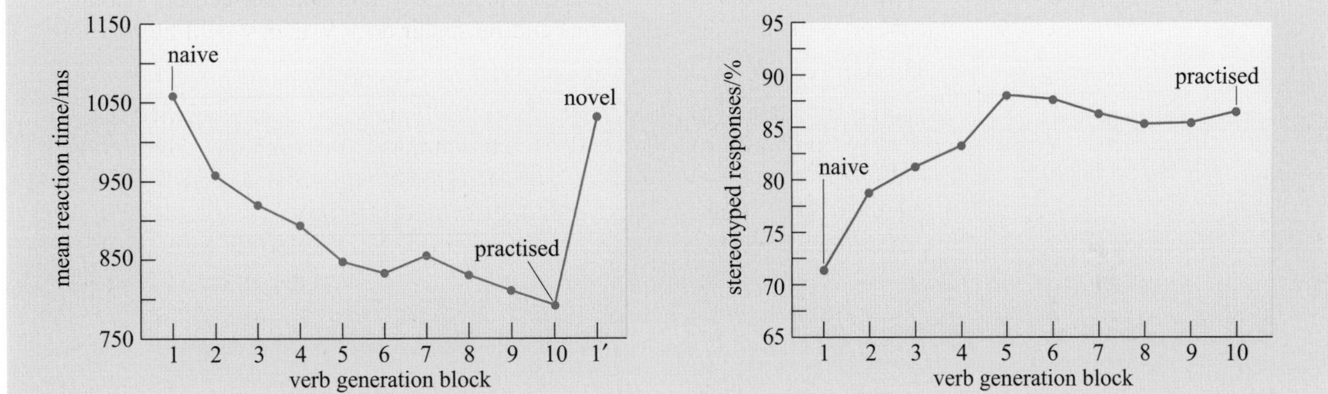

Figure 4.4 Mean time taken by participants to generate (i.e. say) an appropriate verb, e.g. 'hit', when presented with a noun, e.g. 'hammer'. Blocks 1–10 consisted of the same 40 nouns, presented at the rate of one every 1.5 seconds. In block 1 (the naive phase), participants were unfamiliar with the nouns. By block 10 (practised phase), they were familiar with them. Then in block 1′ a novel set of 40 nouns was introduced for the exercise. Reaction times were significantly lower in the practised phase than in the naive or novel phases.

Figure 4.5 Mean percentage of stereotyped responses made by participants who had to generate (i.e. say) an appropriate verb when presented with a noun. The same 40 nouns were presented in each of blocks 1–10. If a subject came up with the same verb for a particular noun in six or more blocks, this was considered a stereotyped response. After the experiment, the percentage of nouns in each block that generated a stereotyped response was calculated. There were significantly more stereotyped responses in the practised phase than in the naive phase.

About 85% of their noun–verb pairings were now stereotyped – for instance, 'hammer' might always produce the response 'hit' (Figure 4.5). Thus, in effect, their responses had become less effortful, or more automatic. A new list of nouns was now introduced (the *novel* phase), and verb generation times shot back up to the levels seen in the *naive* phase (Figure 4.4).

Raichle and his colleagues monitored the brain activity of participants engaged in these experiments and found marked differences between the naive and practised phases. In the naive phase, when people had to cast around for appropriate verbs, a range of high-level cognitive areas in the forebrain, such as the left prefrontal cortex (PFC) (see Figure 3.15b and relevant paragraphs in Section 3.6) and the **anterior cingulate cortex (ACC)**, showed increased activation. (The ACC is the anterior end of the cingulate cortex, which you met in Figure 3.16.) The PFC is thought to be involved in planning and memory, while it has been suggested that the ACC is an important part of the attention system, concerned with selecting between one of a number of competing responses. As the exercise was repeated and participants became more practised at the task, activation in the PFC and the ACC faded away.

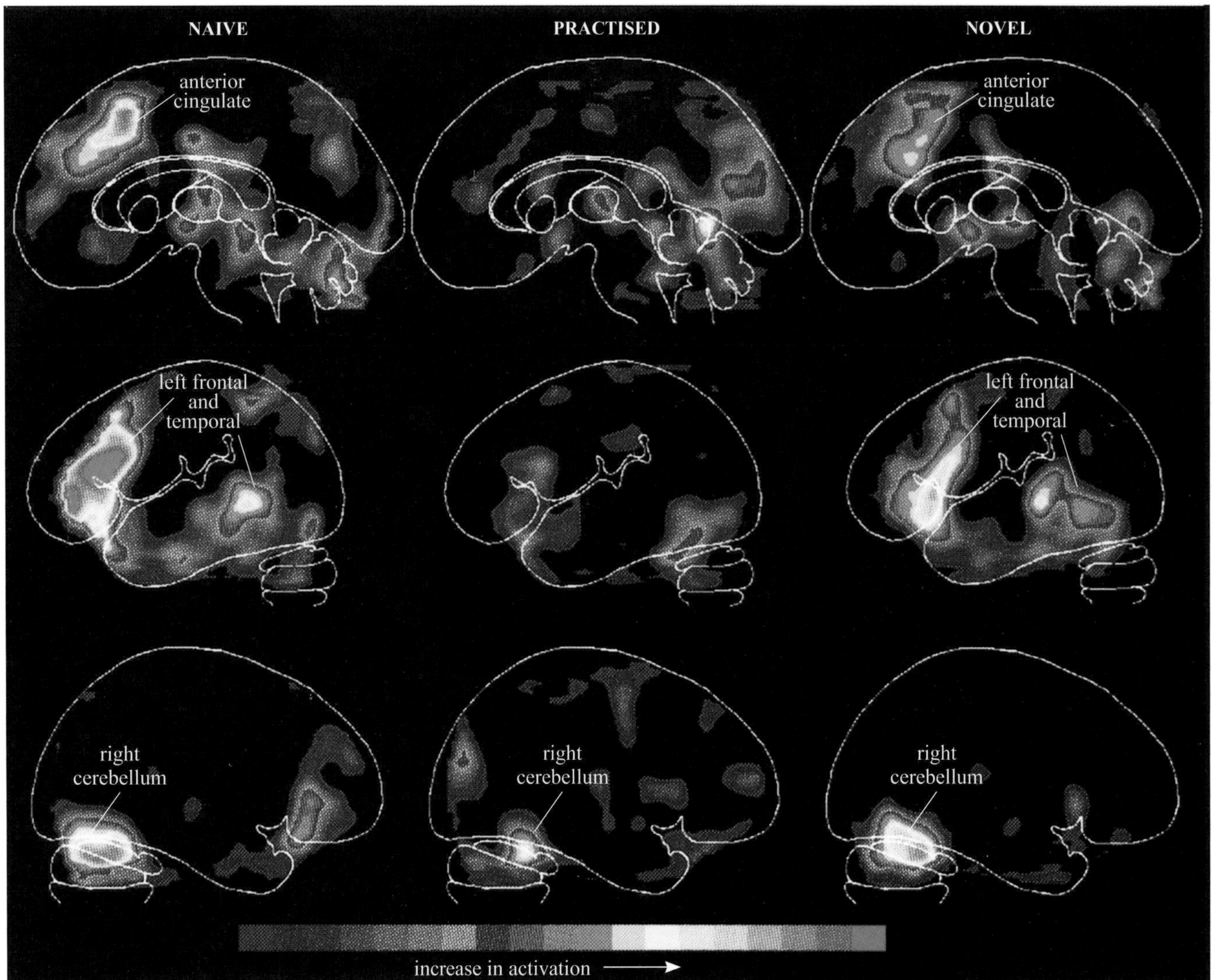

Figure 4.6 Activity *increases* in some parts of the brain when people generate verbs to accompany new nouns, compared to when the nouns are familiar. Participants had to think of and say an appropriate verb (e.g. 'hit') for a visually presented noun (e.g. 'hammer'). In the naive phase (left hand), the nouns were new; in the practised phase (centre), they were familiar through repeated presentation; and in the novel phase, a new list of nouns was shown. The images are derived from PET scans (discussed in Book 3, Section 2.4.1), in which increased brain activity is measured by increased blood flow.

- ◇ What would you expect to happen to prefrontal cortex (PFC) and anterior cingulate cortex (ACC) activation in the novel phase, compared with the practised phase, and why?
- ◆ It would be expected to increase, as participants once again need to pay more attention to the nouns presented, think of possible verbs, and select appropriate verbs.

This was indeed what happened. Figure 4.6 illustrates the changes in brain activity observed.

In fact, Raichle and his team discovered there was a whole suite of changes in brain activation between the more effortful (naive or novel) phases and the more automatic practised phase. In addition to the increases in brain activation shown in Figure 4.6, activity in other areas of the brain (the left and right sylvian–insular cortices) actually *decreased* in the effortful phases (Figure 4.7). Finally, in the more automatic practised phase, activity in the left medial occipital cortex *increased* (Figure 4.8).

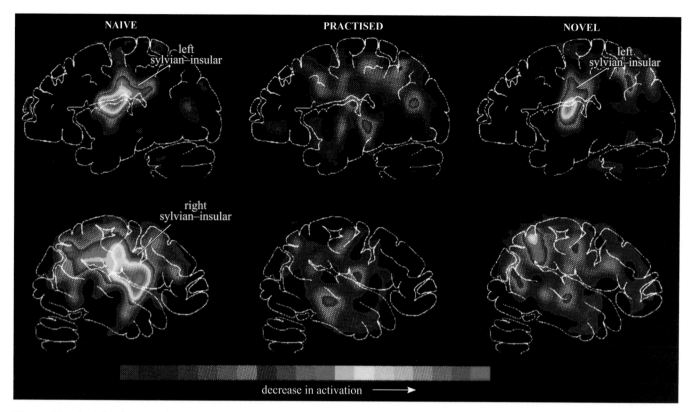

Figure 4.7 Activity *decreases* in some parts of the brain when people generate verbs to accompany new nouns, compared to when the nouns are familiar. Note the marked decrease in both left and right sylvian–insular cortices in the naive phase, which disappears in the practised phase and reappears partially in the novel phase. The images are derived from PET scans (Book 3, Section 2.4.1), in which decreased brain activity is measured by decreased blood flow. Note that the scale here shows *decrease* in activation to the right.

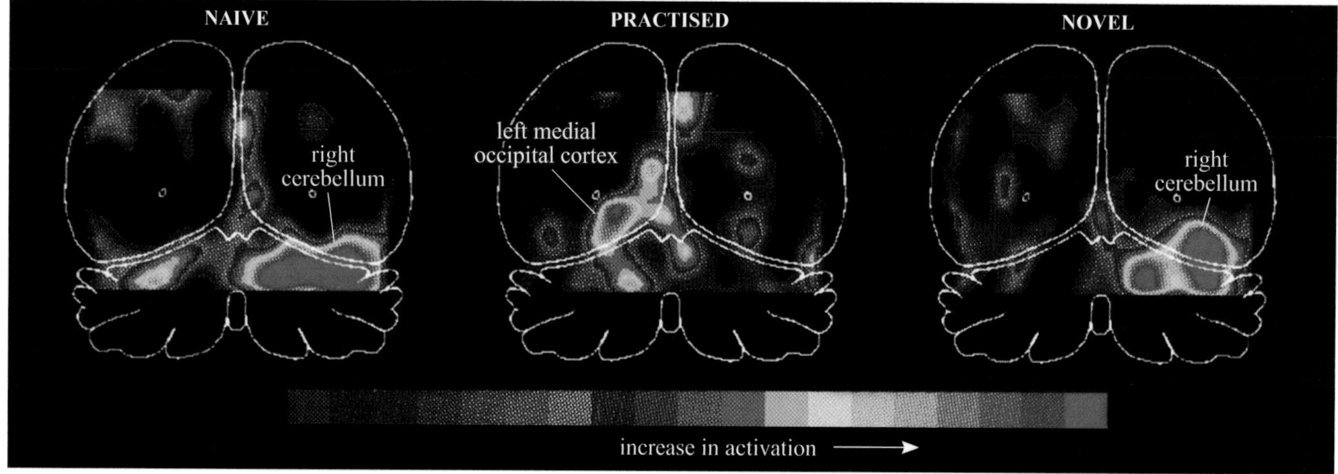

Figure 4.8 Activity in the left medial occipital cortex *increases* when people are performing a practised task – in this case, generating a verb to accompany a noun they have seen many times (practised phase: see Figure 4.6 and text for further definition). Coronal sections of the brain show increased activity in the left medial occipital cortex in the practised phase, compared to the naive and novel phases. (As in Figure 4.6, increased activity in the right cerebellum in the naive and novel phases is also shown; clearly, these do not show increased activity in the practised condition.) Note that this scale returns to an *increase* in activation to the right.

What does this pattern of changes in activation signify? Raichle and his colleagues suggest that they can be understood in terms of two different pathways, one operating when attentive, sharply conscious verb generation is required, the other pathway operating when a more practised or automatic response is possible.

- What structures seem to support (a) the conscious, effortful verb generation pathway, (b) the more practised, automatic verb generation pathway?
- (a) The left prefrontal cortex, the anterior cingulate cortex and the right cerebellar hemisphere; (b) the left and right sylvian–insular cortices, and the left medial occipital cortex.

Raichle's study focused on a verbal learning task, but other researchers have shown that comparable changes occur during other forms of skill learning in the transition from 'unpractised' to 'practised'. For instance, in one experiment (Toni *et al.*, 1998) participants had to learn a keypad typing task while their brains were being scanned. They were asked to work out an unknown sequence of eight taps using trial and error. Learning was rapid, and on average participants learned the correct sequence in 8–9 minutes. However, they were asked to keep tapping the sequence long after they had discovered it: altogether, they tapped for 40 minutes, by which time the action had become virtually automatic.

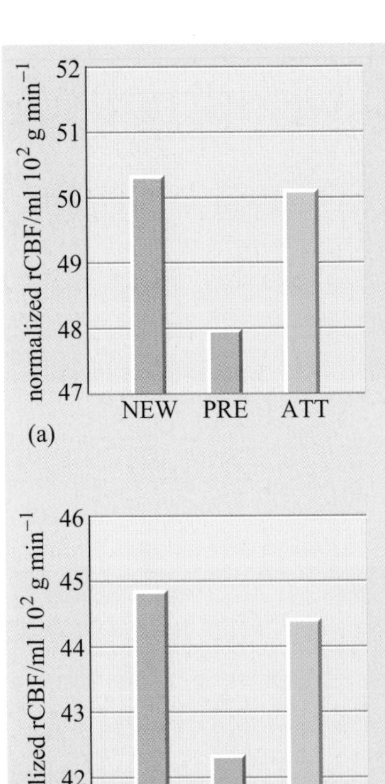

Figure 4.9 Graphs showing increases in the regional cerebral blood flow (rCBF) in (a) the anterior cingulate cortex (ACC), and (b) the prefrontal cortex (PFC) while participants were performing a keypad typing task under three different conditions: (1) NEW – participants new to the task; (2) PRE – participants who had pre-learned the task and were highly practised at it; (3) ATT – participants who were highly practised at the task but had to pay attention to each key press. Increases in blood flow signify increased brain activation.

The experimenters compared brain activity during the initial and final stages of this task and found marked differences. In the learning phase, where people had to remember what they had just discovered while groping for the next step, many regions of the brain were activated. As in the Raichle study, these included the prefrontal cortex and anterior cingulate cortex, as well as the basal ganglia and cerebellum. Within minutes of learning the sequence, however, most of this activity disappeared, and the remaining activity was confined to a small set of motor areas, such as the putamen (part of the basal ganglia), parts of the cerebellum and the motor cortex, all of which are involved in motor responses.

Again, these results suggest that *attending consciously* to a new task is linked to extensive activation in areas of the brain such as the left prefrontal cortex (PFC) and the anterior cingulate cortex (ACC). This activation is maintained while the task is being learnt. However, once the problem has been solved, the brain no longer has to attend to the operations performed while tackling the problem and the response can be reduced to its bare essentials, creating a memory trace in the motor or language area that lies dormant until the correct input passes by again.

The involvement of the PFC and the ACC appears essential for participants to be able to be sharply conscious of a mental event. In an experiment carried out by Jueptner and his colleagues (Jueptner *et al.*, 1997), participants who knew a keypad sequence well, and were able to type it without thinking, had to pay close attention to it again when asked to think of each key press in advance. When they did this, the PFC and ACC became active again, attaining levels similar to those seen in people new to the typing task (Figure 4.9). Not only this, but their performance became more jerky, just as when they were exploring the task.

A further experiment by Passingham and his colleagues (Passingham, 1996) suggested that the need to use high-level areas such as the PFC and the ACC may explain why it is so difficult to focus attention properly on more than one thing at a time. Before the experiment proper, 20 participants learned an eight-key sequence until they could tap it out in one run without error. They then tapped it for a further 12 trials. However, on trial 3, when the task was still relatively new (*early stage*) and on trial 12, when the task was very familiar (*late stage*) they had to perform an additional task while typing. Half the participants had to repeat a noun shown on a computer screen, while continuing to type. (It is known that repeating a noun does *not* activate the PFC or the ACC as it is a relatively undemanding activity.) The other 10 were asked to generate (and say aloud) a verb appropriate to the noun they were shown, again while continuing to type. As this involves thinking of an appropriate verb, it is a more demanding activity. Figure 4.10 shows the results of using two measures of typing competence – the average time taken per keystroke, and the average number of keystroke errors per trial.

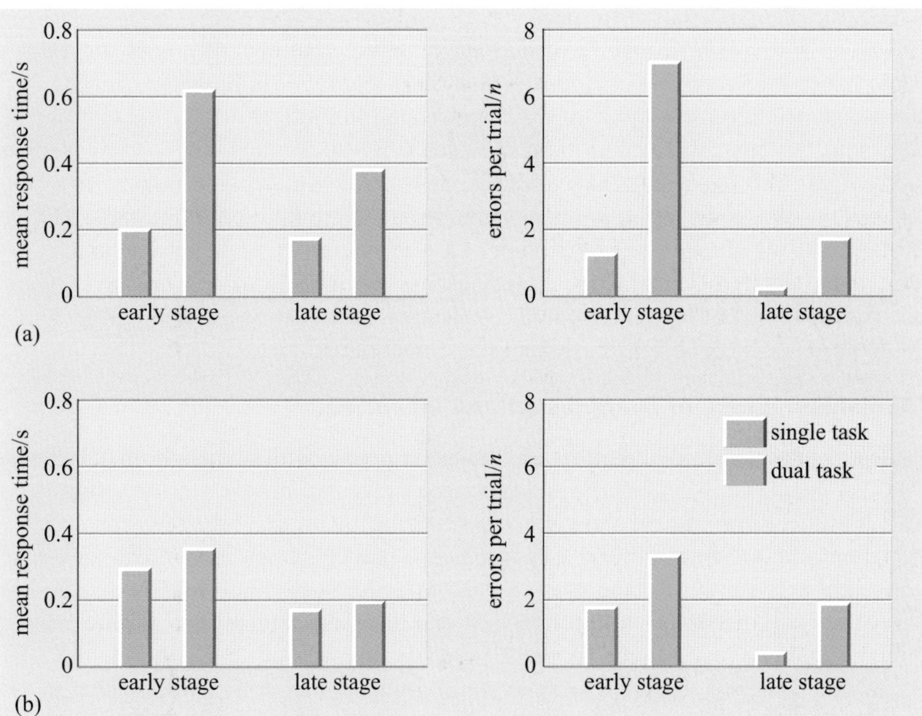

Figure 4.10 Average time taken by participants to press a key while typing a pre-learned eight-key sequence (the motor sequence task), and average number of mistakes made per eight-key trial, under different conditions. 'Early stage' denotes trials soon after a participant had learned the eight-key sequence; 'late stage' denotes trials after the participant had had more practice with the eight-key sequence. 'Single task' denotes trials where only typing was required. 'Dual task' denotes trials when participants had to perform a verbal task as well as typing. (a) While typing the sequence, participants had to generate an appropriate verb when shown a noun; (b) while typing the sequence, participants simply had to repeat a noun they were shown.

- ◆ From Figure 4.10, when is the motor sequence task most demanding?
- ◆ In the early stage of the experimental condition in which it needs to be combined with verb generation.

As we saw above, both the motor sequence task and the verb generation task make demands on the frontal areas when relatively unpractised. Hence a plausible interpretation of the results is that when both tasks are new, interference occurs in these areas. However, when the motor task is familiar, it is less demanding, and interference is significantly reduced. Dealing with a new problem engages large parts of the brain, but once a suitable response has been worked out activity becomes restricted to a pathway that directly connects a given sensory input to its matching motor or mental output.

Over time, therefore, we form a large repertoire of habitual or automatic responses, both perceptual and motor. These allow us to process familiar situations quickly and automatically, with little or no call on conscious attention. But if something unexpected happens, we can switch back to a more attentive and conscious response. The two modes have been characterized by the psychologist James Reason as analogous in some ways to the two modes of piloting a modern aircraft: we can either operate with conscious attention (analogous to having our hands on the controls), or we can switch to automatic pilot. Reason also suggested that the two modes were finely balanced in normal human behaviour. This is evident from the 'slips of habit' or absentmindedness we all experience from time to time. Reason gives the example of a man who went into his garage to get his car out to go to work. He was deep in thought at the time. The next thing he knew, he was dressed in the gardening overalls he also kept in the garage, and about to pick up a trowel! Going into the garage was the cue for more than one activity, and in this case he unconsciously chose the wrong one.

4.3.4 Conscious processing – what are the benefits?

It is clear from much that we have said above that a great deal of processing can occur beneath consciousness, and it is also clear that this can be an enormous advantage. But are some kinds of processing only possible or effective when one is conscious? In other words, are there limits to what can be achieved via unconscious processing? This is an important question, answers to which could help us to understand how consciousness operates, and shed some light on its possible evolutionary advantages (see Section 4.2.2). Unfortunately, while there is much speculation about the function of consciousness (see also Book 6, Chapter 4), there is not a great deal of current research in this area. However, some findings do hint at the importance of conscious processing in a number of contexts.

Blindsight: a lack of imagination and intention?

First, it is apparent from a number of studies on people with blindsight that, although they can unconsciously perceive and process a great deal of visual information in their blindfield, they do not show any *spontaneous* intentional behaviour towards visual objects in their blindfield. For instance, a patient known as G.Y. cannot use blindsight to reach out for and grasp a glass of water in his blindfield, no matter how thirsty he is. Someone has to tell him first that the glass is there. Nor can he create thoughts and imaginings out of what he perceives in his blindfield, claiming that: 'I can't replicate the sensation of an event in my imagination. I can't actually go home and think that's what it looked like to me'.

Control of action

There is some evidence to suggest that conscious processing may give an advantage when control of action is required. For instance, in a study carried out by Debner and Jacoby (1994), a word was flashed up in front of participants in two conditions. In condition A, the target word was flashed up very briefly (for 50 ms), followed by another visual stimulus, also a word. The second word acted as a mask, as described in Section 4.3.2. Hence, subjects were not consciously aware of the target word, though it was perceived subliminally, as expected. In condition B, the target word was flashed up for 150 ms before the second visual stimulus. In this case, because the target word had been flashed for longer, the second stimulus was ineffective as a mask, and participants consciously perceived the word. After the word flash, participants in both conditions were shown the first three letters of the target word (the word stem). They could all see the word stem consciously and were asked to complete it with the first word that came to mind *except* the word that had just been flashed. So, if the target word *frigid* had been flashed up, participants needed to complete the word stem *fri*, but without using the target word *frigid.* (There are of course several other possibilities, such as *friend*, *fright*, *frilly*.)

The results showed that those participants who had consciously seen the target word *frigid* (in condition B) were much more likely to follow the instructions given than those who had not consciously perceived the target word *frigid* (in condition A).

- ◆ Which participants were more likely to complete the word stem *fri* to create the word *frigid*?
- ◆ Those who experienced the word flash *frigid* for 50 ms and did not perceive the word consciously.

It appears, therefore, that perception with awareness may enable a perceiver to exert greater control over actions, whereas perception without awareness leads to more automatic reactions.

Summary of Section 4.3

This section began by considering what we mean by conscious and unconscious in the context of biological psychology. By conscious states, we mean states in which an individual is able to report from introspective insight on what he or she is experiencing, albeit this may be the lack of an experience. It is important to note that individual report is essential to establish the state of awareness, as in many cases evidence from other measures (whether behavioural, physiological or scans of brain activity) cannot yet adequately establish this. For instance, discriminative ability (a behavioural measure) can be good in the absence of awareness, as in blindsight.

There is a wealth of evidence that information processing and perception can occur unconsciously. Detailed evidence of unconscious perception in a variety of cases (prosopagnosia, backward masking using words or human facial expressions, and masked priming using words), and using a variety of measures (behavioural, physiological, brain scans) is considered. In the context of the fear and visual attention systems, the value of fast unconscious subcortical pathways operating in conjunction with slow conscious cortical pathways was discussed.

Brain activity during conscious focused attention while performing complex effortful tasks (e.g., involving thinking, making choices or learning new motor routines) is compared with activity when the task has become automatic, inattentive and unconscious. The former state is characterized by pronounced activation of the prefrontal cortex (PFC), thought to be important in planning and memory, and the anterior cingulate cortex (ACC), thought to be important in focused attention. Evidence that focused attention can set a limit to how many things can be done at once is considered. Finally, there is a brief consideration of some possible advantages of conscious processing, which may allow greater control over actions as well as imaginative access to experiences.

4.4 Neural correlates of consciousness

4.4.1 The search strategy

If consciousness is linked to brain activity, then, many researchers hypothesize, we should be able to find **neural correlates of consciousness (NCCs)**. The focus of current research on NCCs is generally on the specific contents of phenomenal consciousness, for example seeing a particular image or object, rather than on the states of consciousness. Hence, the common definition of NCC as 'a specific pattern of brain activity that correlates with particular conscious experiences' (Rees *et al.*, 2002; Crick and Koch, 2003).

Using brain-imaging methods, brain activity can be monitored while a participant is aware or unaware of a given stimulus. The basic assumption is that the brain activity of a participant who is aware of a particular stimulus will differ in some measurable way from when the participant is unaware of this stimulus, although awake and attentive.

- Does this method finally provide an alternative to first-person reports of consciousness?
- No – experimenters are still dependent on participants telling them when they are or are not aware of a particular stimulus. As we have already seen, this is important because brain activity can occur in response to stimuli of which the participant says he or she is *not* aware.

The *difference* in brain activity between the aware and unaware conditions, particularly if it is reliably replicated across participants and studies, may point to a possible NCC.

In practice, the search for NCCs poses formidable difficulties. Changes in brain activity occur at many different levels. For instance, the concentration of a particular neurotransmitter (Section 2.4.3), the firing rate of a particular nerve cell, or the coordinated activity of different areas in the brain can all vary. If several changes happen at once, as they normally do, or if there is a sequence of changes, which one might be the NCC? At any moment, brain activity related to many different events will be taking place – including a variety of thoughts, movements and emotions. To isolate brain activity related to the event of interest, other factors that could affect brain activity need to be kept as constant as possible. Current recording techniques make it difficult (though not impossible – see Book 3, Section 2.4.1) to monitor changes at more than one level at once. Even at a given level, they often provide a very limited window on what is happening. Some ways of monitoring brain activity are relatively imprecise – for instance, brain-imaging studies tell us about the level of activity in particular brain regions, but nothing about what is happening at the level of particular neurons. Recording the activity of individual neurons is a potentially powerful way of identifying NCCs, as we shall see below. However, this is considered too invasive for use on humans (unless it is needed during neurosurgery) and so is generally restricted to animals such as monkeys.

Another source of possible information about NCCs is damage (or lesions) to particular areas of the brain. In the past, this was the main source of information about where a NCC might be located, and has provided valuable pointers to those using other methods about where to focus their efforts. However, lesions inevitably damage, to a greater or lesser extent, the normal structure and working of the brain. Hence, any inferences from their consequences about the normal activity of the brain have to be made with great caution. As the distinguished Israeli neurobiologist Yadin Dudai notes, there are basic problems 'involved in all research which infers function from dysfunction'. As an illustration, consider a simple example, from a friend whose old fan-operated oven developed a fault. The fan no longer operated and the correct temperature was not maintained. After some exploration, the only damage an electrical engineer could locate was to the oven clock. Consider this dysfunction: the oven does not maintain its temperature, and it is found that the clock is damaged. Anyone who did not know what a clock was might be tempted to infer that the 'function' of the clock is to regulate the oven temperature. In fact, the circuit that maintained the temperature was connected via both the fan and the clock, so a fault in the clock affected the operation of the fan and hence the temperature the oven could maintain. The engineer solved the problem by the simple expedient of rewiring the circuit so it bypassed the clock.

4.4.2 Vision with and without awareness

Blindsight

As described in Section 1.1.6, individuals such as D.B., with damage to the primary visual cortex in one hemisphere, lack visual awareness in the contralateral part of the visual field (consequently known as the blindfield). (The primary visual cortex is also called **V1**, or the **striate cortex**.) However, careful studies have revealed that people like D.B. have residual, albeit unconscious, visual function in the blindfield – a phenomenon named blindsight. Blindsight is studied by presenting a stimulus in the blindfield and then asking the subject to decide which of two stimuli (one of them correct) was shown. This kind of 'forced choice' experiment might, for instance, require the participant to decide whether the orientation of visual stripes presented in the blindfield was 'horizontal' or 'vertical'. As participants say they are not actually conscious of the stimulus, they are forced to guess, and tend to choose whichever possibility 'feels' right.

◆ There are two possible answers: horizontal or vertical. What are the chances of getting the answer right purely by chance?

◆ The chances of getting the right answer are 1 in 2, or 50%.

In fact, people with blindsight choose the right answer very much more often than 50%, and almost as often as people who can see the stimulus consciously. Human participants with V1 damage have been reported who are even able to tell colours apart (Stoerig and Cowey, 1992). Particularly impressive was the ability of a monkey with blindsight called Helen. The whole (not just one half) of her primary visual cortex had been destroyed, so she was totally cortically blind. However, she learned to avoid obstacles in her path and was even able to reach out accurately for tiny objects such as currants (Figures 4.11 and 4.12).

Figure 4.11 Helen runs for a currant in an arena.

Figure 4.12 Helen, a rhesus monkey with blindsight, reaching out for a currant.

What is the basis of blindsight? In one pathway of normal primate vision, signals from the retina travel to the thalamus and then to the primary visual cortex. This, the **geniculostriate pathway**, is the main pathway from the eyes to the brain and is a cortical pathway. It provides the fine-grained information needed for the identification and analysis of visual images. However, there are several other pathways. A particularly important one is the subcortical pathway (or **collicular pathway**) that carries visual information from the retina to the superior colliculus. For so-called lower animals, this is probably the more important system. The projection to the cortex is a more recent evolutionary development, and is particularly important in primates such as ourselves and monkeys. Like other subcortical pathways (see above), the collicular pathway is fast and unconscious. Compared with the cortical pathways, it provides only rough information about the location and identity of stimuli, as it cannot resolve fine detail. The subcortical system is particularly sensitive to stimuli falling on the periphery of the retina, that is, for ambient vision – what is seen out of the corner of the eye. A movement or object here can capture attention, and the colliculus then directs a quick reflex eye movement response towards the stimulus; this rapid response is thought to have evolved to support predator avoidance or prey capture. It has been suggested that the collicular pathway may underlie blindsight.

Conscious and unconscious cortical pathways

We tend to believe that what we consciously see exerts powerful control in directing our vision-based activities and movements. For instance, looking for and then reaching out to pick up a pen, I feel that it is my visual awareness of its position that guides my hand accurately towards it. But what about the tennis player successfully returning a 134 mph serve at Wimbledon, or the world-class cricketer hitting a boundary off a fast bowler? In cases like this, it is difficult to believe that the very rapid motor response needed to return the ball is controlled by conscious visual perception of the trajectory of the ball (Figure 4.13). Rather, it is thought to depend on unconscious prediction of the probable trajectory of the ball.

In line with this is the suggestion that 'what we think we "see" is not what guides our actions' (Milner and Goodale, 1995). Their essential idea is that 'online',

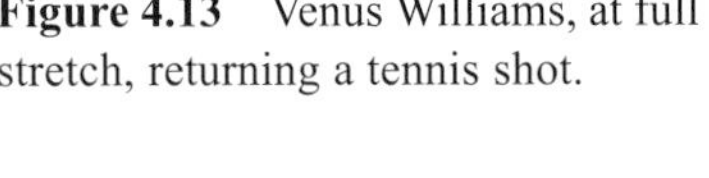

Figure 4.13 Venus Williams, at full stretch, returning a tennis shot.

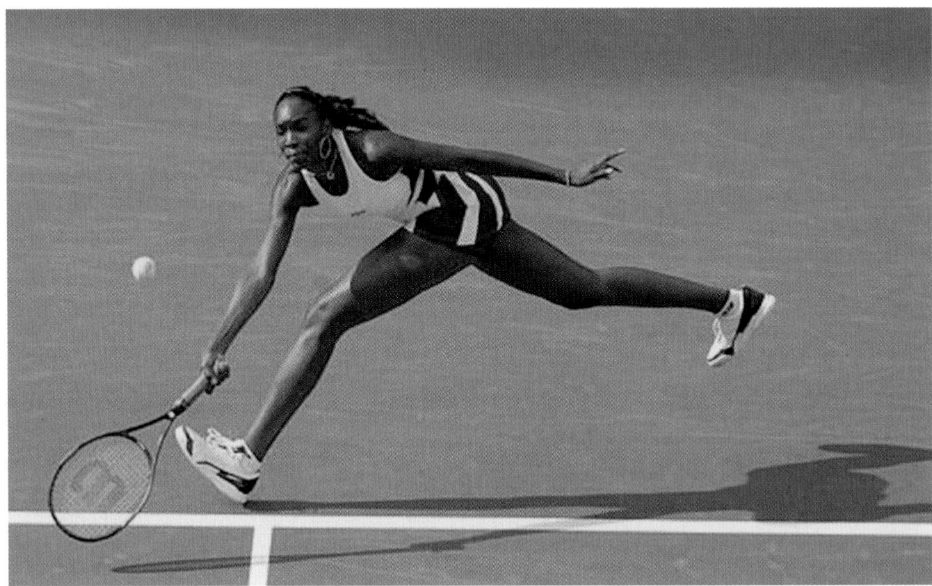

'here-and-now' visually guided action is in fact unconscious, and is supported by visual cortical pathways that are different from, and partly independent of, those that support conscious visual experience. Conscious visual experience includes the ability to recognize and name visual objects, and to use them in imagination or planning. Based on an analysis of some disorders described below, Milner and Goodale suggested that we possess two 'visual brains', only one of them involving conscious visual awareness. The neuroanatomical basis for these so-called brains lies in the fact that the visual pathway in the cortex of primates, including ourselves, divides into two streams, a **ventral stream** and a **dorsal stream** (Figure 4.14; see also Tables 4.1a and b).

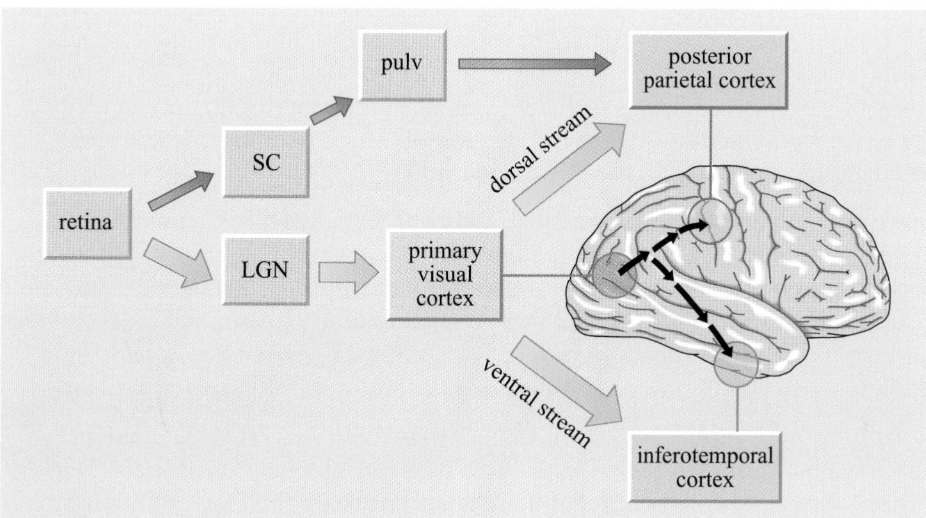

Figure 4.14 Dorsal, ventral (and subcortical) visual processing streams, shown schematically. Information from the retina travels via the lateral geniculate nucleus (LGN) to the primary visual cortex, and thence to the dorsal and ventral streams. Cortical projections of the dorsal and ventral streams on the right hemisphere of a macaque monkey brain are also shown. The subcortical pathway leads from the retina to the posterior parietal cortex via the superior colliculus (SC) and the pulvinar nucleus (pulv).

Table 4.1a Classification of visual systems: cortical and subcortical systems.

	System:	
	cortical (geniculostriate path)	subcortical (collicular path)
route	retina → LGN → primary visual cortex (V1)	retina → superior colliculus
function	focal vision; identification; fine-grained analysis	ambient vision; detection; localization; coarse analysis; eye movement control
characteristics	slow	fast
evolutionary appearance	new	old

Table 4.1b Classification of cortical systems: ventral and dorsal streams.

	Cortical systems:	
	ventral stream	dorsal stream
route	visual cortex → inferotemporal cortex	visual cortex → posterior parietal cortex
function	'what' information	'where' information; movement
characteristics	slow; colour-sensitive; foveal input; associated with conscious visual processing	fast; less colour-sensitive; peripheral input; associated with unconscious visual processing
evolutionary appearance	new	old

The dorsal stream ends in the posterior parietal cortex, and is evolutionarily the older of the two cortical pathways. It is also called the 'where' pathway, as it is responsible for visually guiding 'online' movements such as those I make in the here-and-now to reach out and pick up my pen. It is unconscious and fast – so it is very likely to be the one (perhaps in conjunction with the subcortical pathway, also unconscious and fast) to be involved when Venus Williams manages to return that tennis serve so superbly and fluently.

The ventral stream, also called the 'what' pathway, ends in the **inferotemporal cortex**, and is, in evolutionary terms, the newer of the two cortical pathways. (The inferotemporal cortex is the ventral part of the temporal cortex described in Section 3.4.6; see also Figure 3.26.) It supports conscious visual experience, and underlies any planning and decisions that are based on the 'insight, hindsight and foresight' we have acquired about the visual world (Milner and Goodale, 1998). This kind of conscious awareness links in with our learning and memory of the way in which the visual world behaves. It is involved when we know what to do with a tennis ball, a needle and thread, a bar of soap and so on.

The two visual brains are not totally independent but act together in everyday life. For example, conscious vision is used to select the *blue mug* on the *left* and to decide on a grip appropriate to *drinking* rather than *throwing*. But then the non-conscious dorsal stream works out how to implement these plans and ideas. When we keep looking while doing something, we feed visual information to *both* these systems – one visually conscious, the other unconscious, but acting in tandem.

What is the point of this division of labour? It has been suggested that it might make 'computational' sense given the need to achieve such different goals. The 'where' system that controls the visually guided reach for the blue cup has to process and track information about the position of your own hand and body in relation to the cup rather rapidly if the hand and cup are to meet smoothly. The 'what' system is geared for the very different task of identifying visual objects and selecting appropriate behaviour towards them, based on past experience.

Figure 4.15 Examples of D.F.'s ability to recognize and copy line drawings. She did not recognize the drawings on the left, and was unable to copy them (centre). On another occasion, when asked to draw an apple or open book, she produced reasonable images (on the right), probably from long-term memory, suggesting that her finger and hand control were not at fault. However, when she was later shown the drawings she had done from memory, she did not recognize what they were!

The different operations of these two 'visual brains' are apparent from the effects of brain damage to the different pathways. One of Milner and Goodale's patients, D.F., was a young woman who had suffered brain damage as a result of oxygen deprivation following carbon monoxide poisoning. She suffered from *visual form agnosia.* In other words, she appeared to have no conscious visual perception of the shape, size or orientation of objects, and was unable to describe these characteristics verbally or manually. Shown 120 standard line drawings of common objects, she was able to identify only 13. As Figure 4.15 shows, she was hopeless at copying line drawings.

(Interestingly, according to Milner and Goodale, she was often able to identify real objects such as fruit and vegetables, as her appreciation of surface visual characteristics such as colour and texture was unimpaired. And although she could not identify letters or digits visually, she was able to identify them using touch.) Although D.F. showed no conscious awareness of the form of objects, her actions indicated that she was able to behave in an appropriate manner towards them. For instance, although she could not recognize a slot, when given a card she was able to orient it correctly and push it through the slot!

◆ Which visual stream do you think was damaged in D.F.?

◆ It was the ventral stream, which underlies the conscious identification of visual objects (the 'what' pathway).

Conversely, participants suffering from *optic ataxia* are perfectly conscious of the identity of an object, how big it is and where it is in space. Optic ataxia (part of Balint's syndrome) was first described in 1909 by the doctor Rudolf Balint, whose patient had great difficulty reaching for objects with his right hand (but not with his left hand – optic ataxia is often one-sided). 'While cutting a slice of meat, which he held with a fork in his left hand, [the patient] would search for it outside the plate with the knife in his right hand', or 'while lighting a cigarette he often lit the middle and not the end', or 'when asked to grasp a presented object with his right hand, he would miss it regularly, and would find it only when his hand knocked against it'. Like other optic ataxia sufferers, Balint's patient could use other cues to reach out accurately. With his eyes closed, for instance, he could reach out and touch his left ear with his right hand quite accurately. However, he simply could not direct his hand accurately to an object using visual cues. Optic ataxia patients also often angle the hand incorrectly, or mistake the size of grip needed (Figure 4.16).

◆ Which stream is damaged in people with optic ataxia?

◆ The dorsal stream, which controls 'online' fine motor control based on unconscious visual cues (the 'where' pathway).

There appears to be a dissociation, for these participants, between the information represented in the ventral pathway, which determines conscious perception, and that represented in the dorsal visual pathway, which calculates the motor response.

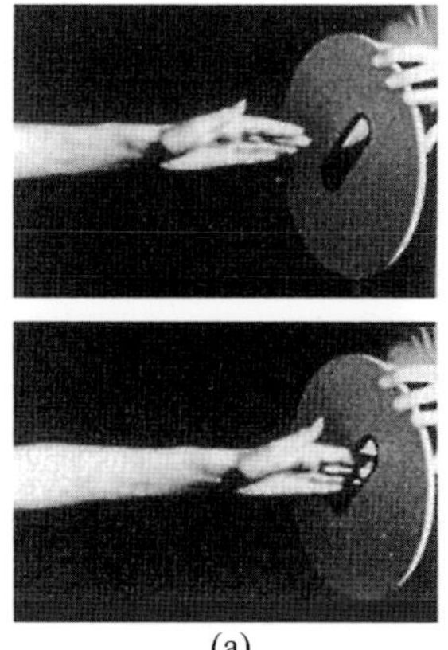

(a)

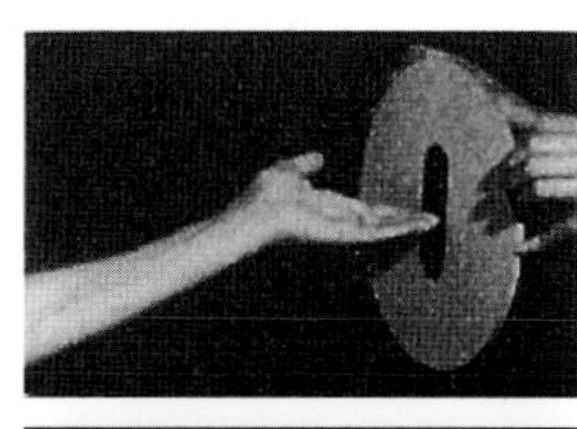

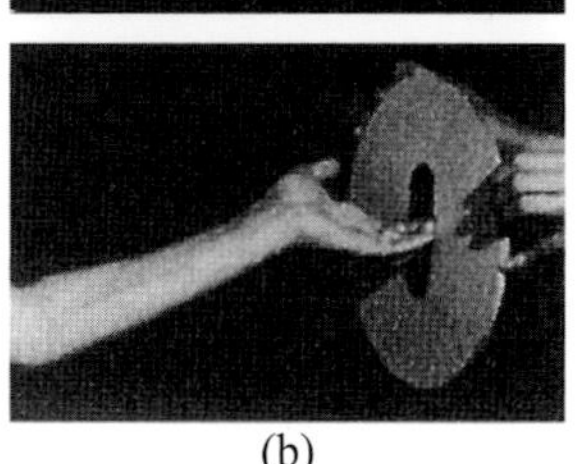

(b)

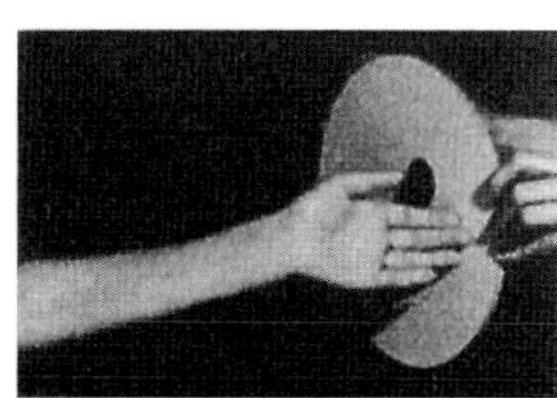

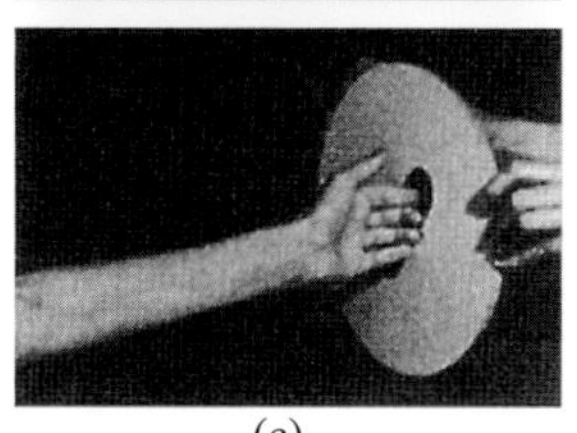

(c)

Figure 4.16 A patient with optic ataxia reaching out to pass her left hand through an oriented slot. She had a tumour in the right parietal lobe, affecting her left visual field. When the oriented slot was in her right (unaffected) visual field, her reaching response was normal (a). However when the slot was in the left visual field, she made errors of hand orientation (b) or errors of hand placement (c).

Based on the findings above, Milner and Goodale hypothesized that the neural correlate of visual consciousness in primates is situated in the ventral visual processing stream.

Binocular rivalry in monkeys

To test Milner and Goodale's ideas about the location of the NCC for vision more directly, for instance by examining neural activity, we need a method that allows us to differentiate brain activity linked to consciousness from unconscious brain activity in response to visual stimuli. Ideally, what is needed is a stimulus that does not alter physically, yet is sometimes consciously perceived and sometimes not, leading to changes in the 'content' of phenomenal awareness. Fortunately, there are two excellent candidates: ambiguous figures and binocular rivalry (Figure 4.17a–e).

Figure 4.17 Ambiguous figures. (a) 'My Wife and My Mother-in-Law'. (b) A vase produced by the Kaiser Porcelain Company for the Silver Jubilee of Queen Elizabeth II and Prince Philip, whose profiles can be seen. (c) Dark or light arrows? (d) An Inuit stepping outside, or the profile of a native American face? (e) 'Paranoic Figure' by Salvador Dali – half a face lying in the sand, or group of seated figures in front of an African hut?

Ambiguous figures, which many of you will have seen, give rise to **bistable percepts**. A single pattern of retinal input gives rise to two alternating perceptual interpretations (or percepts). Because these changes in perception occur in the absence of any change in the stimulus itself, they are related directly to subjective perception or subjective awareness.

The second candidate, which we will focus on (no pun intended!), is **binocular rivalry**. This was first reported by the inventor of the stereoscope, the physicist Sir Charles Wheatstone, in 1838. He noticed that two letters or patterns presented in a stereoscope, so that only one could be seen by each eye, did not fuse into one image but instead competed for visual awareness. Sometimes the image from one eye was consciously seen, sometimes the image from the other eye, and sometimes the two images overlapped.

Nikos Logothetis (Logothetis, 1998) and his colleagues at the Max Planck Institute in Germany used the binocular rivalry phenomenon to try to identify the neural correlate of visual consciousness in monkeys. The reason monkeys were used is first, their visual system is very similar to that of humans, and secondly researchers were allowed to insert electrodes into the brains of the monkeys to record the activity of *single neurons*. The monkeys were trained to squeeze different levers when confronted with different images, such as faces and sunbursts (Figure 4.18).

Figure 4.18 (a) Non-rivalry tasks during training and (b) rivalry tasks during the experimental condition in monkeys. In the non-rivalry training condition (a), a monkey was trained to squeeze the left lever for a sunburst display, the right lever for a face display and not to respond (or to let go of a lever if already squeezed) on perceiving an overlapping or blended image of the two. Once trained, a monkey was presented with two stimuli at once, one to each eye (b). It responded by squeezing the levers, in effect reporting what it was seeing: a sunburst, a face or a blended image of the two.

Logothetis and his colleagues recorded electrical activity from single neurons located at several stages in the (conscious) ventral stream that culminates in the inferotemporal cortex. By taking recordings from cells at various points in the pathway *before* the experiment began, they established that certain neurons respond preferentially to certain stimuli: to sunbursts, for example, or to faces. These neurons were then monitored in the binocular rivalry situation, to see how well their activity correlated with what the monkey reported it was 'seeing'.

It turned out that activity in the primary visual cortex (V1) of the monkey did *not* correlate well with what the monkey reported seeing. When the monkey was shown faces and sunbursts in the binocular rivalry situation, most of the cells in V1

40%
MT
40%
V4
20%
V1
1 cm
IT
90%

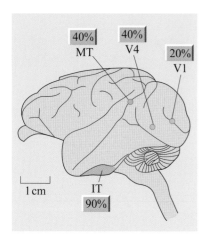

Figure 4.19 Percentage of neurons in different areas of the macaque monkey visual pathway whose response is correlated with the monkey's subjective perception (or visual percept) of the stimulus in a binocular rivalry task, rather than with the stimulus falling on the retina (visual input). The left hemisphere of a macaque monkey brain is shown. The percentage of percept-related neurons was greater in the inferotemporal cortex (IT). It was relatively low in V1, the primary visual cortex, and intermediate in areas such as V4 and the middle temporal cortex (MT).

fired irrespective of whether the monkey subjectively perceived faces or sunbursts. The pattern falling on the retina seemed the only factor determining their firing (as reported by use of the lever). Thus, on the whole, cells in V1 seemed to correlate with the retinal stimulus, not with the visual percept. But further into the visual system, for instance in V4, the percentage of cells whose firing correlated with the visual percept increased, until in the inferotemporal cortex, the activity of nearly all the neurons matched the monkey's subjective perception. When the monkey was stimulated with a sunburst and a face and reported perception of a face, virtually all the relevant face cells in the inferotemporal cortex fired, but almost none of the sunburst cells did. When the monkey's response switched, indicating that it was now perceiving a sunburst, the cell response switched accordingly.

These ingenious experiments demonstrated that whereas the firing of most neurons in the primary visual cortex, V1, reflects the visual input and not the visual percept during rivalry, activity further into the ventral pathway, culminating in the inferotemporal cortex, shows increasing correlation with the perceptual state of the animal. At this stage of processing, therefore, neural activity reflects the brain's internal view of a visual scene rather than the retinal stimulus itself (Figure 4.19).

- Where, in this example, is the neural correlate of visual consciousness?
- In the ventral stream, in the inferotemporal cortex.

Thus, the work of Logothetis and his colleagues seems to strengthen the evidence for a 'neural correlate' of visual consciousness in the primate inferotemporal cortex.

4.4.3 Is there a neural correlate for visual consciousness?

The above findings sound promising, and suggest that a neural correlate of visual consciousness might exist. However, the situation that is emerging is in fact more complex than this. Although there is evidence that a number of areas are *necessary* for visual consciousness, there is no evidence at present that any of them are *sufficient* for visual consciousness. Table 4.2 summarizes this evidence.

Primary visual cortex (striate cortex or V1)

The **primary visual cortex (V1)** is the lowest cortical visual area, being the first cortical area to receive input from the retina. As we have seen, if V1 is damaged, patients report that they have no visual awareness in their blindfield. Damage to V1 appears to have a general effect on conscious visual perception, in that all visual attributes (such as colour, motion, size, orientation and so on) are affected (though see the case of the blindsight patient G.Y. below). V1 therefore appears *necessary* for normal visual perception. However, even if it is necessary, experiments such as those done by Logothetis suggest that it is not *sufficient.*

- In what way do they suggest this?
- Because the firing of V1 cells in monkeys represents stimulus characteristics rather than the conscious percept.

In other words, activity in V1, in and of itself, may not give rise to conscious visual perception – further processing of visual information may also be needed, as discussed below.

Table 4.2 The neural correlate of visual consciousness: a summary of potential candidates.

Visual area	Consequences of damage	Comments
Primary visual cortex	Cortical blindness results in the contralesional visual field. Blindsight is the name given to the visual functions that remain in the cortically blind area of the visual field (blindfield).	Firing of V1 neurons in monkeys correlated with stimulus characteristics rather than conscious percept The case of G.Y. (see below) suggests that conscious vision may be possible without V1
Extra-striate visual cortex (EVC) (contains functionally specialized areas or essential nodes) V4, in the occipito-temporal cortex (in humans) Fusiform face area (FFA), in inferotemporal cortex V5/MT or motion cortex, in medial temporal cortex	Achromatopsia: inability to perceive colours Prosopagnosia: inability to recognize a familiar face Akinetopsia: inability to perceive moving stimuli	Single cell activity at some levels of EVC correlates strongly with conscious vision. However, fMRI scans suggest location may not be enough: experiments with blindsight patient G.Y. suggest unconscious stimuli evoke less response than conscious stimuli, in the essential node for motion (V5/MT).
Parietal and prefrontal cortex	Neglect syndrome: a deficit of spatial attention	Activity here may be important in association with activity in essential nodes in the EVC

Extra-striate visual cortex

The **extra-striate visual cortex (EVC)** lies beyond V1, in the temporal cortex. It is an area where different aspects of the visual scene are processed and organized in different *functionally specialized* areas. For instance, there are areas for features such as colour, face recognition and movement (Figure 4.20).

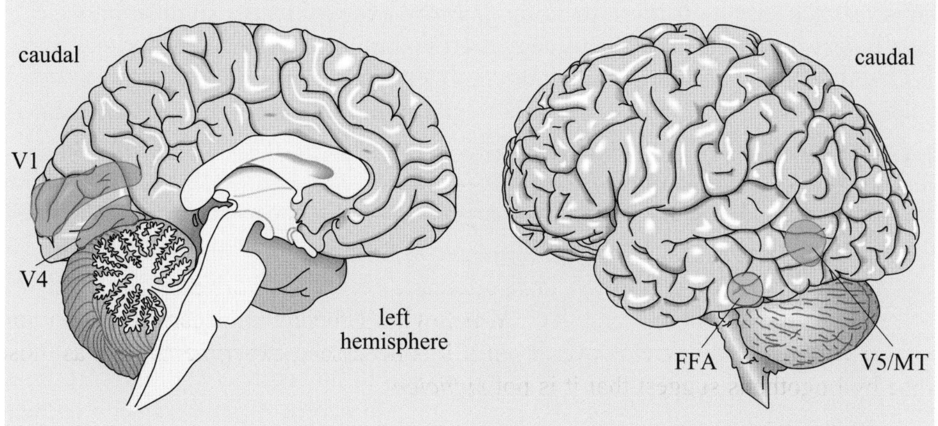

Figure 4.20 Some areas of the extra striate cortex, the visual cortex beyond V1 (the primary visual cortex or striate cortex) are functionally specialized: V4, for colour; V5/MT for motion and FFA, the fusiform face area, for face recognition. Each area receives inputs via V1. Lesions in V4 produce achromatopsia, the inability to perceive colour; in V5/MT lesions produce akinetopsia, the inability to perceive motion, and in the FFA lesions produce prosopagnosia, an inability to recognize familiar faces.

Damage to any of these specialized areas (which the British neuroscientist Semir Zeki has called **essential nodes**) causes corresponding damage to consciousness. Thus, for instance, damage to the colour area V4 (in the occipito-temporal cortex in humans) causes **achromatopsia**, lack of awareness of colour; damage to the face recognition area, the fusiform face area (FFA) in the inferotemporal cortex causes prosopagnosia, the inability to recognize familiar faces (as discussed above and in Book 4, Chapter 2); and damage to the movement area (V5/MT, in the dorsal visual stream; on the lateral surface of the medial temporal cortex) causes **akinetopsia** – patients have no *conscious* perception of movement. For instance, L.M., a woman with this condition, sees the tea emerging from the spout of a teapot as a solid curved cylinder (L.M. herself described it as a frozen glacier). However, she is able to catch a ball thrown at her quite normally!

- How could L.M. catch a ball thrown at her if she has no conscious perception of movement?
- The unconscious *dorsal* visual and subcortical visual pathways are still intact in L.M., and as shown above are important in visually guided 'online' motor responses.

The above suggests that activity in the essential nodes is *necessary* for consciousness of the visual attribute (e.g. colour) analysed in that area. It is striking that damage to these areas results in very specific deficits in visual awareness, compared to the more general deficit seen with damage to V1. One aspect of a person's visual consciousness (such as perception of colour) can be affected, leaving other aspects, such as motion, unaffected. This has led Semir Zeki to propose that, in effect, an essential node can be regarded as a neural correlate of a particular **micro-consciousness** – that is, consciousness of a single attribute such as colour or motion. There is neurophysiological evidence that activity at essential nodes is associated with awareness. For instance, brain scans of people with schizophrenia and others experiencing spontaneous visual hallucinations show that the reported attributes of the hallucination (e.g. colour or a face) correspond exactly to the activation seen in essential nodes. And when most of us perceive motion while looking at a static picture that implies motion (such as Venus Williams hitting a return in Figure 4.13), the essential node for visual motion, V5/MT, is activated.

Could activity in an essential node be sufficient, in itself, to generate consciousness (albeit a 'micro-consciousness')? It is known that in patients with blindsight, stimulation of the blindfield by a moving stimulus in the blindfield activates cells in V5/MT. This activation is not *always* accompanied by consciousness. Interestingly, however, this may be because the *level of activity* caused by the stimulation is insufficient in some cases. This is suggested by some experiments carried out by Zeki and the psychologist Dominic ffytche (1998) on a blindsight patient, G.Y. When a moving stimulus was presented in his blindfield, G.Y. sometimes felt he had caught a glimpse of 'something'. He was tested with slow-motion and fast-motion stimuli in his blindfield. As he had blindsight, G.Y. was able to identify the direction of movement of both kinds of stimuli, if offered a choice of answers (one correct, the other incorrect). However, only in the case of fast-moving stimuli did he *consciously* see the stimuli. It was found that the degree of activation in the motion cortex (V5/MT) was higher in the fast-motion aware condition than in the slow-motion unaware condition (Figure 4.21).

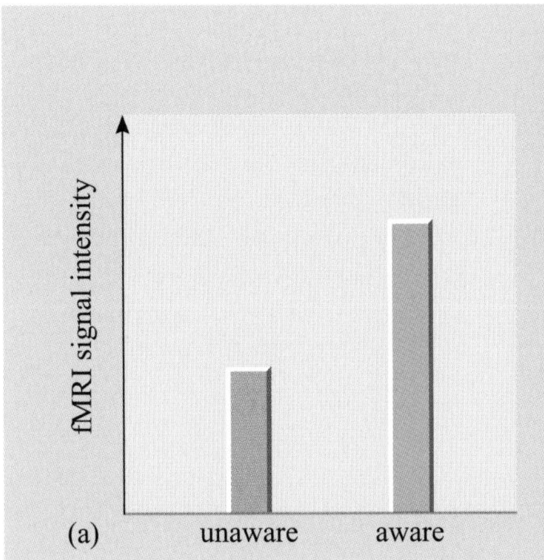

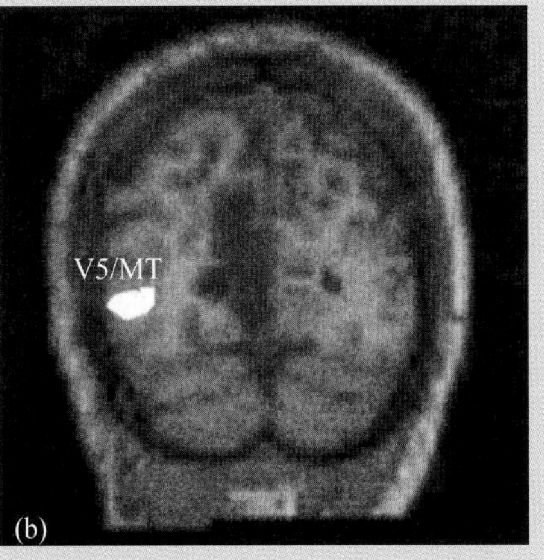

Figure 4.21 (a) The level of brain activation in the motion area (V5/MT) of G.Y., a blindsight patient, is greater when he is aware of a moving stimulus in his blindfield than when he is unaware of it. Moving stimuli of which he is aware are fast-moving while those he is unaware of are slow-moving. (Brain scanning using fMRI is discussed in Book 3, Section 2.4.1.) (b) V5/MT is shown in white, in a coronal section of G.Y's brain. The left of G.Y.'s brain is to the left of the image.

It is not clear at present what this might mean in neurobiological terms. However, one possibility is that more neurons in the essential node for motion, V5/MT, were activated by the fast stimuli. This raises the possibility that it is not just the *location* of activation that might be a candidate neural correlate of consciousness (NCC), but that some threshold of activation might need to be passed for awareness.

Overall, the data suggest that activity in essential nodes is necessary for conscious experience of specific features, and that there is generally a strong correlation between activity in such areas and conscious experience. However, as with V1, although activity in essential nodes is *necessary*, it may not be *sufficient* for conscious visual experience.

Parietal and prefrontal cortex

Recent neuroimaging investigations into the neural correlates of binocular rivalry in humans indicate that activity in the parietal and prefrontal cortices might be associated with visual awareness (Figure 4.22). So although activity in the extra-striate visual cortex is a consistent neural correlate of consciousness, it might be insufficient to produce awareness without an additional contribution from parietal and prefrontal loci. The activation in parietal and frontal cortices is in areas that overlap with those that have been associated with attention (see Section 4.3.3). This seems to support the idea that awareness and attention are closely linked. Perhaps, therefore, there is a common neural basis to some aspects of attention and consciousness?

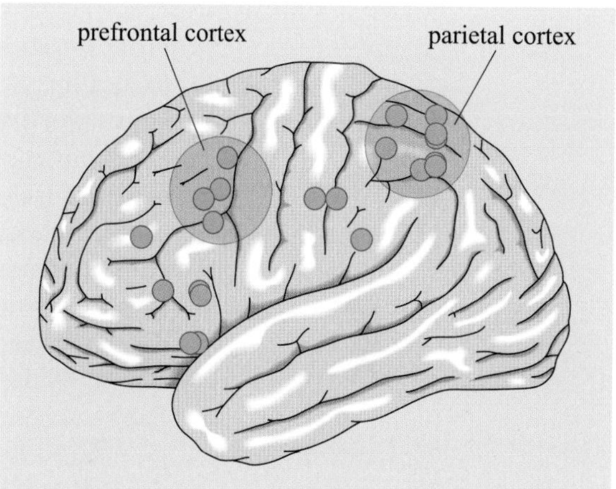

Figure 4.22 Parietal and prefrontal correlates of changes in visual consciousness. The left hemisphere of a human brain is shown, with the areas that show changes in activity correlated to changes in visual consciousness. The small pink circles show centres of clusters of activation, as seen in different studies. Large blue circles highlight the most prominent clusters, which are in the superior parietal cortex and dorsolateral prefrontal cortex.

Consistent with this idea, it is known that disturbances of visual attention and visual awareness in humans can occur after damage to the parietal or frontal cortex. For example, damage to the right of the parietal cortex can result in visual extinction, a common component of the **neglect syndrome**. This is a syndrome in which patients behave as if they are not aware of visual stimuli in the contralesional (in this case, left) visual field. For instance, they tend to ignore food on the left side of their plate, and even to ignore the left side of their bodies while dressing and undressing. Syndromes such as this illustrate that visual awareness for particular regions of visual space can be lost even when the visual cortex V1, the extra-striate visual cortex, and the input from the eyes are all intact. Thus, although these areas are necessary, they are not sufficient for visual awareness.

It has been suggested that the lack of awareness in **visual extinction** may be linked to attention. This is a phenomenon where, if a stimulus is presented just on the left (in the contralesional field), it is clearly seen by the patient, but if stimuli are presented on both sides, the patient is no longer aware of the stimulus on the left – it is 'extinguished'.

- ◆ Which hemisphere of the brain would be involved in processing input from the left visual field?
- ◆ The right hemisphere.

fMRI scans show that, as expected, a single consciously seen left-field stimulus activates the striate and early extra-striate visual cortex in the right hemisphere.

However, so does an unseen, 'extinguished' left-field stimulus! This suggests that the activation of the striate cortex and extra-striate visual cortex by a visual stimulus is not sufficient to evoke awareness.

It is of course possible, as in the case of G.Y. and motion perception above, that the *level* of activity in the conscious state is greater than in the unaware state, and there is some evidence to support this. However, it has also been suggested that awareness may be linked to other aspects of the activity, such as how synchronized the firing of neurons in the activated areas is, or whether such areas interact with other areas (such as the parietal cortex). The precise nature of the difference between neural activity in the aware and unaware states is therefore still unclear, and is currently the subject of intensive research.

From the above, it seems clear that we cannot say there is a specific area, pathway or locality for the NCC for visual awareness, although there is widespread agreement that the ventral visual pathway, interacting with areas of the prefrontal and parietal cortex, is an important part of it. Moreover, the emerging picture is that visual consciousness is modular, rather than a single entity, and that our experience of a seamless, unified visual consciousness of an object (or a **macro-consciousness**, as Zeki calls it) is somehow generated from a number of distinct visual micro-consciousnesses. As we saw above, the areas linked to micro-consciousness (e.g. the essential nodes for colour or motion) are spatially distinct. Recent evidence suggests that micro-consciousnesses are also temporally distinct – that is, separated in time. For instance, there is some evidence (which we will not go into) to suggest that when we look at an object, colour is perceived split seconds (around 80 ms) before motion. Visual processing and perception apparently occur in the order: location, colour, orientation, motion. However, this is not our experience – we are not aware of the asynchrony but conscious only of a unified object. When, where and how this binding (see also Sections 4.2.2 and 4.5.3) occurs is still unclear, but is currently the topic of intensive research. So far, there is no evidence of a particular place in the brain where everything comes together to generate the unified conscious visual experience with which we are familiar.

Summary of Section 4.4

The neural bases of conscious vision, and attempts to identify them, are the main focus of this section, but neural bases of unconscious visual processes are considered to some extent. For example the subcortical collicular visual pathway is thought to underlie unconscious visual processing in blindsight. In addition, behavioural studies of individuals with brain damage reveal two major cortical visual pathways – the ventral or 'what' path, and the dorsal or 'where' path. Damage to the ventral path can cause visual form agnosia (no conscious recognition of what a visual object is), while damage to the dorsal stream can cause optic ataxia (impaired ability to reach out to a visual object in space). The ventral path is associated with conscious visual experience.

The search for neural correlates of consciousness (NCCs) in the visual system currently involves attempts to measure brain activity using techniques such as single cell recording and fMRI scanning. NCCs could be spatial, or could depend on the level of neural activity at a specific location. Here, NCC is defined as the correlate of a very specific visual experience (such as awareness of a particular visual object). The underlying assumption is that there is a measurable difference in brain activity when an individual is aware of a particular visual object (i.e. has a particular visual percept) compared to when the same individual is unaware of it. The binocular rivalry paradigm has helped researchers relate an individual's visual percept to brain activity. Results suggest that the visual percept is correlated with activity in the further reaches of the ventral visual stream (in the inferotemporal cortex) rather than with activity in the primary visual cortex (V1). However, the emerging picture is complex and suggests that many different areas need to operate together to generate visual consciousness – each area may be necessary, but none is sufficient. Thus, activity in functionally specialized areas of the extra-striate visual cortex (EVC) (essential nodes) is needed for awareness of visual attributes such as colour or motion. (Damage to these areas causes achromatopsia and akinetopsia, respectively.) Activity in the parietal cortex and prefrontal cortex, which are involved in attentional processes, may also be needed, as damage to these areas causes visual extinction.

Overall, visual consciousness appears to be modular, rather than unified – there does not appear to be any one area in the brain where conscious visual experience is 'located'. At present, it is not clear how different aspects of visual consciousness are brought together or 'bound' to create our unified conscious experience.

4.5 Illusion and reality

Having come so far through this chapter, you will have had hints that conscious experience contains an element of illusion. Cast your mind back to the blindspot exercise you carried out in Section 4.2.3. As you will recall, there is an area on each retina that is not supplied with light receptors, so we are in effect blind in this part of our visual field.

◆ Recall that the orange square disappeared when in the area of the blindspot. What did you see in its place?

◆ The area where the orange square was became 'filled-in' with the purple of the surrounding disc. There was certainly no hole!

The brain clearly tricked us into seeing something that we knew was not there. This convincing illusion is ever-present – as we look around (even with one eye closed), we experience no hole in our visual field. The brain seems to make a 'best guess' of a plausible filler and normally we notice nothing unusual. It takes special manipulation, such as that carried out in the exercise, to demonstrate the existence of the blindspot. There are numerous other illusions which suggest that what we are conscious of can be a distortion of what is actually there. In this section, we briefly consider some phenomena that may help us to explore the relationship between reality and illusion in the generation of conscious experience. Some important parts of our conscious experience may be underpinned by the brain 'jumping to conclusions' or applying rules of thumb.

4.5.1 Free will

In the course of our daily lives, we make many willed (i.e. voluntary) movements, that is movements we are aware of making and have consciously decided to make. For instance, a moment ago I decided I would like some coffee, so I reached out, picked up the mug at my side and lifted it to my mouth for a sip. All these actions I experienced as voluntary. I could have decided to leave the coffee until later, or to have a big gulp rather than a small sip.

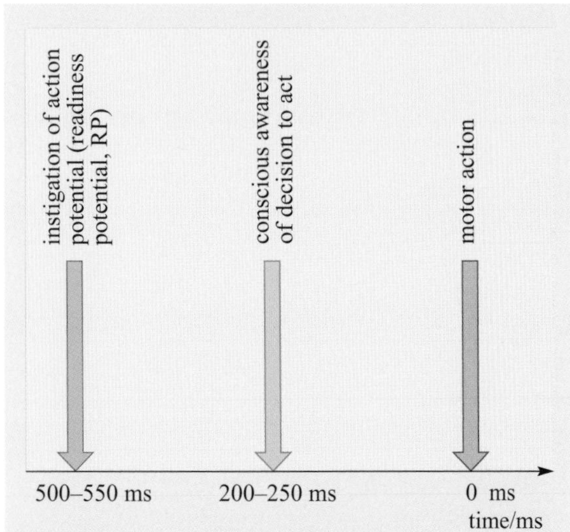

Figure 4.23 Observed time sequence of components of a willed action, based on Benjamin Libet's experiments. The motor action (moving the hand) occurs at 0 ms, and is preceded by reported conscious awareness of the decision to move the hand. However, even before this, a readiness potential (RP) is seen in the motor cortex, indicating initiation of the movement.

Our experience of ourselves as constantly making conscious decisions in our day-to-day life, and hence as beings with a choice, is closely linked to our assumptions of free will, self-control, responsibility and, indeed, culpability. So it is startling and indeed disturbing for many people to learn that there is evidence to suggest that the electrical impulse in the brain that initiates motor action may occur *before* our conscious decision is made.

This finding came from an experiment carried out by Benjamin Libet at the University of California (Libet, 1985). It was already well-established that around 500 ms before a willed action, a surge of electrical activity called a **readiness potential (RP)** takes place in the cerebral cortex. Reflex actions such as a knee jerk, that are not willed, are not preceded by an RP.

Libet set up an experiment in which participants were fitted with EEG sensors (see Section 1.3.2 and Book 3, Section 2.4.1) to pick up any RPs. Participants were told they could make a specified hand movement whenever they wished. Each hand movement, being willed, was preceded by an RP, of which the participants were unaware. The time at which the RP took place was noted by the experimenter. The participants were also asked to note exactly when they decided to move their hand, by noting the position of a spot of light as it moved round a large clock face. Over hundreds of trials, Libet found that the decision to move the hand, instead of coming before the RP as one might expect if the decision triggered the movement, was consistently placed about 250–300 ms *after* the RP. The movement itself took place about 200–250 ms after the reported decision (Figure 4.23).

What does this result mean? It suggests that the unconscious brain kicks off a movement and that the conscious decision to make it may or may not be a decision, in the usual sense of the word, at all. One possibility is that conscious will does not actually *cause* the actions that we experience as willed or voluntary – even though we have the very strong impression, indeed conviction, that it does. Our experience of free will is perhaps an illusion created by the brain.

Libet himself seemed unwilling to accept the implications of his findings, and in effect tried to eat his cake and have it too. He suggested that conscious will might enable us to veto an action already begun, by aborting it during the 200–250 ms between the feeling of decision and the actual movement.

- ◆ What is the problem with this suggestion?
- ◆ The difficulty is that the conscious decision to abort the act may itself be an illusory decision. So, for instance, the motor command RP to *halt* the raising of a finger would have arisen 250–300 ms *before* the conscious decision to halt the raising of the finger.

Libet's results do, however, suggest that consciousness is not as instantaneous as it seems to us. A variety of estimates suggest it can take 100–500 ms for us to become conscious. We are not consciously aware of many events that happen faster. For instance, we are not aware of television frames of around 30 ms.

Given that the paradigm Libet used was contrived and unnatural to an extent, as well as relatively simple, it is still unclear whether a similar lack of a causal role for conscious will would be expected in more complex cases of planning and decision-making. However, the idea that conscious will could be a trick of the mind is taken increasingly seriously by students of the mind. For instance, the Harvard psychologist Daniel Wegner (Wegner and Wheatley, 1999; Wegner, 2002) has suggested a possible model for how the illusion of apparent mental causation could arise (Figure 4.24). To understand Wegner's argument, as described in the caption to Figure 4.24, you may need to remind yourself of the difference between *correlation* and *causation* (see Section 1.4.4).

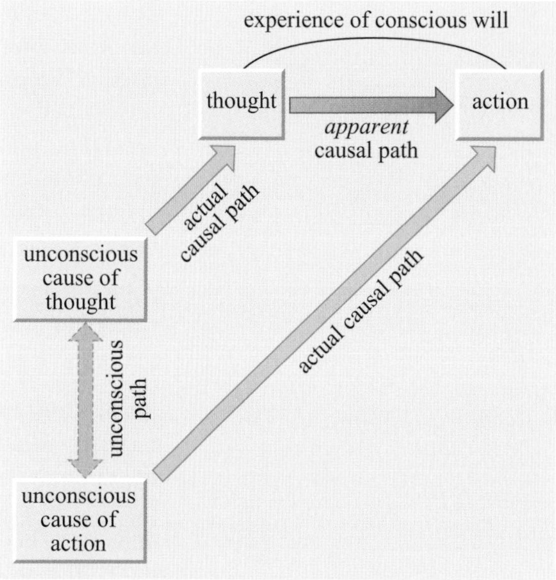

Figure 4.24 Wegner's model for how the illusion of conscious will might arise. He suggests that: 'the experience of conscious will arises when a person infers an apparent causal path from thought to action [purple arrow]. The actual causal paths [green] are not present in the person's consciousness. The thought is caused by unconscious mental events, and the action is caused by unconscious mental events, and these unconscious mental events might also be linked to each other directly or through yet other mental or brain processes. Conscious will is experienced as a result of what is apparent, not what is real.'

In other words, the experience of conscious will may arise when the mind *infers* a causal relationship – for instance, when an action follows a thought and is consistent with it. The inference may not, of course, be correct. Wegner suggests that 'if conscious will were an illusory add-on to action, we could begin to explain all the odd cases when action and conscious will do not properly coincide'. Cases where there is a dissociation between conscious will and action include the alien hand syndrome and the feeling that some people with schizophrenia have that someone else is controlling their actions.

At this stage, you may well be wondering why, if there is no actual causal connection between a thought and an action, the brain bothers to create the illusion of one. If there is such an illusion, what might its function be? We will return to this idea in Book 6, Chapter 4, when we revisit the concept of self.

4.5.2 The embodied self

As a subjective phenomenon, consciousness is, by definition, always linked to an individual. As humans, we experience our 'selves' in a phenomenal sense. For instance, I have a distinct awareness that this is 'me' sitting here at my computer keyboard, that these are 'my' fingers and it is 'I' and no one else who is deciding to tap these keys to produce these words. Our sense of self is so strong that our normal experience is infused through and through by the first-person perspective.

Some philosophical traditions such as Hinduism and Buddhism have always regarded the self as a fragile, illusory construct. The Scottish philosopher David Hume (1739) independently came to a similar conclusion. The only method of examination available to these philosophers was introspection (guided, in the case of Eastern traditions, by a rigorous discipline of meditation, and in Hume's case by the different but equally rigorous rules of logic). Introspection, Hume concluded, suggests that we have no palpable identity: we are 'nothing but a collection of perceptions which succeed each other with inconceivable rapidity and are in perpetual flux and movement'. The self, he felt, was therefore an illusion.

How does the idea of the self stand up to more scientific enquiry? First, we need to be clearer about some of the concepts that underlie our normal sense of self. One of the most fundamental is the me/not me distinction that is based on body boundaries. So I know this is my hand and that is your hand, and when the nurse gives me an injection it is in my arm that I experience the pain. We have a sense of knowing about our own bodies in a way we do not know about other people's bodies. We also feel that the thoughts we are thinking and the emotions we are feeling belong to us. All in all, we have a strong sense of *ownership* of our bodies, sensations and thoughts. We also have a strong sense of ourselves as the agents of our actions. We feel we can decide what to do and hence that we cause our actions. Finally, we feel that we are coherent selves with a continued existence in time – a past, a present and a future.

As we shall see below, these convictions, which seem so strong and well-based at first sight, are in fact rather vulnerable constructs based on the interaction between the brain, body and environment.

As Section 3.4.6 showed (Figure 3.25), there is a topographical map (pictorially represented as a sensory homunculus) of the body in the somatosensory cortex of the brain. As you also saw there, the right side of the body is represented in the left cortex (i.e. contralaterally) and vice versa. Strokes, which are a common cause of damage to the right side of the brain, can cause partial paralysis of the left side of the body (Box 3.4). The result, for the patients concerned, is a sudden and startling change in their sense of ownership and agency in relation to their body. Many patients refuse to believe that a paralysed limb belongs to their own body – while the limb is there, there is no access to the somatosensory brain map that represents that limb. Conversely, individuals who have lost a limb as a result of an accident or amputation often feel that the lost limb is still present and functional. In this case, of course, while the limb has gone, the body map is still accessible in the brain, and the illusion of a so-called **phantom limb**, together with appropriate sensation, can be generated with appropriate stimulation. The Indian neuroscientist V. S. Ramachandran suggested how this might come about. In the sensory homunculus, it is noticeable that areas of the somatosensory cortex representing the hand lie adjacent to areas representing the face and the upper arm (Figure 3.25).

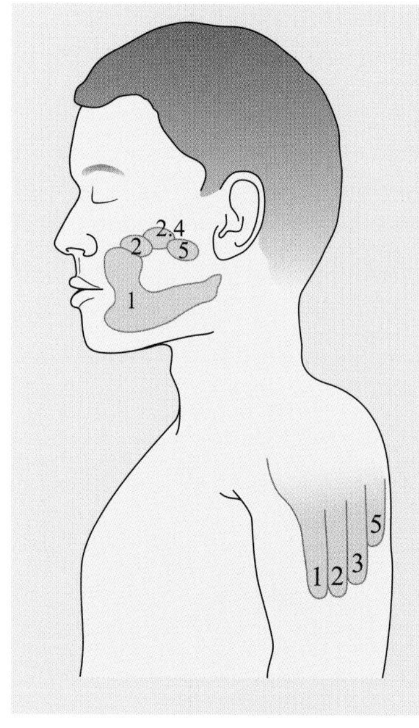

Figure 4.25 Phantom hand represented on the skin surface of the upper arm and face. 1 represents the thumb, and 2, 3, 4, 5 the digits. Touching the skin on the face or upper arm in this case makes the person feel that specific digits on the missing hand are being touched. The arrangement of the digits on face and upper arm is fairly topographic but not all the digits are represented in the case illustrated.

Ramachandran's studies (Ramachandran and Blakeslee, 1998) suggest that the phantom limb phenomenon might occur because the part of the cortex that normally looks after the hand becomes linked to other parts of the body. When the hand is lost, the neuronal infrastructure representing it in the somatosensory homunculus becomes inoperative through lack of sensory input. As a consequence, afferent neuronal connections from the upper arm and the face invade the hand territory from either side. A remarkable corollary of this is that the phantom hand often comes to be quite accurately represented on the skin of the face and upper arm. Stimulation of these sites feels to the participant like stimulation, at precisely located points, of the phantom hand (Figure 4.25).

Some body-ownership phenomena resulting from brain damage, for instance from strokes, can seem even more bizarre. Damage to the anterior cingulate cortex (ACC) can create an *anarchic* or *alien hand.* Not only does one well-studied patient who suffers from this syndrome not recognize her hand as her own, but she feels the hand can *behave* as if it has a will of its own and carry out actions which she does not consciously intend. For instance, the hand has been known to undo buttons as fast as the other hand does them up. Some of these experiences of lack of agency have parallels in the experience of people with schizophrenia (Book 6, Chapter 3).

What lies behind our sense of ownership of our own bodies? How does the brain construct a body image? One clue is that we can predict the sensations that relate to the actions of our own bodies but not those belonging to someone else. When I move my own arm or leg, my brain is able to anticipate the changes in feeling and location very accurately, for the simple reason that it is *my* brain that is commanding and directing the movements of the muscles involved, and is receiving feedback from them and from the other senses involved. When these control mechanisms are disrupted, for instance due to brain damage, our sense that we own our body parts and actions is also disrupted. The brain does not even have to be damaged – it can be fooled by the information it is receiving into a false sense of ownership. This is demonstrated, for instance, by the *phantom nose illusion* generated by Ramachandran and Hirstein (1997).

In their experiment, the participant sat blindfolded in a chair, with an accomplice sitting in front of him, facing in the same direction. The experimenter stood near the participant, and with his left hand took hold of the participant's left index finger and used it to tap and stroke the nose of the accomplice repeatedly and randomly, while at the same time, using his own right hand, he tapped and stroked the participant's nose in precisely the same manner, and in perfect synchrony. After a few seconds of this procedure, the participant developed the illusion that 'his nose had either been dislocated, or had been stretched out several feet forwards'. Ramachandran suggests that the illusion arises because the participant's brain 'regards it as highly improbable that the tapping sequence on his finger and the one on his nose are identical simply by chance and therefore assumes that the nose has been displaced'.

As the above examples show, our model of our body, which seems to us to be so stable and solid, is in fact virtual and highly reliant on the often fragmentary information provided by the senses.

4.5.3 Seeing and illusion

Many of you will be familiar with visual illusions such as the Kanizsa figure (Figure 4.26).

Here, most people see two triangles, one of which is above and so partly blocks the other as well as parts of the three black discs. Although we know they are not actually present, we perceive the hidden parts of the lower triangle and discs. Films and videos are another example of an illusion the brain creates for us – when presented with a sequence of still pictures at the rate of about 30 per second we perceive continuous movement. Our brains are equipped with many such rules to make sense of incoming information. The most obvious explanation for this is that our perceptual mechanisms have evolved to interpret a given stimulus or sequence of stimuli in the way that has been most probable during our evolutionary history. For instance, it is easy to imagine that the ability to 'perceive' an entire tiger from bits glimpsed between obscuring saplings might make the difference between life and death to a potential prey animal.

Our ability to devise unusual sensory inputs and to monitor the resulting perceptions can give us important clues about the rules the brain uses to create our picture of reality. Consider our experience of looking around. Visual experience feels smooth, seamless and richly detailed. We feel confident that if a major change occurred in front of our eyes we would be aware of it. However, a number of findings suggest that this is far from the case. In some circumstances, observers can be unaware of very large changes in a visual scene – a phenomenon termed **change blindness**. Change blindness was first demonstrated in an experiment where participants studied a visual scene on a

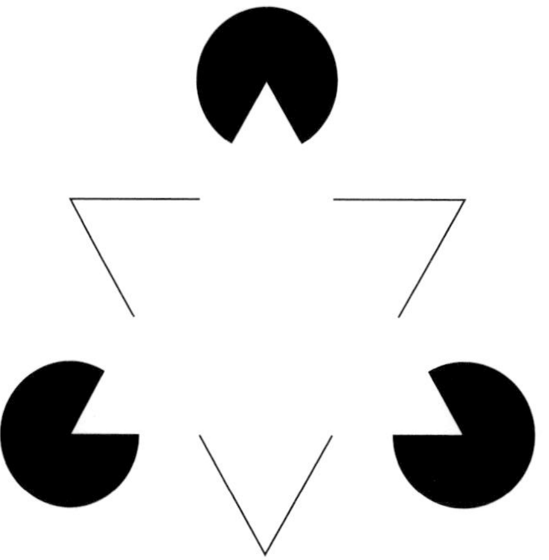

Figure 4.26 The Kanizsa figure.

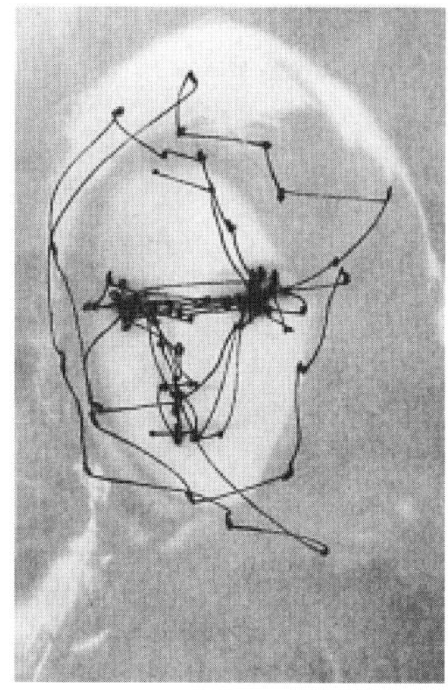

Figure 4.27 An illustration of saccadic eye movements while looking at a woman's face. In between 'leaps' or saccades, the eyes fixate on areas of the picture. It is clear that the eyes and mouth are often revisited during visual exploration of the face.

computer screen. As we examine a visual scene, our eyes move around in a sequence of jumps called **saccades**, alighting first in one place then in another (Figure 4.27), and often returning to some parts of the scene.

Such eye movements help to keep whatever interests us in sharp visual focus – only the central foveal part of our visual field can deliver such sharp focus, so we move it around constantly.

The computer in this case monitored the eye movements of the observer, and while the eye was saccading elsewhere, elements of the scene, such as the colours of flowers and cars, or the presence of a tree (see Figure 4.28) were changed (McConkie and Currie, 1996).

Such changes, to everyone's surprise, went undetected. Since then, change blindness has been demonstrated in a variety of experiments, which have in common that visual changes to a scene are made at the same time as an interruption to visual monitoring of the scene. For instance, observers view film extracts, and at the moment when the camera 'cuts' from one view to another, a large change is made – such as an actor being replaced by a different actor (Figure 4.29).

Many observers do not notice this change. Even more striking, change blindness has been demonstrated in real-life situations. For instance, in a set-up described by Simons and Levin (1998), an experimenter dressed as a construction worker stopped a person in the street and asked for directions. While the person was speaking to the experimenter, workers carrying a door passed between the experimenter and the person, and an accomplice took the place of the experimenter. Most people continued to give directions after the interruption, and only 33% noticed the change even though the experimenter and the accomplice had different heights, wore different clothes and so on (Figure 4.30).

Further experiments have shown that attention is required to notice a change. If something occurs outside the scope of attention, even if it is perfectly visible, it will often not be seen. This is strikingly shown by a study (Simons and Chabris, 1998), in which observers were asked to watch a videotape of a basketball match between a team wearing white and a team wearing black. Observers were asked to attend to one of the teams, and to keep a mental count of the number of passes made by all three members of it. This is a task that requires focused attention. During one of the video clips, which lasted 75 seconds, a person in a gorilla suit or a woman carrying an umbrella strolled across the centre of the court (Figure 4.31a and b), an event that lasted about 5 seconds. About 30% of observers failed to notice this event. A similar level of failure occurred even when, in a separate 62-second clip, the gorilla actually stopped in the middle of the scene, faced the camera and thumped its chest before strolling off, an event that took up 9 seconds (Figure 4.31c)! This is an example of **inattentional blindness**.

Figure 4.28 Example of a change made to a picture during a saccade.

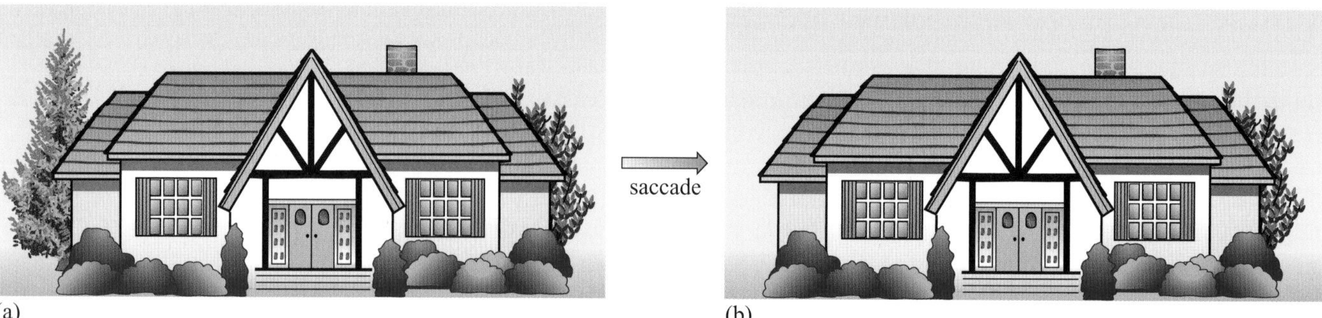

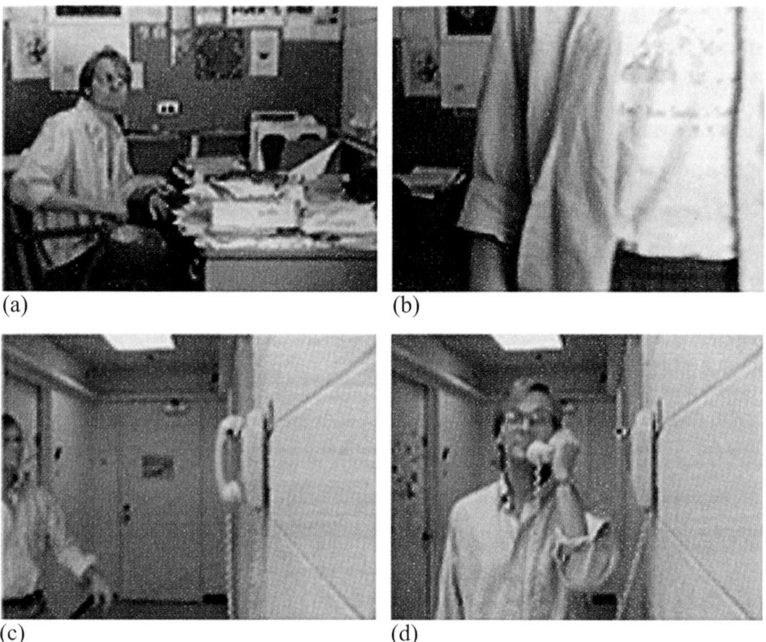

(a) (b) (c) (d)

Figure 4.29 Four frames from a film are shown. During a change in camera angle (b and c), the actor in (a) was replaced by a different actor (in d). Many observers did not notice the change, even though the actor was in the centre of the scene.

Figure 4.30 The experimenter and his accomplice, dressed as construction workers.

(a)

(b)

(c)

Figure 4.31 (a) Woman with umbrella, and (b) person dressed as a gorilla, traversing a basketball match. The event lasted for around 5 seconds about half-way through a 75-second video of the match between the White team (white shirts) and Black team (black shirts). (c) Frame from a video recording showing a 'gorilla' pausing and displaying in the middle of a basketball match. Six out of twelve observers of the video clip failed to notice this event, which lasted 9 seconds and occurred while observers were mentally counting basketball passes by one of the two teams.

The relevance of these phenomena to conscious perception of the visual world is currently a matter of debate. Traditionally, psychologists have assumed that the brain creates detailed internal representations of what we see, and that it is these representations we access when we are conscious of the elements of a visual scene. However, change and inattentional blindness phenomena raise a number of difficulties for this idea. They suggest that the information about a visual scene to which the brain has conscious access is in fact full of holes – it is incomplete. If this is the case, how does the brain manage to create the seamless, vivid and richly detailed visual scenes that we normally experience consciously?

One suggestion is that the brain may indeed form richly detailed and vivid internal representations when looking at a scene, but that *most* of the information is lost within seconds (a form of very short-term memory). This view of visual processing has been called 'inattentional amnesia' (Wolfe, 1999): the idea that we see everything, but forget *most* of it immediately.

- ◆ Why is it unlikely that *all* the information is lost within seconds?
- ◆ If it were all lost, we would not be able to check what had changed in a visual scene – we would have no memory of what it was like before! It is likely that a memory of the most significant or prominent aspects of a scene is stored for longer.

A more radical and controversial solution to the problem has been offered by, amongst others, the psychologist Kevin O'Regan and the philosopher Alva Noë (O'Regan and Noë, 2001). They suggest that the brain does not really need to form a sequence of rich representations of the world as we look around. Put simply, they suggest that the brain always has access to the detailed information it needs in the world itself – the world, in their view, thus acts as a kind of 'external memory'. To become visually aware of details in the world, all we need to do is to move our eyes around. As we do so, whatever we fixate with our foveal vision becomes available for conscious processing. We have the impression of seeing everything because we have visual access to everything, even though without actually fixating it we have no detailed information about it. It is a bit like having a library to which we have immediate access any time we want – we do not need to carry the books with us all the time because we have access to the detailed information they contain whenever we take them off the shelves and read them. Those who favour this view feel that it explains the apparent paradox between the feeling of richness we have of our visual environments, and our striking inability, in change blindness experiments, of knowing what has changed.

Supporters of this view also feel that it offers an answer to the binding problem we mentioned earlier. In effect, this is circumvented, simply because objects *are* bound together in the external world, and that is all that is needed. The brain does not have to perform this feat for every tiny object, all the time, because it does not actually recreate such objects from their components internally.

This view emphasizes that, in an important sense, the environment, brain and body may operate as a system. We generate the feeling of ourselves in a three-dimensional world, a kind of virtual reality machine. It is an idea that will no doubt be debated and tested for some time to come.

Summary of Section 4.5

There is evidence from a variety of sources that several aspects of our conscious experience are the result of 'tricks of the mind'. These illusions may result from the operation of rules-of-thumb, acquired during the course of evolution, that are applied by the brain. Examples include the way the brain 'fills in' the visual world at the site of the blindspot, and the way in which an appropriate sequence of still images presented in rapid succession results in the illusion of movement (as in the movies).

There is some evidence that willed movements are initiated before we are aware of the decision to make such movements. This has led to the suggestion that our experience of conscious (free) will may derive from an inferential jump made by the brain to connect our thoughts with our actions, giving the false impression that our thoughts have caused our actions. Illusions can also affect our conscious awareness of our body, as shown by alien hand and phantom limb phenomena. Finally, the phenomena of change blindness and inattentional blindness suggest that we may not be as consciously aware of the details of our normal visual environment as we generally feel we are.

Learning outcomes for Chapter 4

After studying this chapter you should be able to:

4.1 Recognize definitions and applications of each of the terms printed in **bold** in the text.

4.2 Outline the methods, goals and limits of a scientific study of consciousness.

4.3 Outline the key reasons why consciousness is considered to be a 'problem'.

4.4 Describe the neurobiological bases and functional characteristics of some conscious and unconscious processes.

4.5 Demonstrate understanding of the methods and findings of the search for the neural correlate(s) of consciousness.

4.6 Describe or explain the fallibility and illusory aspects of consciousness, using appropriate examples.

4.7 Be able to describe and discuss ideas and evidence relating to the part played by conscious and unconscious processes in cognition and behaviour.

Questions for Chapter 4

Question 4.1 *(Learning outcome 4.1)*

A woman sees a yellow rose and thinks: 'I've always loved that yellow! It's exactly the colour I want to paint my kitchen'. Suggest, with reasons, two kind(s) of consciousness that must contribute to her thought.

Question 4.2 *(Learning outcome 4.2)*

Which *two* of the following CANNOT provide information that could be used in a scientific study? Explain why.

A A boy watching a football match on television thinks: 'That was a great goal by Beckham'.

B When a woman is shown a picture of a chocolate cake, the pupils of her eyes dilate.

C Jemima feels the others are ignoring a perfectly sensible suggestion she has made.

D Mustafa says: 'This cup of tea is much sweeter than that one'.

E A cat offered a piece of carrot and a piece of cheese ignores the cheese and eats the carrot.

Question 4.3 *(Learning outcome 4.3)*

An eminent physicist suggests that a series of small structures found in cells could be vital in generating conscious experience. State which problem of consciousness this idea is relevant to, giving reasons.

Question 4.4 *(Learning outcome 4.4)*

Is it possible to recognize someone without being conscious of doing so? Give evidence to support your answer.

Question 4.5 *(Learning outcome 4.4)*

Which *two* of the following brain pathways are associated with conscious processing?

A The eye → thalamus → amygdala pathway

B The eye → thalamus → cortex → amygdala pathway

C The subcortical visual pathway

D The dorsal visual stream

E The ventral visual stream

Question 4.6 *(Learning outcome 4.4)*

James is learning how to juggle three balls in the air. He has to focus his attention on what he is doing, as well as plan his next movement. Which *two* areas of his brain are likely to be particularly active while he is doing this, and are also less likely to be active once he is an experienced juggler?

Question 4.7 *(Learning outcome 4.4)*

Rita says: 'If D.B. says he can't see something shown to him but keeps getting the right answer when he's asked to choose which of two images it might have been, he is either lying or mistaken'. Is there another explanation you could offer Rita?

Question 4.8 *(Learning outcome 4.5)*

For each of the following, name (a) the deficit described and (b) the area in the brain that is likely to be damaged:

1 A man looks at and sees an object but cannot reach out accurately for it with his left hand.

2 A woman looking at a train drawing into a station sees it as a sequence of still images.

3 A man can see nothing at all on the left side of his visual field, and ignores the left side of his body while dressing or undressing.

Question 4.9 *(Learning outcome 4.6)*

Explain why, when looking around, we do not see a hole in the visual world where our blindspot is.

Question 4.10 *(Learning outcome 4.7)*

It has been suggested that the phenomenon of conscious will is an illusion (Section 4.5.1). Does this mean that conscious will is an epiphenomenon?

ANSWERS TO QUESTIONS

Question 1.1

We often assume that our conscious awareness of the world as mediated by vision conveys a faithful account of events in the world. D.B. shows that it is possible to react to events that do not reach conscious awareness.

Question 1.2

It means that there is a specific effect of the drug quite apart from any benefit derived by patients based on their expectation of an effect. To ascertain whether there is such an effect, patients would be tested not knowing whether they were receiving the new drug or some neutral substance.

Question 1.3

No. The mind is used to cover both conscious and unconscious aspects.

Question 1.4

Neuron.

Question 1.5

Transmission of information *within* a given neuron is by means of action potentials, pulses of electricity. In the cases discussed so far, transmission *between* neurons is by means of chemical neurotransmitter that is released from one neuron and attaches itself to another.

Question 1.6

A neurotransmitter is a chemical which is released from a neuron and which migrates the very small distance to a neighbouring cell, where it effects action. A hormone is a chemical that is released into a blood vessel at one location and then is conveyed in a blood vessel (or the whole circulation) to effect action at a distant site.

Question 1.7

In functional terms, the animal will be low on nutrients. In order that it should not starve, a high priority is given to searching for food. A causal explanation would be in terms of the detection of the low nutrient level in the body and the biasing of its choice mechanisms in the direction of food seeking.

Question 1.8

Sexual reproduction is the coming together of two cells, one from the mother and one from the father, to form a new individual. Cell division is intrinsic to a given animal and consists of division of a cell and then division of the two products and so on.

Question 1.9

Perhaps the most obvious scale is the 'everyday' one of the physical and social environment that surrounds the whole animal. Another scale is the environment of the cells of the body, i.e. the fluid that surrounds them. At a still smaller scale is the fluid environment within the cells, i.e. the fluid that surrounds the genes and the other cellular structures.

Question 2.1

Nerve nets, like nervous systems in more complex invertebrates and vertebrates, act as communication systems that:

- receive and integrate information from the outside world via a sensory system;
- generate appropriate responses by modulating the activity of different effector systems.

As a result, the animal is able to respond to changes in the external environment.

Question 2.2

Centralized nervous systems are organized into more elaborate neural networks that allow a far greater interchange of information between them. This results in the coordination and control of more complex behaviour than in non-centralized nervous systems (e.g. nerve nets).

Cephalization, the concentration of neurons at the rostral end, allows animals more rapid responses to changes in the environment detected by sense organs such as eyes or ears. As these are mainly located in the leading end of locomotion, it keeps the transmission distance of information between sense organs and neurons in the brain short.

Question 2.3

Similarities:

1 Both nervous systems show bilateral symmetry.

2 Both nervous systems show segmentation.

3 Both nervous systems show centralization.

4 Both nervous systems show cephalization.

5 Neurons of both vertebrate and invertebrate nervous systems function by conducting action potentials.

Differences:

1 The CNS is located dorsally in vertebrates, ventrally in invertebrates.

2 The CNS of vertebrates is larger than that of invertebrates and contains many more neurons.

3 The PNS of vertebrates is divided into the somatic and autonomic divisions whereas the invertebrate PNS has no ANS.

4 Axons of invertebrate neurons are not myelinated whereas many axons of vertebrate neurons are myelinated.

5 Electrical synapses are mainly found in invertebrate nervous systems.

Question 2.4

Check your labels with Figure 2.33.

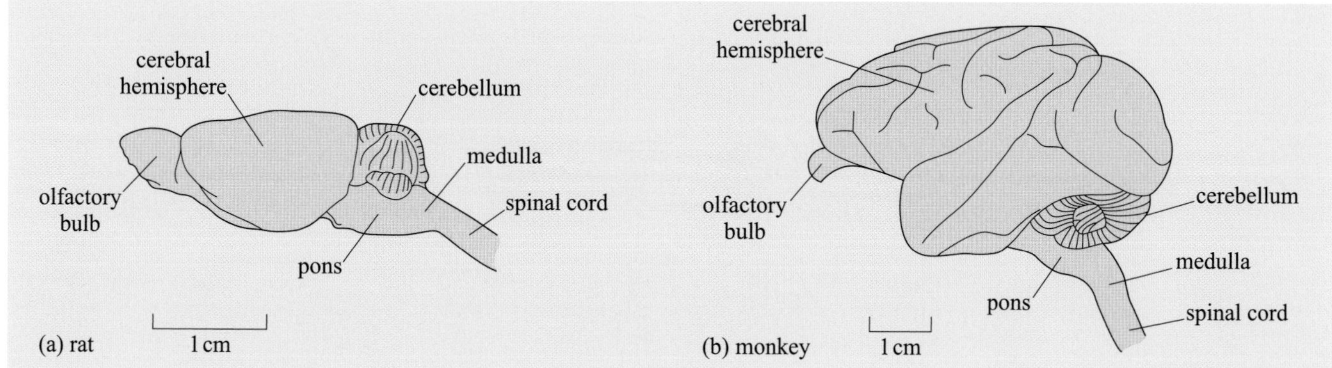

Figure 2.33 Answer to Question 2.4.

Question 2.5

(a) False. The cerebellum lies caudally in relation to the cerebral hemispheres.

(b) True. If you got this wrong, look back at Section 2.2.

(c) False. The size of the olfactory bulbs, the brain structures that process olfactory stimuli, relative to the rest of the brain, are much larger in the laboratory rat than in the rhesus monkey, indicating that rats have a more developed sense of olfaction than monkeys.

(d) False. Primates have the largest relative size of cerebral hemispheres in mammals. This is particularly evident for the outer layer of the cerebral hemispheres, the cerebral cortex.

(e) True. If you got this wrong, look back at Section 2.3.

Question 2.6

(a) 4; (b) 5; (c) 1; (d) 3; (e) 6; (f) 2; (g) 7.

Question 2.7

The fatty molecules of cell membranes are organized into two closely opposed layers (the 'bilayer'). A variety of proteins are immersed within the lipid bilayer arranged in patterns that resemble a 'mosaic'. In addition, membrane proteins have the capacity to float and move laterally within the sea of lipids and, therefore, cell membranes are considered to have a 'fluid' character.

Question 2.8

(a) Check your labels with Figure 2.34.

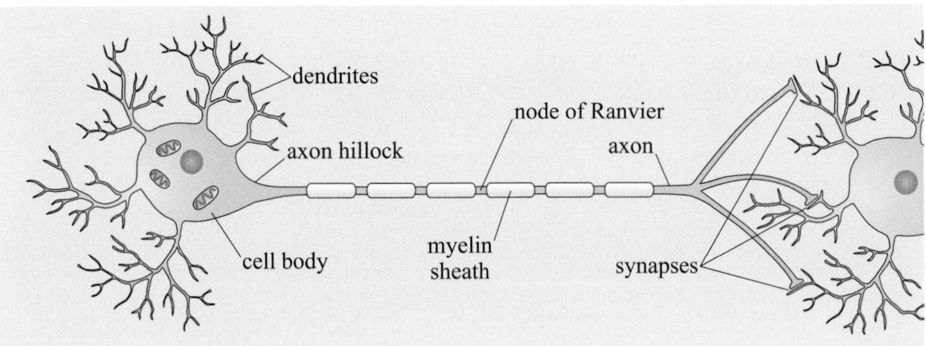

Figure 2.34 Answer to Question 2.8a.

(b) Dendrite: extension of a neuron that receives many inputs in the form of synapses from other neurons and conveys electrical signals towards the cell's body. It does not usually conduct action potentials.

Axon: a long thin structure extending from the cell body of a neuron that by virtue of its excitable membrane conducts action potentials towards the presynaptic terminals.

Cell body: central region of a neuron that contains the nucleus and many intracellular organelles. It represents the metabolic centre of the cell.

Axon hillock: the region of the cell body from which the axon emerges, and where the action potential is generated.

Myelin sheath: an electrically insulating sheath that forms around some axons in vertebrates, so allowing rapid propagation of the action potential over long distances.

Nodes of Ranvier: the area of axons in vertebrate neurons which is not surrounded by the myelin sheath formed by oligodendrocytes in the CNS or Schwann cells in the PNS. They have an important role in the transmission of electrical signals.

Synapse: the area of close contact between neurons or between a neuron and an effector cell (i.e. muscle fibre or gland cell) with which it communicates.

Question 2.9

(a) In vertebrates, the main feature is the presence of a myelin sheath that surrounds many axons. (b) In invertebrates, the main features are the larger diameter of some of the axons and the presence of electrical synapses.

Question 2.10

Both membrane and sensory receptors are concerned with detecting events. However, the membrane receptor signals the presence of a particular substance in the extracellular environment to the cell whereas the sensory receptor signals an event in the external world to the nervous system.

Question 2.11

Glial cells are non-neuronal cells of nervous systems that maintain the local environment surrounding neurons in a way that is optimal for neuronal function. Astrocytes regulate potassium concentration and glucose and oxygen metabolism, and provide structural scaffolding. Oligodendrocytes in the CNS and Schwann cells in the PNS form the myelin sheath that surrounds axons, thereby speeding up the conduction velocity of action potentials. Microglia play an important role in the CNS immune response to infection and injury. Ependymal cells help circulate the cerebrospinal fluid.

Question 2.12

Compare your answer with Figure 2.35.

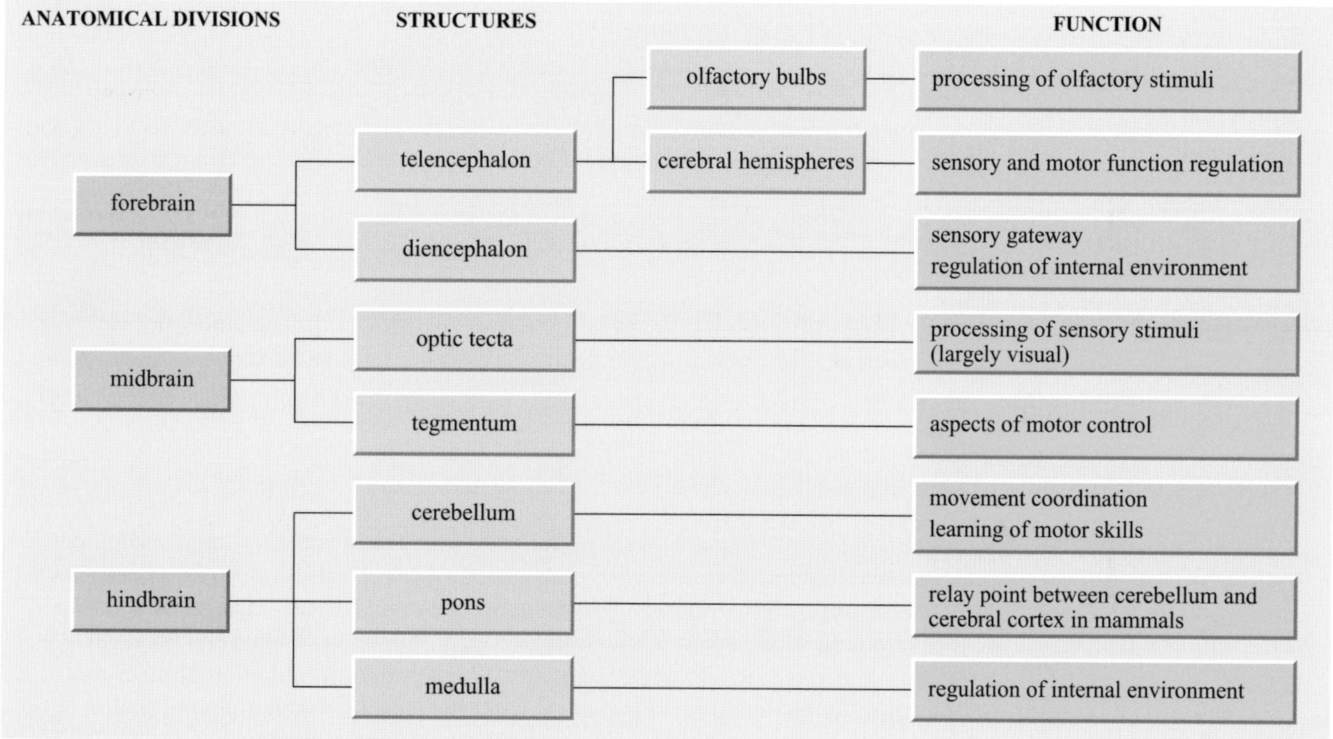

Figure 2.35 Answer to Question 2.12.

Question 3.1

1. Statement (b) is false. The nose cannot be contralateral in relation to any structure as it runs along the midline.
2. Statement (b) is false. The occipital lobe is posterior in relation to the frontal lobe.
3. Both statements are false. At the spinal cord, dorsal and posterior have the same meaning whereas superior is equivalent to rostral. By contrast with the spinal cord, both superior and dorsal indicate the same positions at the brain.
4. Both statements are false. A coronal cut separates the brain into an anterior and posterior half. A sagittal cut separates the cerebral hemispheres into two roughly symmetrical left and right halves.

Question 3.2

Check your labels with Figure 3.44. Neuron 1 is as a sensory neuron. This class of neuron is involved in the detection of sensory information. Neuron 2 is neither sensory nor motor. Rather it falls into a class of neuron that modulates the activity of other neurons. This neuron is logically described as an interneuron which may be either inhibitory or excitatory. Neurons 3, 4 and 5 are called motor neurons (although strictly speaking neuron 4 is an interneuron). They effect action and innervate effector organs. Neuron 3 is a CNS motor neuron as it innervates skeletal muscle. Neurons 4 and 5 are ANS motor neurons. Neuron 4 is a preganglionic neuron whereas neuron 5 is a postganglionic neuron and it may innervate directly smooth muscle, cardiac muscle or glands.

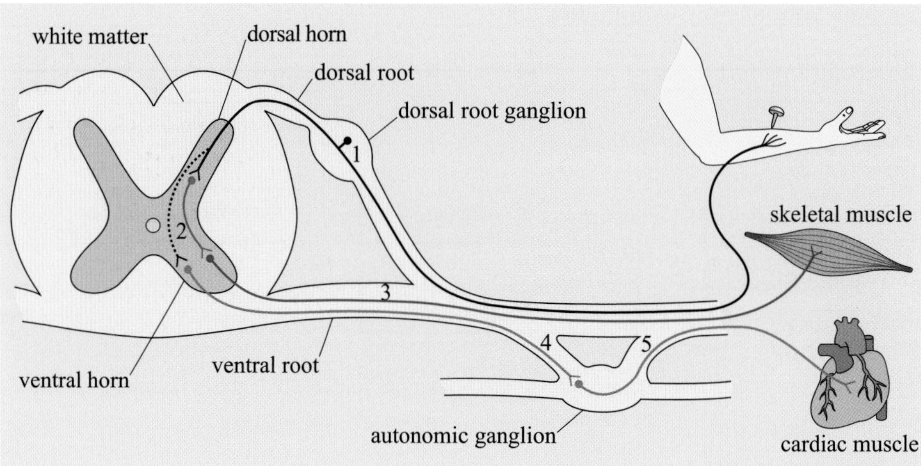

Figure 3.44 Answer to Question 3.2. Completed Figure 3.42.

Question 3.3

(a) Even before you are aware of the pain, you would probably rapidly attempt to remove the limb from the source of pain. In other words, you would experience a withdrawal reflex response. This response may entail the (i) activation of motor neurons such as neuron 3 which induce the contraction of the flexor skeletal muscle responsible for withdrawing the arm and the (ii) inhibition of other motor neurons innervating the antagonistic extensor muscle. Another type of motor response may involve the activation of the ANS which would prepare you for the 'fight or flight' response. The consequences of ANS activation may be generalized such as an increase in the heart rate or in blood pressure (involving neurons projecting to higher centres in the brain). It may also involve neurons that are localized to the damaged area resulting in constriction of skin blood vessels to stop bleeding.

(b) Neuron 1 may be a nociceptor, a type of sensory neuron that responds to tissue damage and mediates the sensation of pain.

(c) A sensory receptor such as neuron 1 innervating the dermatome in the underarm feeds information via a peripheral nerve into the dorsal root of the T1 thoracic segment of the spinal cord.

(d) The input from neuron 1 to the spinal cord thoracic region means that the autonomic ganglion depicted in Figure 3.42 must be sympathetic because sympathetic ganglia run alongside the thoracic (and some lumbar) segments of the spinal cord.

Question 3.4

Check your labels with Figure 3.45.

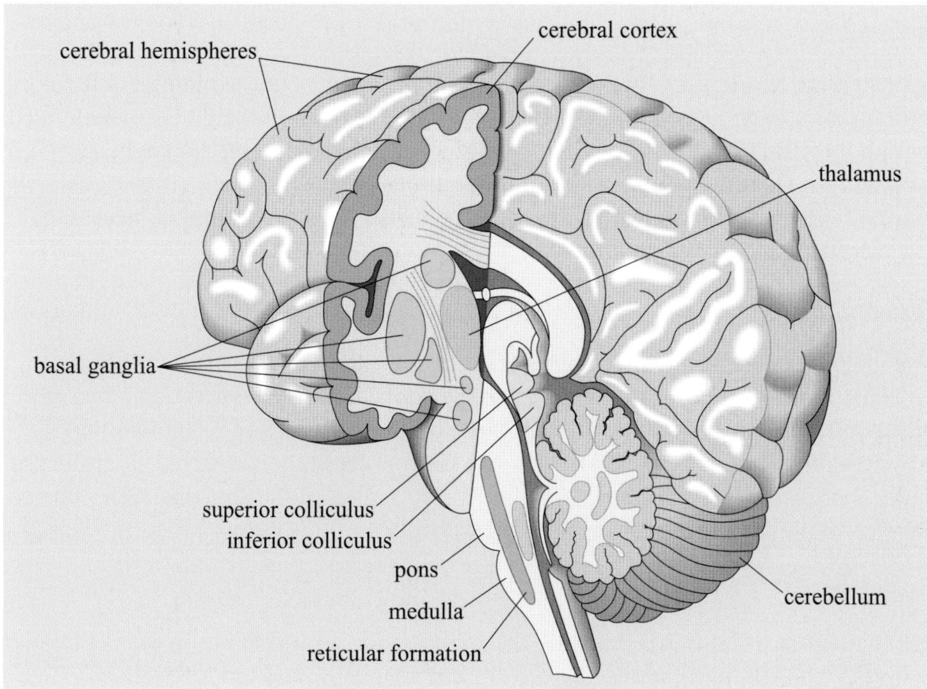

Figure 3.45 Answer to Question 3.4. Completed Figure 3.43.

Question 3.5

The horizontal pattern of organization of the cerebral cortex is formed by six anatomically distinguishable layers due to the location of different types of neurons and variations in the density of cell bodies. Specific sensory information from the thalamus terminates mainly in layer IV whereas other thalamic inputs and those from association areas are much more diffuse, spanning several layers. Output to different structures in the CNS and to other cortical areas are from pyramidal cells in layers V and VI and in layers II and III, respectively. The vertical patterning refers to the organization of the cerebral cortex into basic functional units termed columns which form complex local networks between them.

Question 3.6

Unimodal association areas in the cerebral cortex, which process information from a particular sensory modality, project to higher order multimodal association areas where information from different sensory modalities is integrated and refined. An example of a multimodal association area is the posterior parietal cortex which combines visual and spatial information to give a single percept. Other multimodal association areas include the temporal association cortex, the parahippocampal cortex and the cingulate cortex.

Question 3.7

The sympathetic division of the ANS, together with the adrenal glands, are responsible for preparing the body for an emergency, when the heart beats faster, hairs stand on end and sweat glands are activated. The adrenal gland releases the hormone adrenalin which has a widespread and relatively long lasting action on target organs. An interesting point is that the symptoms were the result of a danger that was perceived by the person, which may have been real or not. This illustrates the control of autonomic functions by higher centres in the brain.

Question 3.8

Although not an impenetrable physical barrier, the concept of the blood–brain barrier refers to an anatomical feature of the blood vessels in the CNS characterized by tight junctions between endothelial cells. The CNS needs a restrictive barrier separating it from the blood to permit the rigorous control of levels of nutrients, ions and other substances within the nervous tissue microenvironment, necessary for adequate function of neurons.

Question 3.9

The importance of tactile information from the lips and fingers in human life is reflected in their larger representation on the somatosensory cortex, compared to the area of the skin on the lower back, for example. In Chapter 2, we saw that whiskers play an important role in the way rodents sense their external environment and, consequently, they have a large specialized region of the somatosensory cortex devoted to processing sensory information obtained in this way.

Question 4.1

Phenomenal consciousness, because there must arise a raw sensation of 'the colour yellow' when she sees the rose before she can recognize and talk of 'yellow'.

Autobiographical consciousness, as she has a sense of herself, 'I', and is making a plan for the future (to paint her kitchen yellow). Or you might have mentioned introspective awareness, self- or self-reflexive consciousness. Any of these would be correct as the woman clearly shows awareness of herself, her likes and her plans. (See Section 4.2.1.)

Question 4.2

The answer is 'A' and 'C'. The boy has a thought and Jemima has a feeling / thought – but the information in both cases is internalized, subjective and hence not available to outsiders – it falls into the private, phenomenological domain. Scientific study requires information to be accessible to others, that is to third parties. In all the other instances, such information is potentially available. In B, eye pupil dilation could provide a physiological measure of an internal experience (emotional arousal, say). D provides a report of personal experience, and E provides observable data – both D and E fall into the behavioural data domain. (See Section 4.2.3.)

Question 4.3

The idea is relevant to the so-called 'hard problem' of consciousness. Part of this problem is our lack of understanding about the kind of physical mechanisms or laws that might underlie the phenomenon of consciousness. (You may be interested to know that an eminent Oxford University mathematical physicist, Professor Roger Penrose, has actually proposed that cellular structures called microtubules could play a part in generating consciousness, and that new laws of physics may be needed to understand the processes involved. However, at present this idea is not taken seriously by most scientists studying consciousness, and there is no evidence to support it.) (See Section 4.2.2.)

Question 4.4

Yes. The case of prosopagnosia provides an example (Section 4.3.2). Prosopagnosics have difficulty recognizing faces and cannot consciously tell the face of a familiar person from that of an unfamiliar person. However, if their autonomic response is measured using a lie-detector, there is a stronger response to the familiar face than to the unfamiliar face. They are not conscious of this, but this response suggests that recognition has indeed occurred unconsciously.

Question 4.5

The correct answer is pathways B (Section 4.4.2, which also tells you A is incorrect) and E (Section 4.4.2, which also tells you C and D are incorrect).

Question 4.6

The anterior cingulate cortex (ACC) and the left prefrontal cortex (PFC). The ACC is involved in selective attention processes while the PFC is thought to be involved in planning and memory. (See Section 4.3.3.)

Question 4.7

You could tell her that, in fact, D.B.'s brain might be receiving and processing the visual information without his being consciously aware of it. There are a number of visual pathways carrying information from the eye to the brain. In people with blindsight, such as D.B., a major pathway associated with visual consciousness is usually damaged. However, unconscious visual pathways such as that from the retina to the superior colliculus are still operating, so the information can still be processed. It appears to be accessible, albeit unconsciously, as people 'guess' the answer and go for what 'feels' right. (See Section 4.4.2.)

Question 4.8

1 (a) Optic ataxia; (b) the dorsal visual stream on the right side, or more specifically, the right parietal lobe (cf. legend to Figure 4.16).

2 (a) Akinetopsia; (b) the essential node for motion perception, V5/MT, in the extra-striate cortex (see Figure 4.20).

3 (a) Visual neglect syndrome; (b) right parietal cortex. (See Section 4.4.3 and Table 4.2.)

Question 4.9

The area of the blindspot gets filled in with surrounding visual material – as Figure 4.1 demonstrates. The brain appears to have an inbuilt rule that accomplishes this. In effect, therefore, an illusion, of which we are normally completely unaware, is created for us, and we are not aware of the blindspot.

Question 4.10

No, it does not. An epiphenomenon (as defined in this chapter, see Section 4.2.2) is a property that has no function and is simply a by-product. Even if conscious will is an illusion, it is possible it has an important function, hence it does not follow that it is an epiphenomenon.

REFERENCES AND FURTHER READING

Chapter 1

References

Vessie, P. R. (1932) On the transmission of Huntington's chorea for 300 years – The Bures family group, *The Journal of Nervous and Mental Disease*, **76**, pp. 553–73.

Further reading

For a good account of the two-way interactions between the brain and the social context, see Cacioppo, J. T. and Berntson, G. G. (1992) Social psychological contributions to the decade of the brain, *American Psychologist*, **47**, pp. 1019–28.

For the placebo effect, see Harrington, A. (ed.) (1997) *The Placebo Effect: An Interdisciplinary Exploration*, Harvard University Press, Cambridge, MA.

For a good account of the dynamic interactive nature of development, see Michel, G. F. and Moore, C. L. (1995) *Developmental Psychobiology: An Interdisciplinary Science*, The MIT Press, Cambridge.

To develop the ideas found in this chapter and for a good textbook of biological psychology that assumes some prior knowledge of science, see Pinel, J. (2002) *Biopsychology*, Allyn and Bacon.

For an account of biological psychology that assumes no prior knowledge of science, see Toates, F. (2001) *Biological Psychology: An Integrative Approach*, Pearson Education, Harlow, UK.

Chapter 2

Further reading

Butler, A. B. (2001) *Brain Evolution and Comparative Neuroanatomy*, *Encyclopedia of Life Sciences*, Nature Publishing Group, MacMillan Publishers Ltd, England.

Kandel, E. R., Schwartz, J. H. and Jessell, T. M. (2000) *Principles of Neural Science*, 4th edn, McGraw-Hill, New York.

Knott, G. and Molnar, Z. (2001) *Cells of the Nervous System*, *Encyclopedia of Life Sciences*, Nature Publishing Group, MacMillan Publishers Ltd, England.

Matus, A. (2001) *Neurons*, *Encyclopedia of Life Sciences*, Nature Publishing Group, MacMillan Publishers Ltd, England.

Ward, R. (2001) *Vertebrate Central Nervous System*, *Encyclopedia of Life Sciences*, Nature Publishing Group, MacMillan Publishers Ltd, England.

More demanding recent scientific reviews on some topics discussed in this chapter:

Haydon, P. G. (2001) Glia: listening and talking to the synapse, *Nature Reviews Neuroscience*, **2**, pp. 185–93.

Satterlie, R. A. (2002) Neuronal control of swimming in jellyfish: a comparative story, *Canadian Journal of Zoology*, **80**, pp. 1654–69.

Chapter 3

References

Itoh, K,. Fujii, Y., Suzuki, K. and Nakada, T. (2001) Asymmetry of parietal lobe activation during piano performance: a high field functional magnetic resonance imaging study, *Neuroscience Letters*, **309**(1), pp. 41–4.

Maguire, E. A., Gadian, D. G., Johnsrude, I. S., Good, C. D., Ashburner, J., Frackowiak, R. S. and Frith, C. D. (2000) Navigation-related structural change in the hippocampi of taxi drivers, *Proceedings of the National Academy of Sciences of the United States of America*, **97**(8), pp. 4398–403.

Further reading

Kandel, E. R., Schwartz, J. H. and Jessell, T. M. (2000) *Principles of Neural Science*, 4th edn, McGraw-Hill, New York.

Passingham, R. E. (2002) The frontal cortex: Does size matter? *Nature Neuroscience*, **5**(3), pp. 190–2.

Prescott, T. J., Redgrave, P. and Gurney, K. (1999) Layered control of architectures in robots and vertebrates, *Adaptive Behaviour*, **7**(1), pp. 99–127.

Semendeferi, K., Lu, A., Schenker, N. and Damasio, H. (2002) Humans and great apes share a large frontal cortex, *Nature Neuroscience*, **5**(3), pp. 272–6.

Toates, F. (2001) *Biological Psychology: An Integrative Approach*, Pearson Education, Harlow, UK.

More demanding recent scientific reviews on some topics discussed in this chapter:

Bizzi, E., Tresch, M. C., Saltiel, P. and d'Avella, A. (2000) New perspectives on spinal motor systems, *Nature Reviews Neuroscience*, **1**, pp. 101–8.

Miller, E. K. and Cohen, J. D. (2001) An integrative theory of prefrontal cortex function, *Annual Review of Neuroscience*, **24**, pp. 167–202.

Saper, C. B. (2002) The central autonomic nervous system: conscious visceral perception and autonomic pattern generation, *Annual Review of Neuroscience*, **25**, pp. 433–69.

Schieber, M. H. (2001) Constraints on somatotopic organization in the primary motor cortex, *Journal of Neurophysiology*, **86**, pp. 2125–43.

Chapter 4

References

Chalmers, D. (1995) Facing up to the problem of consciousness, *Journal of Consciousness Studies*, **2**, pp. 200–19.

Crick, F. and Koch, C. (2003) A framework for consciousness, *Nature Neuroscience*, **6**(2), pp. 119–26.

Damasio, A. R. (1999) *The Feeling of What Happens*, Vintage Books, Random House, London.

Debner, J. A. and Jacoby, L. L. (1994) Unconscious perception: attention, awareness and control, *Journal of Experimental Psychology: Learning, Memory and Cognition*, **20**, pp. 304–17.

Dennett, D. C. (1991) *Consciousness Explained*, Little Brown & Co., USA.

Dudai, Y. (1989) *The Neurobiology of Memory: Concepts, Findings and Trends*, Oxford University Press, Oxford.

Hume, D. (1739, reprinted 1964) *A Treatise of Human Nature*, L. A. Selby-Bigge (ed.), Clarendon Press, Oxford.

James, W. (1890) *The Principles of Psychology*, Macmillan, London.

Jueptner, M., Stephan, K. M., Frith, C. D., Brooks, D. J., Fracowiak, R. S. J. and Passingham, R. E. (1997) Anatomy of motor learning. I. Frontal cortex and attention to action, *Journal of Neurophysiology*, **77**, pp. 1313–24.

Libet, B. (1985) Unconscious cerebral initiative and the role of conscious will in voluntary action, *Behavioural and Brain Sciences*, **8**, pp. 529–66.

Logothetis, N. K. (1998) Single units and conscious vision, *Philosophical Transactions of the Royal Society of London B*, **353**, pp. 1801–18.

Marcel, A. J. (1983) Conscious and unconscious perception: an approach to the relations between phenomenal experience and perceptual processes, *Cognitive Psychology*, **15**, pp. 238–300.

McConkie, G. W. and Currie, C. B. (1996) Visual stability across saccades while viewing complex pictures, *Journal of Experimental Psychology*, **22**(3), pp. 563–81.

Milner, A. D. and Goodale, M. (1995) *The Visual Brain in Action*, Oxford University Press, Oxford.

O'Regan, J. K. and Noë, A. (2001) A sensorimotor account of vision and visual consciousness, *Behavioural and Brain Sciences*, **24**, pp. 939–1031.

Passingham, R. E. (1996) Attention to action, *Philosophical Transactions of the Royal Society of London B*, **351**, pp. 1473–79.

Raichle, M. E., Fiez, J. A., Videen, T. O., MacLeod, A.-M. K., Pardo, J. V., Fox, P. T. and Petersen, S. E. (1994) Practice-related changes in human brain functional anatomy during non-motor learning, *Cerebral Cortex*, **4**(1), pp. 8–26.

Ramachandran, V. S. and Hirstein, W. (1997) Perception of phantom limbs, *Brain*, **121**, pp. 1603–30.

Ramachandran, V. S. and Blakeslee, S. (1998) *Phantoms in the Brain: probing the mysteries of the human mind*, William Morrow & Co.

Reason, J. and Mycielska, K. (1982) *Absent-minded? The psychology of mental lapses and everyday errors*, Prentice Hall, Englewood Cliffs, NJ.

Rees, G., Kreiman, G. and Koch, C. (2002) Neural correlates of consciousness in humans, *Nature Neuroscience Review*, **3**, pp. 261–70.

Simons, D. J. and Chabris, C. F. (1998) Gorillas in our midst: sustained inattentional blindness for dynamic events, *Perception*, **28**, pp. 1059–74.

Simons, D. J. and Levin, D. T. (1998) Change blindness, *Trends in Cognitive Science*, **1**(7), pp. 261–7.

Staddon, J. E. R. (2001) *The New Behaviourism: Mind, mechanism and society*, Psychology Press, Philadelphia, PA.

Stoerig, P. and Cowey, A. (1992) Wavelength sensitivity in blindsight, *Brain*, **115**, pp. 425–44.

Toni, I., Krams, M., Turner, R. and Passingham, R. E. (1998) The time course of changes during motor sequence learning: a whole-brain fMRI study, *NeuroImage*, **8**, pp. 50–61.

Tranel, D. and Damasio, A. R. (1985) Knowledge without awareness: an automatic index of face recognition by prosopagnosics, *Science*, **228**, pp. 1453–55.

Wegner, D. M. and Wheatley, T. P. (1999) Apparent mental causation: sources of the experience of will, *American Psychologist*, **54**, pp. 480–92.

Wegner, D. M. (2002) *The Illusion of Conscious Will*, MIT Press.

Whalen, P. J., Rauch, S. L., Etcoff, N. L., McInerney, S. C., Lee, M. B. and Jenike, M. A. (1998) Masked presentations of emotional facial expressions modulate amygdala activity without explicit knowledge, *Journal of Neuroscience*, **18**(1), pp. 411–18.

Wolfe, J. M. (1999) 'Inattentional amnesia', in V. Coltheart (ed.), *Fleeting Memories,* MIT Press.

Zeki, S. and ffytche, D. H. (1998) The Riddoch syndrome, *Brain*, **121**, pp. 25–45.

Further reading

Accessible books on consciousness and the mind are being published all the time. Here are some you may enjoy reading:

Carter, R. (1998) *Mapping the Mind*, Weidenfeld & Nicolson, UK.

Carter, R. (2002) *Consciousness*, Weidenfeld and Nicolson, UK.

Crick, F. (1994) *The Astonishing Hypothesis*, Simon & Schuster Ltd.

Damasio, A. R. (1999) *The Feeling of What Happens*, Vintage Books, Random House, London.

Greenfield, S. A. (2000) *The Private Life of the Brain*, Allen Lane, The Penguin Press.

Hauser, M. (2001) *Wild Minds: What Animals Really Think*, Penguin Books.

Ramachandran, V. S. and Blakeslee, S. (1998) *Phantoms in the Brain: probing the mysteries of the human mind*, William Morrow & Co.

Sacks, O. (1985) *The Man who Mistook his Wife for a Hat*, Gerald Duckworth & Co.

The following books are well-written, but intellectually more demanding, as they deal in some depth with philosophical, methodological and psychological issues relating to consciousness and the mind:

Dennett, D. C. (1991) *Consciousness Explained*, Little Brown & Co, USA.

Dennett, D. C. (2003) *Freedom Evolves*, Penguin, Allen Lane, London.

Wegner, D. M. (2002) *The Illusion of Conscious Will*, MIT Press.

There are also a number of scientific journals that regularly publish papers (and occasionally devote special issues) to relevant topics:

The Cognitive Neuroscience of Consciousness (2001) (special issue), **79**(1–2), pp. 1–238; *Journal of Consciousness Studies*; *Trends in Cognitive Science*; *Nature Reviews Neuroscience*; *Nature Neuroscience*; *Trends in Neuroscience*; *Nature*; *Science*; *New Scientist*; *Scientific American*.

ACKNOWLEDGEMENTS

Grateful acknowledgement is made to the following sources for permission to reproduce material within this product.

Figures

Figures 1.2 and 1.3 © 2003 Psychology Press Ltd.; *Figure 1.17a* CC Studio/ Science Photo Library; *Figure 1.17b* Daudier, Jerrican/Science Photo Library; *Figure 1.18a* Pascal Goetghluck/Science Photo Library; *Figure 1.18b* Horne, J. *Why We Sleep* (1988). Reprinted by permission of Oxford University Press; *Figure 1.25a and 1.25b* Copyright © Frederick Toates 2001; *Figure 1.28* Ann Young/ Harvard University;

Figure 2.3a Dr Pat Morris (Photographer); *Figure 2.3b* Amata Hornbruch in Alberts, B. *et al.* (1994) 'Single cells to multicellular organisms', *Molecular Biology of the Cell*, 3rd edn. Taylor Francis, Routledge, Garland; *Figure 2.5a* Professor J. G. Nicholls; *Figure 2.9* Martini, F. H. *et al.* (2000, Table 15–1, p.379) in Toates, F. (2001) 'Describing the brain', in *Biological Psychology*, Pearson Education; *Figures 2.13b and 2.29* Biophoto Associates/Science Photo Library; *Figure 2.14b* Photos from Perry, M. M. and Gilbert, A. B. (1979) *Journal of Cell Science*, **39**, p. 266. The Company of Biologists Limited; *Figure 2.15* Chris Lancashire/Open University; *Figure 2.17* Carpenter, R. H. S. (1990) *Neurophysiology*, Edward Arnold Publishers; *Figure 2.20a* Robert Wagner, University of Delaware; *Figure 2.20b* 'Diagram showing arrangements of neurons connected by synapses', University of Virginia website; *Figure 2.21a and 2.21b* © The Nobel Foundation; *Figure 2.23a* Evans, D. 'Neurofibrillary tangles stained using ...', Newsletter, Issue 5, website. Journal of Cellular Pathology and Greenwich Medical Media Limited; *Figure 2.24a and 2.24b* Mike Stewart/Open University; *Figure 2.27* Ignacio Romero/Open University; *Figure 2.28c* Morrell, P. (ed.) *Myelin*, Plenum Publishing Corporation;

Figure 3.6 Carola, R., Harley, J. P. and Noback, C. R. (1990) *Human Anatomy and Physiology*, (International Edition), McGraw-Hill; *Figure 3.7a* Sovereign ISM/ Science Photo Library; *Figure 3.8* Liddell, E. F. T. and Sherrington, C. (1924) Reflexes in response to stretch (myotatic reflexes). *Proceedings of the Royal Society of London B: Biological Sciences*, **96**, pp. 212–42; *Figures 3.9, 3.10, 3.11, 3.16, 3.24, 3.32a and 3.35a* Martini, F. H., Timmons, M. J. and McKinley, M. P. (2000) *Human Anatomy*, Prentice-Hall, Upper Saddle River; *Figures 3.13, 3.18a and 3.18b* Brodal, A. (1981) *Neurological Anatomy in Relation to Clinical Medicine*, 3rd edn. Copyright © 1969, 1981 by Oxford University Press Inc. (reprinted with permission); *Figures 3.19a and 3.19b* Taken from K. Brodmann's *Localisation in the Cerebral Cortex*, 1909 edition, translated by Laurence J. Garey. Smith Gordon Limited; *Figure 3.20* Stevie Grand/Science Photo Library; *Figures 3.22 and 3.28* Kandel, E. R. (2000) *Principles of Neural Science* 4th edn, Copyright © by The McGraw-Hill Companies Inc.; *Figure 3.23* Kosuke, I. *et al.* (2001) 'Asymmetry of parietal lobe activation during piano performance:...', *Neuroscience Letters*, © Elsevier Science Limited; *Figures 3.24a and 3.26* Kandel, E. R. (2000) 'The functional organization of perception and movement', *Principles of Neural Science*, Copyright © by The McGraw-Hill Companies, Inc; *Figure 3.29* Prescott, T. J., Redgrave, P. and Gurney, K. (1999) 'Layered control architectures in robots and vertebrates', *Adaptive Behavior*, **7**, p.110. International Society for Adaptive Behavior; *Figure 3.31* Torora, G. J. and Anagnostakos, N. P. (1990) *Principles of Anatomy and Physiology*, 6th edn, Harper Collins Publishers; *Figure 3.32b* Courtesy of Dr Luc Bidaut PhD, Memorial Sloan-Kettering Cancer Center, New York, USA *Figure 3.33* Goldstein, G. W. and Betz, A. L. 'The blood brain barrier', p.73, 3 September 1986. © Patricia J. Wynne; *Figure 3.34a* © Robert Wagner; *Figure 3.34b* Ignacio Romero/Open University; *Figure 3.36a* A. Glauberman/Science Photo Library; *Figure 3.36b* Wellcome Department of Cognitive Neurology/Science Photo Library; *Figure 3.37a* Alfred Benjamin/Science Photo Library; *Figure 3.37b* Toporek, C. and Robinson, K. (1999) *Hydrocephalus: A Guide for Patients, Families and Friends*, O'Reilly and Associates, Inc.; *Figure 3.38* Lorelle Raboni; *Figure 3.39* Semendeferi, K. *et al.* (2001) *American Journal of Physical Anthropology* **114** (2001): Copyright © 2001 Wiley-Liss Inc, a subsidiary of John Wiley & Sons Inc. This material is used by permission of Wiley-Liss Inc., a subsidiary of John Wiley Inc; *Figure 3.40* Maguire, E. A. *et al.* (2000) 'Navigation-related structural change in the hippocampi of taxi drivers', *PNAS* April 11, 2000, **97**, No. 8. Copyright 2000 National Academy of Sciences USA; *Figure 3.14* Welker, W. 'Human Homo sapiens', Brain Museum website. University of Wisconsin-Madison;

Figure 4.2 Martini, F. H. *et al.* (2000) *Human Anatomy*, Pearson Education Ltd; *Figure 4.3* Marcel, A. J. (1983) 'Consciousness, masking and word recognition', *Cognitive Psychology*, **15**(2), April, Academic Press Inc.; *Figures 4.4, 4.5, 4.6, 4.7 and 4.8* Raichle, M. E. *et al.* (1994) 'Practice-related changes in human brain functional anatomy during non-motor learning', *Cerebral Cortex*, **4**(1), January/February, Oxford University Press; *Figure 4.9* Jueptner, M. (1997) 'Anatomy of motor learning. II. Subcortical structures and learning', *Journal of Neurophysiology*, **77**, American Physiological Society; *Figure 4.10* Passingham, R. E. (1996) 'Attention to action', *Philosophical Transactions Series B*, **351**, The Royal Society; *Figures 4.11 and 4.12* Humphrey, N. K. (1974) 'Vision in a monkey without striate cortex: a case study', *Perception*, **3**(3) copyright © 1974 Pion Publications; *Figure 4.13* Elise Amendola/Associated Press; *Figure 4.16* Milner, A. D. and Goodale, M. A. 'Disorders in the visual control of action', *The Visual Brain in Action*, © 1995 A. David Milner and Melvyn A. Goodale; *Figure 4.17a, 4.17c and 4.17d* Block, J. R. (2002) 'Ambiguous figures and figure–ground images, *Seeing Double*, Taylor and Francis Books Ltd; *Figure 4.17b* © Porzellan Manufaktur Staffelstein GmbH & Co. KG; *Figure 4.17e* VEGAP (Madrid); *Figure 4.18* Logothetis, N. K. (1998) 'Single units and conscious vision', *Philosophical Transactions Series B*, **353** © 1998 The Royal Society; *Figure 4.19* Leopold, D. A. and Logothetis, N. K. (1999) 'Multistable phenomena: changing views in perception', *Trends in Cognitive Sciences*, **3**(7) Elsevier Science; *Figure 4.20* Zeki, S. (2003) 'The disunity of consciousness', *Trends in Cognitive Sciences*, **7**(5). Elsevier Science; *Figure 4.21* Metzinger, T. (ed.) 'Imaging conscious vision', *Neural Correlates of Consciousness*, © 2000 Massachusetts Institute of Technology; *Figures 4.25 and 4.26* Ramachandran, V. S. (1998) 'Consciousness and body image: lessons from phantom limbs, Capgras syndrome and pain asymbolia', *Philosophical Transactions Series B*, **353**(1377), The Royal Society; *Figure 4.27* Yarbus, A. L. (1967) 'Eye movement during perception of complex objects', *Eye Movement and Vision*, Plenum Publishing Corporation; *Figure 4.29* Collins, P. (1997) 'Person change in a motion picture', *Trends in Cognitive*

Sciences, **1**, Elsevier Science; *Figure 4.30* Simons, D. J. and Levin, D. T. (1998) 'Failure to detect changes to people during a real-world interaction', *Psychonomic Bulletin and Review*, **5**(4), pp. 644–9, Psychonomic Society Inc.; *Figure 4.31* 'Photo of gorilla in a basketball match', *Perception*, **28**, Pion Publications.

Every effort has been made to contact copyright holders. If any have been inadvertently overlooked the publishers will be pleased to make the necessary arrangements at the first opportunity.

INDEX

Glossary terms are in bold. Italics indicate items mainly, or wholly, in a figure or table.

D

E

Q

R

S

T

U

V

W

Z